STO

D1083659

JUN 3 '65

SULFURIC ACID

SULFURIC ACID
Use and Handling

Oscar T. Fasullo
Consolidated Chemical Division,
Stauffer Chemical Company,
Houston, Texas

McGRAW-HILL BOOK COMPANY
New York   San Francisco   Toronto   London

Sulfuric Acid

Copyright © 1965 by McGraw-Hill, Inc. All Rights Reserved. Printed in the United States of America. This book, or parts thereof, may not be reproduced in any form without permission of the publishers. *Library of Congress Catalog Card Number 63-23467*

19995

PREFACE   1299083

Sulfuric acid—a colorless, odorless, oily liquid—contributes much to the comforts and necessities of mankind. Almost all modern industrial products depend upon hydrogen ions of sulfuric acid at some point in manufacture. In fact, sulfuric acid plays an indispensable part in the basic essentials (food, shelter, clothing, transportation, communication) of life although it frequently does not appear in the final product.

Sulfuric acid has long been pre-eminent among basic industrial chemicals. The amount consumed reflects the industrial activity of the nation.

This book is a compilation of facts to help the sulfuric acid consumer handle and use sulfuric acid most efficiently for his purposes. Because data on the subject are widely scattered through a great volume of literature, it is difficult for the busy design or plant engineer, chemist, technician, administrator, foreman or operator to find, in one place, the facts that are of practical interest and use. This book presents sulfuric acid data—both practical and theoretical—in a form readily accessible for use.

The author will welcome having his attention called to errors and to useful data which he has neglected to include. All suggestions will be given careful consideration in any future revision of the book.

The author wishes to thank the many members of Stauffer Chemical Company, especially Sam S. Emison, R. P. Bond, H. Zeh Hurlbut and C. H. Wilson, who have aided in the compilation of data for this book and in many other ways provided invaluable assistance. The author is particularly grateful to Ralph Sadler who rendered invaluable assistance in proofreading and in taking care of the innumerable details associated with the project.

The author also wishes to thank the following organizations for their contributions to this book: Humble Oil & Refining Company; Procter & Gamble Company; United Refining Company; American Cyanamid Company; Atlas Chemical Industries, Inc.; M. W. Kellogg Company; Manufacturing Chemists Association; Betz Laboratories, Inc., Shell Oil Company; Shell Chemical Company; City Public Service Board, San Antonio, Texas; Chas. Lewis & Company; Goodyear Tire & Rubber Company; United States Rubber Company; Olin Mathieson Chemical Corporation; York Transport Company; Shell Development Company; Gulf States Utilities Company; Stanford Research Institute.

Oscar T. Fasullo

CONTENTS

DERIVATIVES OF SULFURIC ACID

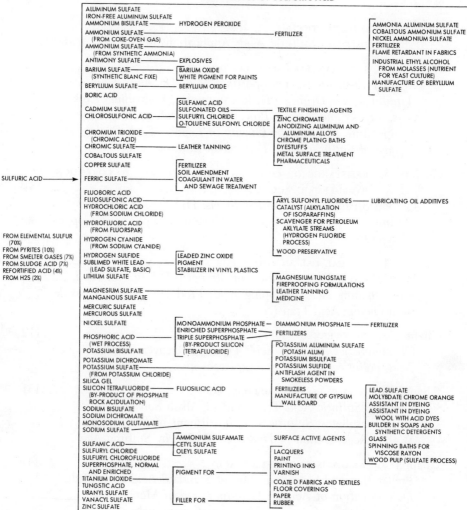

viii

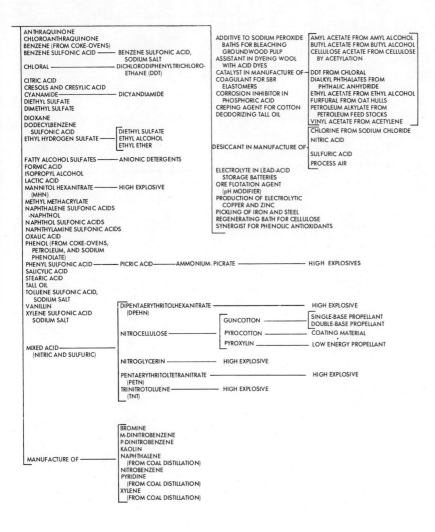

1. INTRODUCTION

Characteristics

Function

Sulfuric acid is not a one-function or one-purpose product. It is used as a drying agent, acidifying agent (pH control), hydrolyzing agent, neutralizing agent, concentrating agent, dehydrating agent, oxidizing agent, polymerizing agent, purifying agent, absorbing agent, leaching agent, catalyst and active reactant in petrochemical and inorganic chemical processes.

Strength

Sulfuric acid is not a one-strength product. It is used in a wide range of strengths from very dilute concentrations for pH control to the strong fuming acids used in the dye, explosives, detergent, pharmaceutical and petrochemical industries. Standard market strengths are: specific gravity 1.250 (33.33%); sp gr 1.400 (50.08%); sp gr 1.500 (59.80%); sp gr 1.835 (93.19%); 60° Baumé (77.67%); 66° Bé (93.19%); 98.0%; 20% oleum (104.5%); 40% oleum (109.0%); and 65% oleum (114.63%).

Quality

Sulfuric acid is not a one-quality product. It is produced and supplied in exact purities for storage batteries, rayon, textile, dye, food and pharmaceutical industries; in less pure grades for steel, heavy chemical, petrochemical, fertilizer, superphosphate and ammonium sulfate industries.

Recoverability

Sulfuric acid needn't be a one-time-use product. It can be recovered easily from some phases in the refining of petroleum and in the manufacture of explosives, petrochemicals, detergents and dyes. It is often re-

1

Synthetic Rubber Polymerization: Sulfuric acid serves as a catalyst in the polymerization of GR-S synthetic rubber in these reactors at Naugatuck, Conn. (*Courtesy United States Rubber Company.*)

TABLE I. SULFURIC ACID CONSUMPTION BY END USES

END USE		1963 ESTIMATE (thousand short tons)
Phosphatic fertilizers		5,995
Petroleum products (total)		2,448
aviation gasoline	1,322	
catalysts	232	
sulfonates (lube oil additives)	232	
others (except sulfonated hydrocarbons)	662	
Ammonium sulfate (total)		1,248
synthetic	720	
coke-oven	528	
Inorganic pigments		1,660
Chemicals not elsewhere classified		1,715
Iron and steel		995
Alcohols		910
Rayon (total)		478
high-tenacity yarn	245	
other	233	
Aluminum sulfate (total)		530
water and sewage treatment	142	
other	388	
Nonferrous metallurgy		970
Industrial explosives		398
Synthetic detergents		555
Regenerated cellulose sheet film (chiefly cellophane)		303
Dyes		187
Insecticides		199
Rubber, including synthetic		170
Hydrochloric acid		82
Chromium chemicals		97
Light oil refining		87
Storage batteries		115
Tall oil		118
Chlorine drying		87
Industrial water treatment		70
Medicinals		78
Textile finishing		43
Copper sulfate		26
Fat-splitting		35
Sulfonated oil		41
Miscellaneous		1,060
TOTAL CONSUMPTION		20,700

covered in a form unsuitable for re-use in the same process but of a strength and quality suitable for use in another process. Sulfuric acid can also be returned to the producer for fortification with sulfur trioxide or for regeneration to strong virgin acid.

Synthetic Rubber Coagulation: Sulfuric acid coagulates a high-purity synthetic rubber in this stainless steel vat in Houston plant. (*Courtesy Goodyear Tire and Rubber Company.*)

Acrylonitrile Synthesis: HCN and acetylene enter these tanks at Fortier, La., to begin the manufacture of acrylonitrile. (*Courtesy American Cyanamid Company.*)

Manufacturing Methods

There are two common methods of sulfuric acid manufacture.

Lead-Chamber Process. Sulfuric acid is produced in the lead-chamber process by burning sulfur or sulfur-bearing ores in a furnace and taking the sulfur dioxide, so formed, to large lead chambers where it reacts

Manufacture: Typical plant for manufacture and recovery of sulfuric acid. (*Courtesy Stauffer Chemical Company.*)

with oxides of nitrogen. This produces an intermediate product, nitro-sulfuric acid, which reacts with water to produce sulfuric acid and to liberate the oxides of nitrogen for re-use. The acid so produced is of low strength and quality.

Contact Process. In the contact process, sulfur dioxide is generated by burning elemental sulfur, roasting sulfur ore and/or decomposing spent sulfuric acid. The sulfur dioxide is oxidized over a catalyst to sulfur trioxide in the presence of oxygen but absence of moisture. The sulfur trioxide is then absorbed in strong sulfuric acid, combining there with water to produce more sulfuric acid. The strongest and best quality sulfuric acid is produced by this process.

Applications

Sulfuric acid is widely used in industry because of its important chemical and physical properties. Other acids have similar properties, but the relative low cost of sulfuric acid makes it the most economical choice for a wide variety of chemical operations. These operations can be conveniently classified by the particular property of sulfuric acid involved.

1. Sulfuric acid is an active acid with a high boiling point. The manufacture of halogen acids (e.g., HCl; HF) and the pickling of steel make use of this high boiling point. Leaching ores, in the manufacture of metal pigments, is more effective with sulfuric acid because high leaching temperatures can be used without loss of acid by volatilization.

2. Sulfuric acid has a great affinity for water. It is widely used for drying gases containing moisture (e.g., cell chlorine). Virtually complete removal of water vapor from these gases is accomplished by a simple scrubbing operation.

Sulfonation and Sulfation: Oleum reacts with alkylbenzene and fatty alcohols to form ingredients of household detergents. (*Courtesy Procter & Gamble Company.*)

Alkylation: Sulfuric acid reacts with petroleum hydrocarbons in this cascade alkylation reactor designed and constructed by M. W. Kellogg for United Refining Company refinery.

3. Sulfuric acid forms hydrolyzable sulfates with many organic compounds. Many alkylation operations of the petroleum and petrochemical industries depend on the ability of this acid to react with hydrocarbons to form intermediate compounds. Aromatic alkylamines important to the dye, photographic and pharmaceutical industries are manufactured with sulfuric acid. The production of industrially important synthetic alcohols is also based on this sulfuric acid property.

4. Sulfuric acid has special catalytic properties, probably related to its affinity for water. These catalytic properties account for its large volume use in the manufacture of aviation gasoline.

5. Oleum is used in the manufacture of organic sulfonates. These materials, used in large quantities, are major ingredients of household detergents. Smaller quantities of special sulfonates are used as lubricants and as additives to automotive lubricants.

6. Sulfuric acid is widely used in acidulation and neutralization processes because it is frequently the most economical acid available for the job. The widespread use of sulfuric acid for pH control, which can be performed satisfactorily by any acid, is a direct result of sulfuric acid's relatively low cost and its availability. The manufacture of phosphate fertilizers is the largest single use of sulfuric acid. Large amounts of sulfuric acid are used in acid coagulation processes (e.g., GRS synthetic rubber) and in regeneration of cationic exchange equipment.

Another major use is that of neutralization agent in production of synthetic fibers.

7. Teamed with relative low cost as a marked advantage of sulfuric acid is availability. Sulfuric acid, in the strengths (96–99%) common to commerce, does not react appreciably with steel. Special containers are needed to transport common commercial grades of hydrochloric and nitric acids, but sulfuric acid can be transported in steel tank cars and tank trucks or shipped in steel drums.

2. SAFE HANDLING OF SULFURIC ACID

General Precautions

The Interstate Commerce Commission classifies sulfuric acid as a corrosive liquid. Because it reacts with most metals and with water, care must be exercised in all handling operations.

In concentrations below 60° Bé (77.67%), sulfuric acid is highly reactive to metals and evolves hydrogen gas on contact. In concentrations above 77.67% it is a strong oxidizing agent, reacting with many organic materials and inorganic reducing agents to evolve considerable heat. It is extremely avid for water and decomposes many oxygen-containing organic materials by dehydration. Addition of water to concentrated sulfuric acid will produce violent steam explosions (spitting).

Sulfuric acid solutions, particularly the more concentrated ones, are rapidly destructive to all body tissues, causing severe burns. Repeated exposure to low concentrations may result in dermatitis. Contact with the eyes is especially hazardous, often causing severe damage and, in some cases, loss of sight.

Inhalation of the concentrated vapor from hot acid or oleum may be very harmful. Inhalation of small concentrations of the vapor over a period of time may cause chronic inflammation of the upper respiratory tract. Sensitivity to the vapor is variable; 0.125 to 0.50 ppm may be mildly annoying; 1.5 to 2.5 ppm definitely unpleasant; and 10 to 20 ppm unbearable.

Although sulfuric acid is not flammable, it must be isolated from organic materials, nitrates, carbides, chlorates and metal powders. Contact of high concentrations of sulfuric acid with these materials can cause ignition. Contact of high concentrations of sulfuric acid with metallic sulfides can cause both evolution of hydrogen sulfide and ignition. Sulfuric acid in drums, tank cars and metal storage tanks evolves hydrogen. Because 4–75% hydrogen by volume with air forms an explosive mixture, open lights or flames and spark-producing tools should be forbidden in the

9

vicinity of such containers. All electrical fixtures in such areas must be vapor-tight.

Sulfuric acid is dangerous if improperly handled. When, however, procedural precautions are taken and adequate protective clothing is worn, there is relatively little danger in handling sulfuric acid, whatever the strength of the acid.

Acid Handling: Personnel dressed in safety suits unload sulfuric acid at Leon Creek Power Plant. Acid is used to treat boiler feedwater and clean boiler feed tubes. (*Courtesy City Public Service Board of San Antonio, Tex.*)

Protective Clothing

Employees who handle sulfuric acid should be provided with the following necessities:

(a) A brimmed felt or treated-fiber hat or a rubber hat; rubber gloves; rubber high-top safety-toe shoes or boots (with tops covered by trousers); woolen outer clothing fitted snugly at neck and wrists; a rubber apron; a rubber acid suit for certain types of tank car loading or unloading.

(b) Water in ample quantity ready for immediate use.

(c) Suitable gas-tight chemical safety goggles.

(d) Rescue harness and lifeline for those entering a tank or enclosed storage space; an outside attendant maintaining constant observation.

(e) Proper face masks.

Positive-pressure hose masks must have hose inlet originating in a vapor-free atmosphere.

Air-line masks must have proper reducing valve and filter. These are suitable for use only when conditions permit safe escape in case of failure of the compressed air supply.

Self-contained breathing apparatus with stored oxygen or air allows greater mobility but usually requires more highly trained men. (In tank work, small manholes may make this apparatus unsuitable because of its bulk, but the type known as self-generating is specially designed for entrance and egress through small openings.)

Masks and breathing apparatus must be approved by the United States Bureau of Mines and must be equipped with full face-pieces.

Industrial canister-type gas masks, even those approved by the United States Bureau of Mines, should never be used in emergency circumstances. They may be used only when it is certain that acid concentration is less than two per cent by volume (20,000 parts per million), and oxygen content not less than 16 per cent. Exposure even then must not exceed one-half hour.

Caution: Never depend on creams or ointments to afford protection.

Remember: Personal protective equipment is not a substitute for good, safe working conditions, nor for adequate ventilation.

First Aid

Sulfuric acid causes severe burns. A doctor should be summoned immediately if the acid is swallowed or spilled, sprayed or otherwise allowed to come into direct contact with a workman's skin or eyes. In the meantime:

In Case of Contact. Flush skin or eyes with large quantities of water as quickly as possible and remove all contaminated clothing. Any clothing touched by acid must be removed whether penetration to the skin appears likely or not. The precaution of removal of all contaminated clothing should also be taken in minor accidents where no acid whatsoever has reached or appears likely to reach any part of a workman's body.

Antidote if Swallowed. Drink one or more teaspoonfuls of magnesia or chalk, or small pieces of soap softened in water with milk, mucilage or raw egg white.

Handling Spilled Chemicals

Ventilate room thoroughly. Neutralize spilled acid with soda ash (sodium carbonate) or washing soda. Wash material down the drain with plenty of water. A minimum of 200 pounds of soda ash is necessary to neutralize 13 gallons of 66° Bé sulfuric acid.

For further general information on hygienic practices and standards to be observed in the handling of sulfuric acid, refer to Hygienic Guide Sheet obtainable from the American Industrial Hygiene Association.

Transporting Sulfuric Acid

Twenty million tons of sulfuric acid a year are transported to various parts of the United States primarily by tank car, tank truck or barge.

Large sulfuric acid consumers near a producer's plant can sometimes use pipelines more economically than any other means of conveyance. On the other hand, consumers of very small amounts of sulfuric acid (a total of less than one-half of one percent of the annual tonnage) may receive the acid by common carrier, but in carboys or drums rather than tank cars or tank trucks.

Warning Labels

Each container, including tank cars, must carry identifying labels or stencils (See Fig. 1). Each drum or box containing inside containers (carboys) must bear the ICC white acid-label. Tank cars or box cars carrying one or more containers of sulfuric acid must bear the ICC "DANGEROUS" placard. Motor vehicles, including tank trucks, must be marked in accordance with Part 77, ICC Regulations. The Manufacturing Chemists' Association (MCA), recommending warning labels in addition to those required by regulations, ordinances or statutes, has published "A Guide for the Preparation of Warning Labels for Hazardous Chemicals (Manual L-1)." This pamphlet is available from MCA.

Tank Cars

Tank cars carrying up to 90 tons of sulfuric acid are in common use today.

Cars loaded with sulfuric acid (generally in strengths ranging from 77.67 to 114.6%) must meet Interstate Commerce Commission (ICC) specifications ICC-103A, 103A-W or 111A100-W-2.

Cars carrying weaker strengths of sulfuric acid (51% or less) must be rubber-lined to meet ICC specifications ICC-103B, 103B-W or 111A100-W-5.

Tank Trucks

The sulfuric acid tank truck, consisting of tractor and tank trailer, must meet both ICC regulations and Motor Vehicle Code MC310 or MC311. Bottom outlets are not permitted on the tank trailer; however, the tank is

Fig. 1. Warning labels and placards for sulfuric acid tank cars (above) and carboys (below). Drum label is similar to carboy label.

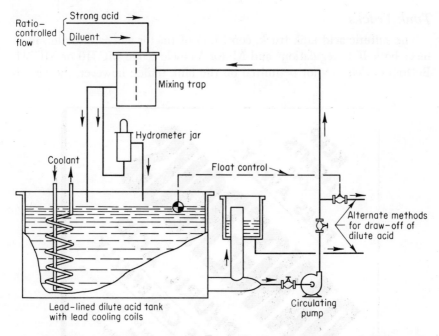

Fig. 2. Continuous dilution of sulfuric acid with recirculation. (*Duecker and West, "The Manufacture of Sulfuric Acid", Copyright 1959 Reinhold Publishing Company.*)

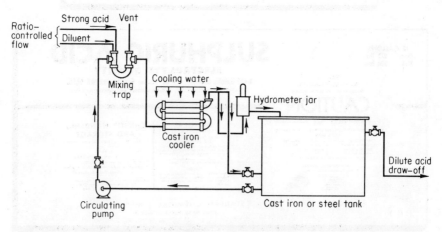

Fig. 3. Continuous dilution of sulfuric acid to strengths of 66° Bé and stronger. (*Duecker and West, "The Manufacture of Sulfuric Acid", Copyright 1959 Reinhold Publishing Company.*)

equipped with a discharge line similar to the deep line on a standard tank car. This line extends from the side of the tank and is equipped with flexible joints for connection to the customer's line at a height of three to four feet from the ground. The tank must be unloaded by pump or air pressure. Transports usually carry their own air compressor and charge a nominal fee for unloading the tank.

Barges

Extremely large amounts of sulfuric acid are usually transported by barges if a waterway is available and distance from supplier to user is more than two miles. Acid has been economically transported by barge for distances up to 500 miles. Barge capacities range from about 1,500 to about 2,000 tons, the equivalent of 30 to 40 fifty-ton tank cars. The amount of sulfuric acid that can be hauled depends on the loaded average draft of a particular barge.

Barges may have either cylindrical or rectangular tanks. These are divided into compartments by bulkheads and valves.

All barges are equipped with pumps that connect to a customer's power stations. Dock facilities are of a special design and if barge deliveries are required, the supplying chemical company is generally contacted for special consultation.

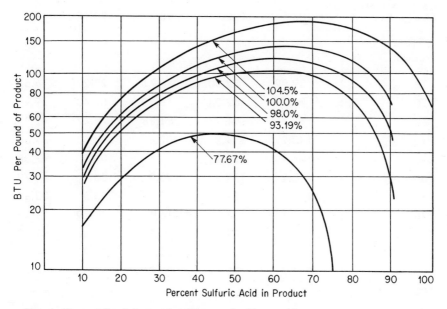

Fig. 4. Heat evolved during the dilution of sulfuric acid.

Dilution of Sulfuric Acid after Shipment

Dilution of strong concentrated sulfuric acid at the customer's plant may be advisable for any or all of these three reasons:

1. To reduce transportation costs by avoiding freight charge on water contained in diluted sulfuric acid.
2. To use heat of dilution for supplying energy to plant process system.
3. To obtain a process strength of acid not available from supplier.

Sulfuric acid of any strength can be diluted without difficulty.

Acid must be added to water (not water to acid) or stronger acid to weaker acid (not weaker to stronger). This avoids generation of excessive heat which might cause violent splattering of the acid.

Whether acid is diluted by batch or continuous method, a great deal of heat evolves, and the diluted acid must be cooled. Typical dilution and cooling systems are shown in Figs. 2 and 3.

The total heat developed and the temperature rise can be calculated by using the enthalpy concentration chart, Figure 68, p. 300. The heat evolved can also be estimated from Figure 4 and Table II.

TABLE II. CALCULATED HEATS OF DILUTION
BTU EVOLVED PER POUND OF PRODUCT ACID

% H_2SO_4 in Strong Acid:	104.5	100	98.0	93.19	77.67
% H_2SO_4 in Product					
10	39.92	32.80	29.71	27.23	16.51
20	76.77	62.54	56.35	51.40	29.97
30	112.5	91.17	81.88	74.47	42.31
40	143.2	114.8	102.4	97.50	49.64
50	164.9	129.3	113.8	101.5	47.88
60	182.2	139.5	120.9	106.1	41.79
65	185.9	139.7	119.5	103.5	33.82
70	188.1	138.3	116.6	99.29	24.25
75	184.7	131.4	108.1	89.62	9.22
80	176.7	119.7	94.95	75.21	——
90	137.7	73.69	45.75	23.57	——
100	71.1	0	——	——	——
104.5	0	——	——	——	——

Handling Carboys

General Safety Measures

Boxed glass carboys are safe, adequate containers when properly handled and maintained. Neglect of precautions, however, creates conditions hazardous to persons and property.

Causes of Breakage

1. Rough handling or dropping.
2. Freezing of contents.
3. Striking neck of bottle.
4. Unfavorable storage conditions, such as placement where bottle necks are in vulnerable locations.
5. Careless use of wire cutters in removing wires.
6. Removal of bottles from carboy boxes. (Consignee should never attempt this.)
7. Excessive internal pressure fracturing bottles. This pressure can be caused by:
   (a) Use of air pressure for emptying.
   (b) Expansion of liquid because of extreme rise in temperature.
   (c) Insufficient air space (outage) in bottle.
   (d) Insufficient venting at the stopper, especially during storage.

There should be no exposed lights, fire, sparks or smoking in the vicinity of filled or empty boxed carboys.

Working areas, particularly in buildings, should be well lighted, well ventilated, properly maintained and connected by ample passageways. Equipment should be kept in first-class condition. Inadequate equipment and poor working conditions are primary causes of carelessness and accidents.

Protection of Personnel

Empty or filled boxed carboys should be handled only by properly clothed men thoroughly instructed in the necessary precautions. Basic rules are:

1. Wear face shields or tight-fitting goggles, rubber boots, aprons and gloves of rubber or acid-resistant material.
2. Inspect with care all incoming carboys and set aside any damaged ones for special handling.
3. Make sure closures are securely fastened before moving filled carboys.
4. Never handle carboys by the closure or neck of bottle.
5. Use specially designed hand trucks for moving boxed carboys about the plant. Names of suppliers of satisfactory trucks may be obtained from the Manufacturing Chemists' Association.

6. Do not use hooks for handling carboys.
7. Do not "walk" carboys on bottom edge because this creates severe strains on the container and can cause breakage.
8. When piling or removing empty boxed carboys, do not tilt neck of bottle toward oneself.
9. Drain empty boxed carboys completely before releasing for transportation. Failure to do this is a violation of Interstate Commerce Commission regulations.

Handling Equipment

Hand Truck. An efficient, safe hand-truck lifts and transports a carboy at a maximum of two inches off the floor or ground. Such a truck is easily operated by one man and allows the man to stay well out of danger at all times. When a carboy is loaded onto the truck, the truck prongs are thrust under the carrying cleats of the carboy. By bearing down on the handles of the truck, a workman can move the carboy to any location without touching the carboy. Upon arrival at destination, the carboy can be placed without jolt or jar. (Handling procedures with this type of truck conform with instructions of the Bureau of Explosives as outlined in Bureau of Explosives Pamphlet No. 6.)

Wood Pallets. Wood pallets have proved successful for handling both filled and empty boxed carboys. The pallets must, however, be specially designed for this service.

Storing Carboys

1. The best flooring for storage of sulfuric acid is concrete treated with sodium silicate.
2. Drainage outlets are needed in case of breakage and spillage.
3. Aisles are necessary for ease of handling.
4. Filled boxed carboys should be stored indoors. Outside storage causes rapid deterioration of the boxes and cushioning material. If outside storage cannot be avoided, boxed carboys should be kept off the ground by placing the bottom tier on suitable dunnage on a properly drained site.
5. Filled boxed carboys should not be tiered more than three carboys high.
6. Filled carboys are closed with porous earthenware, glass or porcelain stoppers, or plastic screw caps. Carboys should be inspected periodically to make certain the contents have not expanded to the point of overflow. Any liquid expanded above top-of-the-box level must be drawn off. Carboys must be securely resealed before moving.

Special Precautions

Always observe the special precautions listed on carboy labels.

Carboys containing sulfuric acid should not be stored where the temperature may drop below the freezing point because freezing can break the bottle. The following are the freezing points of selected strengths of chemically pure sulfuric acid:

Strength (%)	Baumé (°)	Freezing Temperature (°F)
95.50		− 1.3
93.19	66.00	−20.0
91.80	65.75	+ 2.3
90.60	65.50	−16.1
77.67	60.00	+11.6
76.00	59.00	− 7.5

How to Open

1. Keep hands and face to side of carboy (never over neck of bottle)..
2. Use a face-type wire cutter to remove the wire holding the stopper in place.
3. Do not attempt to remove wire by twisting or prying. This can break the neck of the bottle and endanger the workman.

How to Empty

1. An inclinator is the simplest and safest method for emptying carboys.
2. A syphon can be used satisfactorily, but the workman must be careful not to break the bottle while inserting the syphon. Gravity feed must be used. Carboys must not be discharged by air pressure.

Care must be taken in emptying in order to prevent surging or spattering of contents from the bottle mouth.

Storage of Empty Carboys

Empty, boxed carboys should be stored on their flat side in not more than four tiers. Bottle necks must not protrude into aisles or passageways. These precautions help prevent breakage of bottles, accidents to workmen, and collection of water and foreign matter in the bottles.

Empty carboys, like filled ones, should be stored indoors. If outside storage cannot be avoided, the empty carboys should be kept off the ground in the same manner as filled ones.

Boxcar Loading of Empty Carboys

All empty carboys must be completely drained before loading. ICC warning labels must be removed or obliterated to conform with Section 29C of ICC regulations.

Empty carboys must be loaded with care to prevent damage to handles and containers.

Carboys should be packed tightly against the ends of the car and against each other before driving wedges into the center of the car.

All carboy parts—box tops, caps and stoppers, etc.—should be returned to supplier. Small parts should be packed in a small drum or box clearly marked with a description of contents.

If a carboy is damaged, enough repairs should be made on it to allow safe shipment to owner. Damaged carboys should be prominently tagged to call attention of owner to defects.

Handling Steel Drums

General Precautions

If properly handled, unlined steel drums are safe and adequate containers for all except special grades of sulfuric acid. There are, however, certain precautions that must be taken to avoid creation of the following hazardous conditions.

Explosions. Hydrogen is formed by the action of sulfuric acid on steel and accumulates in any loaded drum. Precautions must be taken to avoid striking the drum with tools, etc., because sparks can ignite this hydrogen mixture and cause the drum to explode. For the same reason, there can be no open flames near drums. Filling a used drum with a foreign material can also cause explosions. Care must be taken never to fill a sulfuric acid drum with any other acid or substance unless the drum has been thoroughly and properly cleaned.

Bursting. Bursting of drums can be caused by (1) expansion of the acid because of heat, (2) use of air pressure for emptying, (3) filling drum too full—insufficient air space (outage) in drum, (4) build-up of internal pressure during long-term storage without periodic venting, and (5) allowing water to enter "empty" drum and come into contact with frozen oleum left in drum by last consignee.

Leakage. Leakage occurs because the drum metal has been corroded by weak acid left in "empty" drums. Dilution of the acid is set up by absorption of moisture from the air through loose closures.

The necessity for protective clothing and rules forbidding flames, sparks, smoking, etc., applies fully as much to drum as to carboy shipments. And, as outlined in the preceding discussion of carboys, these rules apply to both empty and loaded containers.

Storage of Drums

Neither full nor empty drums should be stored in direct sunlight or in places where the temperature may exceed 90°F. Storage periods should be kept at a minimum.

Full drums should always be stored with body plug upward. All drums should be vented periodically—at least once a week and more often in warmer weather. Venting is accomplished by loosening the body plug, allowing the internal pressure to vent, and then retightening the plug.

Emptying

Drums should be emptied only by gravity. Application of air pressure is extremely dangerous.

A pipe wrench or plug wrench with a long handle should be used to remove the body plug. The operator should:

1. Face away during the operation.
2. Apply one full turn after plug starts to move, then allow any internal pressure to vent.
3. Remove plug.

If the body plug should fail to start, the drum should be fastened in a suitable holding fixture while even pressure is applied manually by a large pipe wrench with a long or extension handle. If the plug still cannot be moved, the drum should be returned to the supplier.

Drums should be drained completely and plugs securely replaced. Spillage on the outside of the drum should be wiped off and the affected area flushed well with water.

Under no circumstances should water or any substance other than sulfuric acid be introduced into these drums. Drums should always be returned to supplier without washing.

Care should be taken to make certain that closures are securely seated before empty drums are sent back to supplier. In all instances, empty drums should be promptly returned to supplier.

Plastic Containers

The glass carboy is rapidly being replaced by plastic bottles or containers. These plastic containers may be jacketless or have a fiber, wood or steel overpack. The following are the ICC designations.

1. For sulfuric acid concentrations that do not exceed 95%: ICC-IH, ICC-15P, or ICC or 22 metal crate with inside polyethylene carboy or

glued plywood or wooden box or plywood drum with 2T or 2TL polyethylene container.

2. For use with sulfuric acid of 93 percent or greater concentration: ICC-5B, ICC-6J or 37A (single-trip) steel barrels or drums of 55 gallon capacity with inside 2S or 2SL polyethylene liners; all drums to be of at least 16-gage steel.

3. For general use: ICC-16D wirebound wooden overwrap with inside 2T, 2TL, 2S or 2SL polyethylene container.

4. For general use: ICC-21C fiber drum with inside 2T polyethylene container.

5. For single-trip use: ICC-37A metal drums with inside polyethylene containers (specification 27). Removable heads of steel drums may have holes of suitable size to provide for protruding neck and closure of inner container.

6. For general use: ICC-16A wirebound wooden box with inside (specification 2U) polyethylene container. The container must be separated from the wooden box by a complete corrugated fiberboard liner and top and bottom pads.

Handling of polyethylene containers is the same as that of glass carboys and steel drums. There is no formation of hydrogen, thus the chance for explosion is nil.

Unloading Tank Cars, Tank Trucks and Barges

General Precautions for Unloading

Sulfuric acid within the range of 60° Bé to 65% oleum can be safely unloaded from tank car or tank truck by either pump or air pressure. Sulfuric acid of any strength can be unloaded by pump if suitable precautionary measures are taken and proper handling procedures used. Computation of air pressure necessary for a specific unloading is discussed on page 110.

Unloading of tank car and tank truck shipments is the consumer's responsibility. (See page 27.) Water in ample quantity must be readily available at unloading racks.

No naked flame of any kind should be permitted near any opening of the tank for any purpose whatsoever. An incandescent electric light with gas-proof socket and connection, or an explosion-proof flashlight, can be used with safety.

Smoking is strictly forbidden in the vicinity of a dome.

Tank car fittings should never be struck with ordinary tools or other hard objects. Tools made of brass or any "non-spark" material may be used when necessary. Use of these tools should, however, be kept at a minimum.

A tank must not be used for a product other than that last contained because of the possibility of damage to the tank or generation of an explosive gas.

Unauthorized personnel should not walk through or under the loading racks or in or between the tank cars while unloading operations are in progress.

Experience has shown the most frequent causes of accidents are personal rather than environmental; that is, failure to stay alert, forgetfulness, overfatigue and poor judgment. These human failings most often cause overflow of the storage tanks and inadequate bleed-off of air pressure in tank cars before opening.

General Design of Acid Loading and Unloading Ramps

A good ramp design provides ample capacity for handling the desired number of the largest tank cars in use. The elevation of the rack should correspond to the average height of the tank-car platforms. The drop-down ramps should be counter-balanced with a handrail on one or both sides. Storage boxes or cabinets for miscellaneous tools and pipe fittings should be placed at convenient locations along the walkways to help prevent accidents caused by stumbling.

Loading and unloading arms, made of rigid steel pipe with swivel joints, have proved quite successful. Plastic pipe or tubing should be thoroughly evaluated before placing into large-scale use. Loading arms must be chained down to the body of the tank car while acid is being loaded. Pump pressure has a tendency to place into motion, or whip around, parts of a loading arm that have not been permanently or tightly secured. For the same reason, a word of caution is needed if unloading arms are also doubling in use as loading arms. This concerns the end section of the arm which is pointing downward and is inserted into the dome opening of the car during the loading operation. This section is at least 18 inches long, frequently longer, to preclude the possibility of its working out of position by pump pressure and, thereby, spraying a full stream of acid over the surrounding area. This is particularly important in the use of cars with large dome openings. Permanent metal stands for receiving movable ends of the loading arms while not in use are excellent. Ample maintenance to correct or avoid corroded piping keeps down injuries and prevents loss of sulfuric acid. A PVC or lead cup should be used to catch drippings from unused lines. This cup can be easily attached by putting a flexible wire over the open end of the line.

Spotting Acid Cars in Proper Position

The unloading location should be in the open. There should be a visible directional sign, such as "Spot Dome Here", so that the train crew can

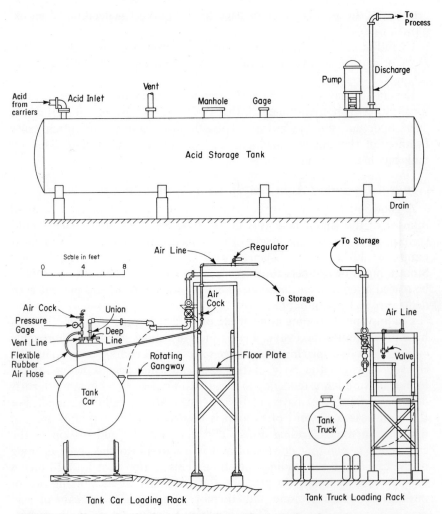

Fig. 5. Loading and unloading facilities for tank cars and tank trucks.

accurately spot the car. In the case of tank trucks, similar guidance should be provided so that the driver can accurately spot the trailer. If the tank is placed wrong, respot the car by some mechanical means rather than by using temporary loading-arm extensions. The brakes should be set and the wheels blocked before any car is unloaded. Caution signs, such as "Stop, Tank Car Connected", should be displayed to alert anyone in the area.

If the car is not protected by a switch gate, derails should be placed at open end or at ends of siding approximately one car-length from the car being unloaded.

Loading and unloading facilities for tank cars and tank trucks are illustrated in Figures 5 and 6.

Inspection

The dome fitting should be inspected for leaks and other defects before unloading. This helps avoid acid spillage and spraying.

Tank Car Fittings

The fittings on all tank cars are not alike; however, they all are designed to discharge by air pressure. Typical dome arrangements are shown in Figures 7 and 8. Each dome contains:

1. Dome cover (hinged or secured by center screw)
2. Discharge (deep line or eduction) pipe (closed with cap, plug or valve)
3. Air connection:
   a. A short pipe closed with a safety vent or
   b. A separate air connection closed with a cap, valve or plug cock.
   (If tank car contains two vent openings, the sealed cap with the pipe must not be removed. The other opening is the correct vent and should be removed so that air can be applied at that opening.)
4. Safety vent, equipped with a frangible disc which ruptures when the pressure inside the tank car builds up and exceeds a maximum of 45 pounds per square inch.

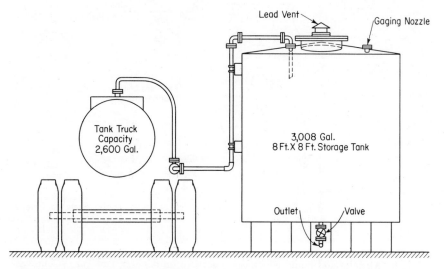

Fig. 6. Unloading sulfuric acid from tank truck.

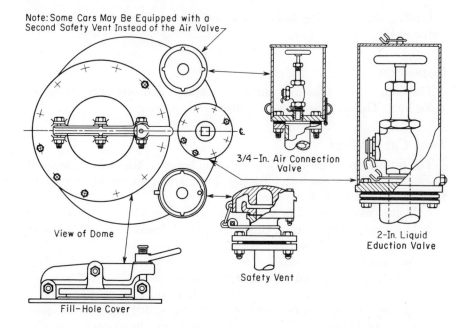

Note:Some Cars May Be Equipped with a
Second Safety Vent Instead of the Air Valve

3/4-In. Air Connection
Valve

2-In. Liquid
Eduction Valve

View of Dome

Safety Vent

Fill-Hole Cover

Fig. 7. Air inlet and liquid eduction valves on dome of tank car. (*Courtesy Manufacturing Chemists' Association, Inc.*)

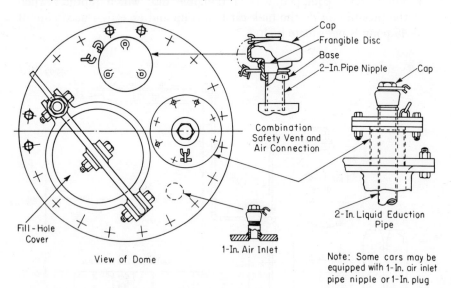

Cap
Frangible Disc
Base
2-In.Pipe Nipple
Cap

Combination
Safety Vent and
Air Connection

2-In. Liquid Eduction
Pipe

Fill-Hole
Cover

View of Dome

1-In. Air Inlet

Note: Some cars may be
equipped with 1-In. air inlet
pipe nipple or 1-In. plug

Fig. 8. Air inlet and liquid eduction connections on dome of tank car. (*Courtesy Manufacturing Chemists' Association, Inc.*)

Unloading and loading connections for tank cars and tank trucks are illustrated in Figs. 9 and 10, respectively.

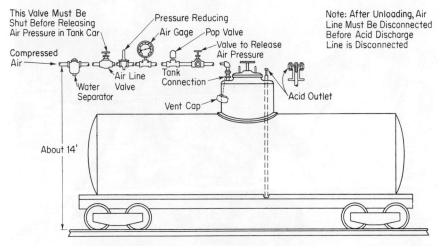

Fig. 9. Air-piping setup for unloading acid tank cars. (*Courtesy Manufacturing Chemists' Association, Inc.*)

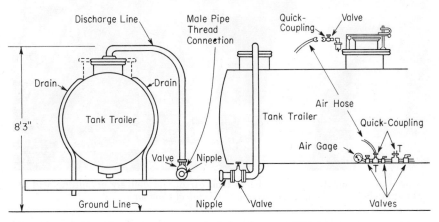

Fig. 10. Loading and unloading connections for acid tank trucks. (*Courtesy York Transport Company.*)

Unloading with Air Pressure

Compressed air used for unloading should be free from oil, moisture and other foreign matter. The air line (which is idle between receipts) should be blown clear before making connections with the tank car. Any efficient means of drying air ahead of the shut-off valve is satisfactory.

Tank Car Shipment: Operator checks tank car during delivery of sulfuric acid at Houston chemical plant. (*Courtesy Shell Chemical Company.*)

It is important to remember that not more than 30 psi pressure should be used to unload any tank car.

As the first step in actual unloading, relieve internal pressure—sometimes developed in transit—by *slowly* loosening air vent cap or dome cover. If air vent cap is loosened, wait until hand control assures that no pressure remains. Then remove cap. If dome cover is loosened, open lid cautiously on far side. When certain that pressure is relieved, open dome cover completely, gage depth of contents and take a sample of acid as described below.

Vacancy gaging, though sometimes providing a satisfactory approxima-tion, can often be misleading.

A very reliable method of gaging is to use a metal (stainless steel) rod marked off in inches and obtain the actual depth of the acid. Care must be taken to avoid damage to the coating if the car is lined with protective material. Also, any overhead electrical wiring near acid cars must be re-routed to prevent the gage rod from touching any wiring during gaging of the tank car. (Procedures for determining gage, temperature and specific gravity are presented in detail on page 33.)

Another important precaution concerns opening of the deepline of a full tank car of acid in preparation for the unloading operation. Although the main dome cover is relieved of pressure and is open to atmosphere, the deepline may still contain pressure. It is recommended that care be taken to first partially unscrew the deepline cap, relieving the pressure, before removing the cap completely.

After the sample has been taken, secure the dome cover tightly in place.

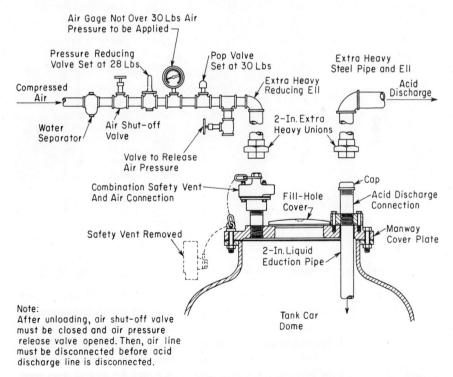

Fig. 11. Closeup of air-piping setup for unloading acid tank cars. (*Courtesy Manufacturing Chemists' Association, Inc.*)

Seal the gasket. Remove the cap from the deepline and make connections with the unloading line.

Make connections of air supply to air line (or air vent) on the dome as shown on Figure 11. The air line must have a pressure-reducing or safety valve set at not over 28 psi. Extreme caution is advisable when using air to unload sulfuric acid cars containing hydrocarbons, as is the case with shipment of certain spent acids.

TABLE III. REQUIRED PRESSURES FOR UNLOADING VARIOUS STRENGTHS

Total Head (Ft)	Air Pressure (Lbs/Sq. In. Gage)					
	60 Be'	66 Be'	98%	104.5%	109%	114.6%
1	0.7	0.8	0.8	0.8	0.9	0.9
2	1.5	1.6	1.6	1.7	1.7	1.8
3	2.2	2.4	2.4	2.5	2.6	2.7
4	3.0	3.2	3.2	3.3	3.4	3.5
5	3.7	4.0	4.0	4.1	4.3	4.4
6	4.4	4.8	4.8	5.0	5.2	5.3
7	5.2	5.6	5.6	5.8	6.0	6.2
8	5.9	6.4	6.4	6.6	6.9	7.1
9	6.7	7.2	7.2	7.5	7.7	8.0
10	7.4	7.9	8.0	8.3	8.6	8.8
15	11.1	11.9	12.0	12.4	12.9	13.3
20	14.8	15.9	16.0	16.6	17.2	17.7
25	18.5	19.8	20.0	20.7	21.5	22.1
30	22.2	23.8	24.0	24.9	25.8	26.5
35	25.9	27.8	27.9	29.0	30.1	31.0
40	29.6	31.8	31.9	33.2	34.4	35.4
45	33.3	35.8	35.9	37.3	38.7	39.8
50	36.9	39.7	39.9	41.5	43.0	44.2
55	40.6	43.7	43.9	45.6	47.3	48.6
60	44.3	47.7	47.9	49.8	51.6	53.1
65	48.0	51.7	51.9	53.9	55.9	57.5
70	51.7	55.6	55.9	58.1	60.2	61.9
75	55.4	59.6	59.9	62.2	64.4	66.3
80	59.1	63.6	63.9	66.4	68.7	70.8
85	62.8	67.6	67.9	70.5	73.0	75.2
90	66.5	71.5	71.9	74.7	77.3	79.6
95	70.2	75.5	75.9	78.8	81.6	84.0
100	73.4	79.5	79.9	83.0	85.9	88.4
(Lbs/Cu. Ft.)	106.4	114.47	114.99	119.5	123.74	127.36

Apply air pressure slowly until the acid flows normally into the storage tank, vented to atmosphere or scrubber in case of fuming acid. Remember that air pressure must not exceed 30 psig. A drop in pressure accompanied by the noise of air being blown through an empty vessel indicates the tank car is empty. Continue air flow until the discharge line is completely empty, then shut off the air, open the relief valve and allow the acid pipe to drain.

When the tank car has reached atmospheric pressure and the acid has drained, disconnect plant—air fittings from the safety vent assembly or cap air inlet. Catch drippings from the plant acid line in a PVC or lead cup. If any spillage occurs on the tank car, wash with plenty of water.

Table III lists pressures required to unload various strengths of sulfuric acid. Pressures above maximum allowable—30 psi—are for information only.

Unloading by Pump

When unloading by pump, follow the above procedure but connect the deepline to the pump inlet. When the tank car is empty, the pump will operate faster.

Cold-weather Unloading

Frozen or congealed acid can be detected with the gaging rod through the vent or air connection.

Never attempt to thaw a tank car with fire or open flame. A car may be thawed by covering with a tarpaulin and then heating with live steam. A second method is to place a car in a heated building and then use live steam. When a car is thawed, the procedures outlined above can be used for unloading.

Return of Empty Tank Cars

The four 10¾- x 10¾-inch ICC placards on the sides and ends of the tank car must be turned over and reattached to the tank by the unloader.

Barge Shipment: Barge is loaded at Stauffer Chemical Company's sulfuric acid plant in Houston.

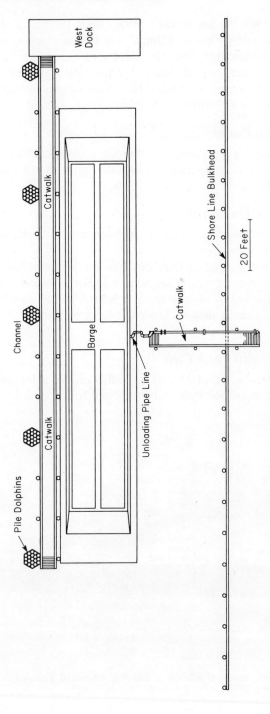

Fig. 12 Barge unloading facilities.

Tank Truck Unloading

Procedure and precautionary measures for unloading tank trucks are substantially the same as described for tank cars. For connections etc., see typical arrangement (Fig. 11, page 29).

Barge Unloading

Most of the above unloading procedures are applicable to receipt of sulfuric acid shipments by barge. Unloading facilities for barges are illustrated in Figs. 12 and 13.

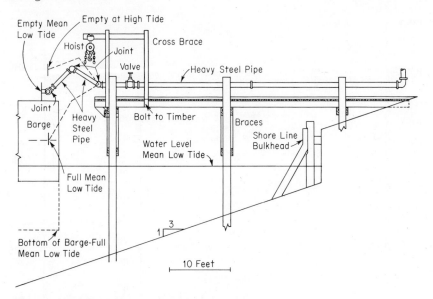

Fig. 13. Catwalk and piping for unloading acid barge.

Procedures for Determining Gage, Temperature and Specific Gravity of Loaded Tank Cars

A tank car loaded with sulfuric acid is generally gaged with a steel rod marked at one-inch intervals. Read the level of the acid on the rod at the nearest one-half-inch mark below the acid level.

After the gage reading, fill a laboratory sample bottle from the tank car. Clamp this bottle, which is generally eight ounces in volume and wide-mouthed in design, to a stainless steel rod or rigid wire three to four feet long. Immerse the bottle in the acid, fill, rinse, empty and refill before removing from the tank car. Bring up the first refill and empty into a hydrometer cylinder or laboratory graduate, generally 13 by 1⅜ inches in size. Rinse the cylinder with the acid. Then pour the acid back into the tank car. Take another acid sample, rinse and empty. Retain the third sample in the cylinder. (Rinsing removes traces of previous samples and brings the temperature of the cylinder nearer to that of the tank car.)

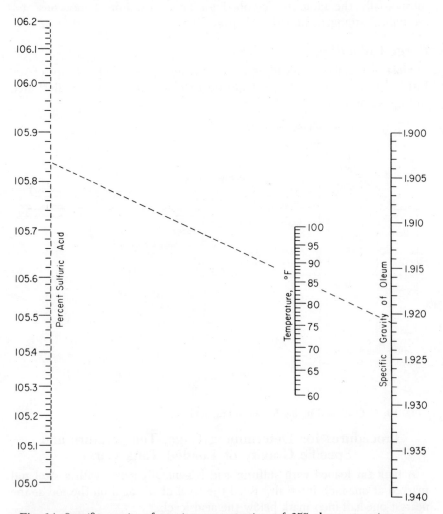

Fig. 14. Specific gravity of varying concentrations of 25% oleum at various temperatures. (*Chemical Processing, March 1960, Copyright Putman Publishing Company.*)

Take the sample immediately to the loader's shelter on the rack, generally a distance of 50 to 150 feet. Place a Tagliabue or similar floating-type thermometer, graduated at 1° F intervals from 0 to 230° F, in the cylinder, agitate and read. Place a Tagliabue or similar gravity hydrometer, graduated in 0.001 division from 1.750 to 1.850, in the cylinder and read. Read the hydrometer as described on page 36. If the observed value is between graduations, the first higher one is recorded (1.8055 is 1.806, etc.). Take all readings quickly to minimize the temperature differential.   **1299083**

In the following example, the loader's gravity is compared with calculated gravity from laboratory analysis. Gravity at true car temperature is also given. Figs. 14 & 15 are useful in determining acidity from specific

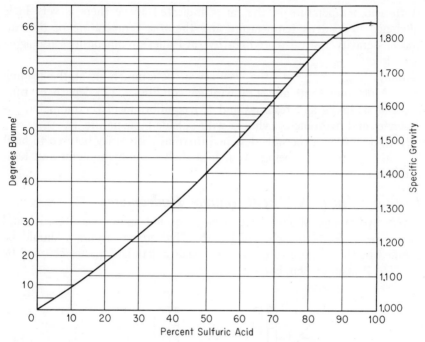

Fig. 15. Density of aqueous solutions of sulfuric acid at 60°/60°F.

gravity. True temperature of the car is obtained by placing a thermometer in the sampling bottle and holding it in the tank car below the dome opening in order to eliminate any cooling effect from wind or outside atmosphere.

Difference in car weight is the difference in weight between loader's gravity and calculated gravity, using the true temperature of the tank car. "Plus" indicates weight should be added, "minus" that weight should be subtracted—both in comparison to weight at loader's gravity. All temperatures are Fahrenheit scale. Acidities and gravities are rounded off to one and three decimal places, respectively.

Example

Car No. 1 ....93.49%

> Weather: Cloudy—84°—Wind South 24 mph
> Temperature at car...............................95°F
> Loader's temperature ....95°F
> Loader's gravity 1.817
> Gravity from acidity at loader's temperature...........1.8175
> Gravity from acidity at car temperature...............1.8175
> Difference in car weight ....+32 lbs.

With acid temperature in the range indicated above there is very little difference in loader's temperature and the true temperature of the car. Loader's gravity and calculated gravity (at loader's temperature) also agree very closely.

Many things enter into the accuracy of determinations at the loading rack. Most important are: (1) weather conditions, (2) length of time between sampling and readings and (3) equilibrium of thermometer, hydrometer and hydrometer cylinder with outside temperature.

In cold weather a specially designed thermos bottle may be used to hold the sample while it is being taken into shelter for hydrometer and temperature readings.

Testing Sulfuric Acid with Baume' Hydrometer

The hydrometer should have a range of not more than 10° Bé and should be at least 10 inches in length. Hydrometer accuracy should be certified by the manufacturer or tested against standard glasses certified by the U.S. Bureau of Standards.

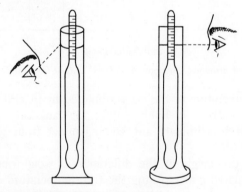

Fig. 16. Correct method of reading a hydrometer.

Reading the Hydrometer

The correct method of reading the hydrometer is shown in Figure 16.

The sample of sulfuric acid is placed in a clear jar or graduate. The hydrometer is carefully immersed in it to a point slightly below that at which it naturally sinks, and then allowed to float freely.

The reading should not be taken until acid and hydrometer are free from air bubbles and at rest.

In taking an hydrometer reading, the eye should gaze first in a plane slightly below that of the surface of the acid. The eye should then be raised slowly until the acid surface, first seen as an ellipse, becomes a straight line. The point at which this line cuts the hydrometer scale should be taken as the reading of the instrument.

Temperature Correction

The thermometer must be used with the hydrometer in taking the Baumé reading of an acid.

Hydrometers do not show correct strength of a liquid unless read at the exact temperature indicated on the spindle; that is, at 60°F. Accurate readings may be obtained by cooling or warming H_2SO_4 to this temperature, but in most instances a correction can be accurately applied by using a temperature correction table. The correction is added when the test is made above 60°F and subtracted for tests below 60°F.

Temperature Corrections

At 10°Bé: (range 5–15°) 0.029°Bé or 0.00023 SpGr per °F
At 20°Bé: (range 15–25°) 0.036°Bé or 0.00034 SpGr per °F
At 30°Bé: (range 25–35°) 0.035°Bé or 0.00039 SpGr per °F
At 40°Bé: (range 35–45°) 0.031°Bé or 0.00041 SpGr per °F
At 50°Bé: (range 45–55°) 0.028°Bé or 0.00045 SpGr per °F
At 60°Bé: (range 55–63°) 0.026°Bé or 0.00053 SpGr per °F
At 63°Bé: (range 63–66°) 0.026°Bé or 0.00057 SpGr per °F
At 66°Bé: 0.0235°Bé or 0.00054 SpGr per °F

Note: Because sulfuric acid above 93% may have the same specific gravity at different concentrations, a direct analysis of acid strength above 93% is recommended. (See Table XIII, p. 86, which lists values for sulfuric acid dilution tests.)

At 94%: 0.00054 Sp Gr per °F.
At 96%: 0.00053 Sp Gr per °F.
At 97.5%: 0.00052 Sp Gr per °F.
At 100%: 0.00052 Sp Gr per °F.

Conversion Formulas for Density Scales (Heavy Liquids)

$$\text{Degrees Baumé} = 145 - \frac{145}{\text{Sp Gr}}$$

$$\text{Specific Gravity} = \frac{145}{145 - \text{Deg Bé}}$$

Fig. 17 facilitates correction of specific gravity and Baumé readings to standard temperature.

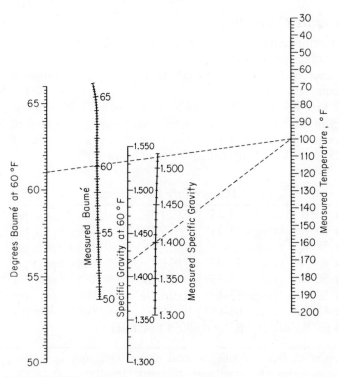

Fig. 17. Correction of specific gravity and Baumé readings to standard temperature. (*Chemical Engineering, Copyright McGraw-Hill, Inc.*)

Storage of Commercial Sulfuric Acid

Facility

The capacity of a consumer's sulfuric acid storage facility is dependent upon:

1. Daily requirements.

2. Method of transportation (rail, truck, barge, etc.) determining, in part, size (tonnage) of delivery.
3. Time required for transportation.
4. A minimum storage capacity at least equal to the amount of sulfuric acid necessary for two weeks of plant operation.

Elevation of the storage tank depends upon the distribution system within the plant. If sulfuric acid is delivered to the consuming point by gravity, then the tank is elevated. If delivery is by pump, either submerged or outside, the tank is constructed on a foundation approximately three feet from ground level. Sometimes, sulfuric acid is pumped to an elevated head tank and then distributed by gravity. In other cases, the storage tank has a bottom outlet connected by a blow-case where the acid is delivered by air pressure. The storage tank itself is never pressurized.

For strengths of 60° Bé (76.67%) sulfuric acid or stronger (including oleum), the tank is generally made of flange-quality steel with all–welded construction meeting the latest ASME code. ASTM A7 (mild steel) can also be used. Welds are both inside and outside. Horizontal cylindrical dished-head tanks with capacities up to 300 tons are stock items of tank manufacturers.

Storage tanks for strengths weaker than 77.67% sulfuric acid should have either lead or phenolic linings.

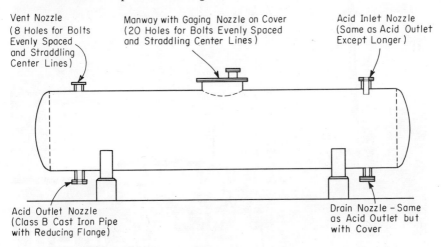

Fig. 18. Typical sulfuric acid storage tank. See also Fig. 5.

Tanks of 300-tons-plus capacity are usually vertical, field-erected, with conical roof and flat bottom. The thickness of the construction plate depends on the tank capacity: 75 tons requires ⅜-inch plate; larger tanks, ½-inch plate. The tank should contain a plug valve in the outlet line to

Acid Transfer: Piping, pumps and tanks supply sulfuric acid to alkylation plant at Houston refinery. In the top photograph, an operator puts another pump on line charging fresh acid. The bottom photo shows a cascade alkylation reactor in the background. (*Courtesy Humble Oil & Refining Co.*)

guarantee positive shut-off. The valve is operated by a mechanism extending through the top of the tank.

The foundation of a storage tank should be designed so that the entire tank, including the bottom, is visible for inspection and maintenance. Some of the larger tanks are constructed on concrete slabs at ground level.

The tank should be equipped with a vent (see Figure 18) to allow normal intake and release of atmosphere caused by changes in acid levels and to release any build-up of internal pressure. The tank is thus maintained at atmospheric pressure. Because of extremely corrosive atmosphere at the vent, the vent should be made of a corrosion-resistant material such as PVC, Saran-lined steel or lead-lined steel. Tank vents and other openings must be protected against entry of rain or snow.

The tank should be equipped with stairs for access to the manhole, vent and nozzles in the top.

Gaging the tank for inventory or acid level is easily done with steel tape equipped with plumb bob, steel rod (if tank is not over eight feet deep) or liquid-level indicators. The use of liquid-level indicators requires special calibrations for different gravities of acid; sight glasses are not recommended. Tanks should be painted with light-color corrosion-resistant paint to reflect heat. Heavy applications of paint protect the metal in case of spillage.

Tank capacities can be calculated from Figures 19 (horizontal tanks) and 20 (vertical tanks). In Fig. 19, connect a line between the tank diameter (scale D) and the liquid height, as a percent of tank diameter (scale H), and read the gallons per foot of length of tank from its intersection with scale V. If the tank has bulged ends, use the same values in constructing a line from D to h, and read the corresponding total gallonage of both ends from its intersection with scale v.

Example: Suppose it is desired to know the contents of a horizontal tank 20 feet long having a diameter of 90 inches and a liquid depth of 27 inches if the tank has bulged ends.

Solution:

1. $\frac{27}{90} = .30 =$ height of liquid as a percent of depth $= 30\%$
2. Connect 90 on the D scale with 30 on the H scale.
3. Read 83 gal./ft. from the V scale.
4. $20 \times 83 = 1660$ gal. in main tank.
5. Connect 90 on the D scale with 30 on the h scale.
6. Read 66 gallons total in both ends.
7. $1660 + 66 = 1726$ gallons total in the tank.

TABLE IV. CAPACITIES OF RECTANGULAR TANKS IN U.S. GALLONS AND CUBIC FEET PER FOOT IN DEPTH

Upper figures gallons; lower figures cubic feet (1 gal. H_2O = 8.345 lbs; 1 ft³ H_2O = 62.43 lbs.)

Width of Tank	LENGTH OF TANK													
	4'	4'6"	5'	5'6"	6'	6'6"	7'	7'6"	8'	8'6"	9'	9'6"	10'	10'6"
2'	59.84 / 8.00	67.32 / 9.00	74.81 / 10.00	82.29 / 11.00	89.77 / 12.00	97.25 / 13.00	104.73 / 14.00	112.21 / 15.00	119.68 / 16.00	127.17 / 17.00	134.65 / 18.00	142.13 / 19.00	149.61 / 20.00	157.09 / 21.00
2'6"	74.80 / 10.00	84.16 / 11.25	93.51 / 12.50	102.86 / 13.75	112.21 / 15.00	121.21 / 16.25	130.91 / 17.50	140.26 / 18.75	149.61 / 20.00	158.96 / 21.25	168.31 / 22.50	177.66 / 23.75	187.01 / 25.00	196.36 / 26.25
3'	89.77 / 12.00	100.99 / 13.50	112.21 / 15.00	123.43 / 16.50	134.65 / 18.00	145.87 / 19.50	157.09 / 21.00	168.31 / 22.50	179.53 / 24.00	190.75 / 25.50	201.97 / 27.00	213.19 / 28.50	224.41 / 30.00	235.63 / 31.50
3'6"	104.73 / 14.00	117.82 / 15.75	130.91 / 17.50	144.00 / 19.25	157.09 / 21.00	170.18 / 22.75	183.27 / 24.50	196.36 / 26.25	209.45 / 28.00	222.54 / 29.75	235.63 / 31.50	248.73 / 33.25	261.82 / 35.00	274.90 / 36.75
4'	119.69 / 16.00	134.65 / 18.00	149.61 / 20.00	164.57 / 22.00	179.53 / 24.00	194.49 / 26.00	209.45 / 28.00	224.41 / 30.00	239.37 / 32.00	254.34 / 34.00	269.30 / 36.00	284.26 / 38.00	299.22 / 40.00	314.18 / 42.00
4'6"		151.48 / 20.25	168.31 / 22.50	185.14 / 24.75	201.97 / 27.00	218.80 / 29.25	235.62 / 31.50	252.47 / 33.75	269.30 / 36.00	286.13 / 38.25	302.96 / 40.50	319.79 / 42.75	336.62 / 45.00	353.45 / 47.25
5'			187.01 / 25.00	205.71 / 27.50	224.41 / 30.00	243.11 / 32.50	261.82 / 35.00	280.52 / 37.50	299.22 / 40.00	317.92 / 42.50	336.62 / 45.00	355.32 / 47.50	374.03 / 50.00	392.72 / 52.50
5'6"				226.28 / 30.25	246.86 / 33.00	267.43 / 35.75	288.00 / 38.50	308.57 / 41.25	329.14 / 44.00	349.71 / 46.75	370.28 / 49.50	390.85 / 52.25	411.43 / 55.00	432.00 / 57.75
6'					269.30 / 36.00	291.74 / 39.00	314.18 / 42.00	336.62 / 45.00	359.06 / 48.00	381.50 / 51.00	403.94 / 54.00	426.39 / 57.00	448.83 / 60.00	471.27 / 63.00
6'6"						316.05 / 42.25	340.36 / 45.50	364.67 / 48.75	388.98 / 52.00	413.30 / 55.25	437.60 / 58.50	461.92 / 61.75	486.23 / 65.00	510.54 / 68.25
7'							366.54 / 49.00	392.72 / 52.50	418.91 / 56.00	445.09 / 59.50	471.27 / 63.00	497.45 / 66.50	523.64 / 70.00	549.81 / 73.50
7'6"								420.78 / 56.25	448.83 / 60.00	476.88 / 63.75	504.93 / 67.50	532.98 / 71.25	561.04 / 75.00	589.08 / 78.75
8'									478.75 / 64.00	508.67 / 68.00	538.59 / 72.00	568.51 / 76.00	598.44 / 80.00	628.36 / 84.00

These tanks are commonly used for pickling, not for bulk storage of acid.

TABLE IV. CAPACITIES OF RECTANGULAR TANKS IN U.S. GALLONS AND CUBIC FEET PER FOOT IN DEPTH

Upper figures gallons; lower figures cubic feet (1 gal. H_2O = 8.345 lbs; 1 ft^3 H_2O = 62.43 lbs.)

Width of Tank	LENGTH OF TANK											
	11'	11'6"	12'	12'6"	13'	13'6"	14'	14'6"	15'	15'6"	16'	16'6"
2'	164.57 / 22.00	172.05 / 23.00	179.53 / 24.00	187.01 / 25.00	194.49 / 26.00	201.97 / 27.00	209.45 / 28.00	216.93 / 29.00	224.41 / 30.00	231.89 / 31.00	239.37 / 32.00	246.85 / 33.00
2'6"	205.71 / 27.50	215.06 / 28.75	224.41 / 30.00	233.76 / 31.25	243.11 / 32.50	252.46 / 33.75	261.81 / 35.00	271.16 / 36.25	280.51 / 37.50	289.86 / 38.75	299.21 / 40.00	308.56 / 41.25
3'	246.86 / 33.00	258.07 / 34.50	269.30 / 36.00	280.53 / 37.50	291.76 / 39.00	302.99 / 40.50	314.22 / 42.00	325.45 / 43.50	336.68 / 45.00	347.91 / 46.50	359.14 / 48.00	370.37 / 49.50
3'6"	288.00 / 38.50	301.09 / 40.25	314.18 / 42.00	327.27 / 43.75	340.36 / 45.50	353.45 / 47.25	366.54 / 49.00	379.63 / 50.75	392.72 / 52.50	405.81 / 54.25	418.90 / 56.00	431.99 / 57.75
4'	329.14 / 44.00	344.10 / 46.00	359.06 / 48.00	374.02 / 50.00	388.98 / 52.00	403.94 / 54.00	418.90 / 56.00	433.86 / 58.00	448.82 / 60.00	463.76 / 62.00	478.72 / 64.00	493.68 / 66.00
4'6"	370.28 / 49.50	387.11 / 51.75	403.94 / 54.00	420.77 / 56.25	437.60 / 58.50	454.43 / 60.75	471.26 / 63.00	488.09 / 65.25	504.92 / 67.50	521.75 / 69.75	538.58 / 72.00	555.41 / 74.25
5'	411.43 / 55.00	430.13 / 57.50	448.83 / 60.00	467.53 / 62.50	486.23 / 65.00	504.93 / 67.50	523.63 / 70.00	542.33 / 72.50	561.03 / 75.00	579.73 / 77.50	598.43 / 80.00	617.13 / 82.50
5'6"	452.57 / 60.50	473.14 / 63.25	493.71 / 66.00	514.28 / 68.75	534.85 / 71.50	555.42 / 74.25	575.99 / 77.00	596.56 / 79.75	617.13 / 82.50	637.70 / 85.25	658.27 / 88.00	678.84 / 90.75
6'	493.71 / 66.00	516.15 / 69.00	538.59 / 72.00	561.03 / 75.00	583.47 / 78.00	605.91 / 81.00	628.35 / 84.00	650.79 / 87.00	673.23 / 90.00	695.67 / 93.00	718.11 / 96.00	740.55 / 99.00
6'6"	534.85 / 71.50	559.16 / 74.75	583.47 / 78.00	607.78 / 81.25	632.09 / 84.50	656.40 / 87.75	680.71 / 91.00	705.02 / 94.25	729.33 / 97.50	753.64 / 100.75	777.95 / 104.00	802.26 / 107.25
7'	575.99 / 77.00	602.18 / 80.50	628.36 / 84.00	654.54 / 87.50	680.72 / 91.00	706.90 / 94.50	733.08 / 98.00	759.26 / 101.50	785.44 / 105.00	811.62 / 108.50	837.80 / 112.00	863.98 / 115.50
7'6"	617.14 / 82.50	645.19 / 86.25	673.24 / 90.00	701.29 / 93.75	729.34 / 97.50	757.39 / 101.25	785.44 / 105.00	813.49 / 108.75	841.54 / 112.50	869.59 / 116.25	897.64 / 120.00	925.69 / 123.75
8'	658.28 / 88.00	688.20 / 92.00	718.12 / 96.00	748.04 / 100.00	777.96 / 104.00	807.88 / 108.00	837.80 / 112.00	867.74 / 116.00	897.66 / 120.00	927.58 / 124.00	957.50 / 128.00	987.42 / 132.00

These tanks are commonly used for pickling, not for bulk storage of acid.   (continued over)

TABLE IV. CAPACITIES OF RECTANGULAR TANKS IN U.S. GALLONS AND CUBIC FEET PER FOOT IN DEPTH

Upper figures gallons; lower figures cubic feet (1 gal. H_2O = 8.345 lbs., 1 ft³ H_2O = 62.43 lbs.)

Width of Tank	\	LENGTH OF TANK										
	17'	17'6"	18'	18'6"	19'	19'6"	20'	20'6"	21'	21'6"	22'	22'6"
2'	254.33 / 34.00	261.81 / 35.00	269.29 / 36.00	276.77 / 37.00	284.25 / 38.00	291.73 / 39.00	299.21 / 40.00	306.69 / 41.00	314.18 / 42.00	321.66 / 43.00	328.14 / 44.00	335.62 / 45.00
2'6"	317.91 / 42.50	327.26 / 43.75	336.61 / 45.00	345.96 / 46.25	355.31 / 47.50	364.66 / 48.75	374.01 / 50.00	383.36 / 51.25	392.72 / 52.50	402.07 / 53.75	411.42 / 55.00	420.77 / 56.25
3'	381.60 / 51.00	392.03 / 52.50	404.06 / 54.00	415.29 / 55.50	426.52 / 57.00	437.75 / 58.50	448.98 / 60.00	460.21 / 61.50	471.26 / 63.00	482.39 / 64.50	493.72 / 66.00	504.95 / 67.50
3'6"	445.08 / 59.50	458.17 / 61.25	471.26 / 63.00	484.35 / 64.75	497.44 / 66.50	510.53 / 68.25	523.62 / 70.00	536.71 / 71.75	549.80 / 73.50	562.89 / 75.25	576.00 / 77.00	589.09 / 78.75
4'	508.64 / 68.00	523.60 / 70.00	538.56 / 72.00	553.52 / 74.00	568.48 / 76.00	583.44 / 78.00	598.40 / 80.00	613.36 / 82.00	628.36 / 84.00	643.32 / 86.00	658.28 / 88.00	673.24 / 90.00
4'6"	572.24 / 76.50	589.07 / 78.75	605.90 / 81.00	622.73 / 83.25	639.56 / 85.50	656.39 / 87.75	673.22 / 90.00	690.05 / 92.25	706.90 / 94.25	723.73 / 96.75	740.56 / 99.00	757.29 / 101.25
5'	635.83 / 85.00	654.53 / 87.50	673.23 / 90.00	691.93 / 92.50	710.63 / 95.00	729.33 / 97.50	748.03 / 100.00	766.73 / 102.50	785.44 / 105.00	804.15 / 107.50	822.86 / 110.00	841.57 / 112.50
5'6"	699.41 / 93.50	719.98 / 96.25	740.55 / 99.00	761.12 / 101.75	781.69 / 104.50	802.26 / 107.25	822.83 / 110.00	843.40 / 112.75	864.00 / 115.50	884.57 / 118.25	905.14 / 121.00	927.71 / 123.75
6'	762.99 / 102.00	785.43 / 105.00	797.87 / 108.00	820.31 / 111.00	842.75 / 114.00	865.19 / 117.00	887.63 / 120.00	910.07 / 123.00	942.54 / 126.00	964.98 / 129.00	987.42 / 132.00	1009.86 / 135.00
6'6"	826.57 / 110.50	850.88 / 113.75	875.19 / 117.00	899.50 / 120.25	923.81 / 123.50	948.12 / 126.75	972.44 / 130.00	996.75 / 133.25	1021.08 / 136.50	1045.39 / 139.75	1069.70 / 143.00	1094.01 / 146.25
7'	890.16 / 119.00	916.34 / 122.50	942.52 / 126.00	968.70 / 129.50	994.88 / 133.00	1021.06 / 136.50	1047.24 / 140.00	1073.42 / 143.50	1099.62 / 147.00	1125.80 / 150.50	1151.98 / 154.00	1178.16 / 157.50
7'6"	953.74 / 127.50	981.79 / 131.25	1009.84 / 135.00	1037.89 / 138.75	1065.94 / 142.50	1093.99 / 146.25	1122.04 / 150.00	1150.09 / 153.75	1178.16 / 157.50	1206.22 / 161.25	1234.28 / 165.00	1262.34 / 168.75
8'	1017.34 / 136.00	1047.26 / 140.00	1077.18 / 144.00	1107.10 / 148.00	1137.02 / 152.00	1166.94 / 156.00	1196.86 / 160.00	1226.78 / 164.00	1256.72 / 168.00	1281.64 / 172.00	1316.56 / 176.00	1341.48 / 180.00

These tanks are commonly used for pickling, not for bulk storage of acid.

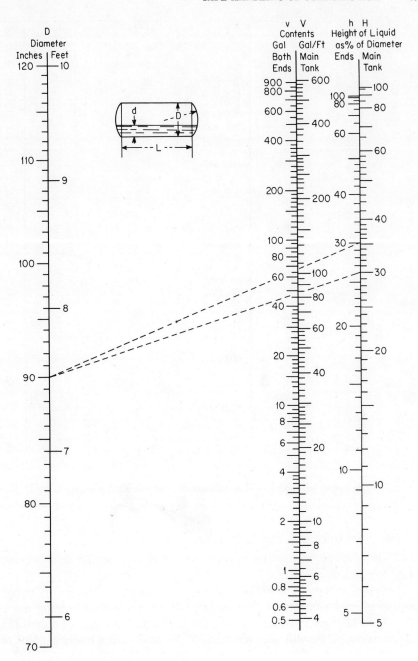

Fig. 19. Capacities of horizontal tanks with flat or bulged ends. (*Chemical Engineering Nomographs by D. S. Davis.*)

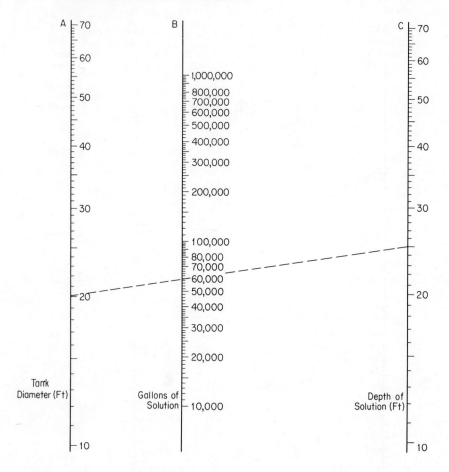

Fig. 20. Capacities of vertical tanks. (*Chemical Engineering Nomographs by D. S. Davis.*)

Outside Storage in Cold Climates

66° Bé sulfuric acid is the most widely used commercial acid because of its low freezing point: −20°F.

Nevertheless, provision for heating may be required when acid is stored outside in cold climates because of large deviations in the freezing point with *slight* changes in concentration. For example, a decrease of only 0.25° Baumé from 66°Bé will produce a 65.75° Bé acid with a freezing point of +2.3°F., or more than 20°F. higher than 66° Bé acid (see opposite). Freezing points for acid and oleum are given in Fig. 21; also in Tables XXII and XXIII, pp. 261 and 269.

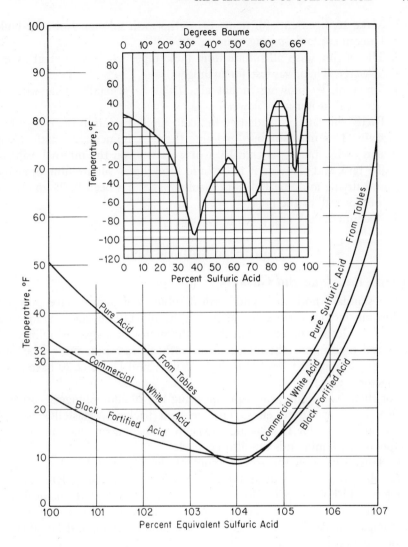

Fig. 21. Freezing points of sulfuric acid (*insert*) and oleum. (*The Betz Indicator, October 1962, Copyright Betz Laboratories, Inc.*)

Cleaning

Over a period of time, there is a slight reaction of strong sulfuric acid on mild steel. This reaction forms ferric sulfate which gradually accumulates and makes it necessary to wash the tank. The removal of this accumulation of iron sulfate from a storage tank can be hazardous.

A recommended procedure is as follows:

1. Make arrangements for neutralizing the wash solution from the tank.
2. Disconnect tank, piping, pumps, etc.
3. Thoroughly wash all sulfate from tank, pipes, etc. Use a great excess of water. Then, gas-test for hydrogen.
4. Dry tank by blowing in hot air. (This is generally done with an electrical heater and blower.)
5. Pacify the tank immediately to avoid rapid formation of iron sulfate again. This may be done by filling the tank immediately with strong acid or by spraying a thin layer of weak acid on the internal walls of the tank and allowing it to dry and form a gray sulfate film. Spraying and drying are repeated until a sulfate coat has been built up on the interior wall of the tank.
6. Reconnect tank and place in service.

Transfer of Sulfuric Acid

Pumps, Packings and Gaskets

The standard horizontal and vertical submerged pumps have provided highly satisfactory service for all strengths of sulfuric acid. Horizontal pumps should be connected directly to the motor by a shaft coupling.

Special precautions should be taken with all cast iron pumps because of the fragility of cast iron. Worthite, Wilfley and Durimet 20 have given satisfactory service.

For chemical feeding, small pumps using FA 20 alloy plungers, cast iron or FA 20 alloy wetted ends, TFE braided packings, Hastelloy C ball checks and Hastelloy D seats are satisfactory. Diaphragm-type pumps with Carpenter 20 liquid ends can also be used.

Packings vary with the specifications of the pump and include: graphited, lubricated, blue African asbestos; braided, lubricated, polytetrafluoroethylene (TFE) and polychlorotrifluoroethylene (CFE). Mechanical seals or packless seals of various kinds may be used for various sizes and speeds of pumps. All Pax No. 5 is recommended. Solid Teflon, and Durabla are recommended for centrifugal pumps.

Gaskets of $\frac{1}{16}$-inch-thick compressed asbestos or Durabla give excellent service.

Piping

Piping for the transfer of sulfuric acid depends on several factors: volume, continuous or intermittent flow, temperature and acid concentration. The most commonly used pipe for strengths above 60° Bé is Schedule-80 black steel with forged-weld fittings and welding neck flanges of all-weld construction. However, regular weld fittings are satisfactory and much cheaper. All piping of this type has good corrosion resistance and gives long service at ambient temperature.

When not in use, acid lines should be kept full in order to cut down corrosion and excessive formation of sulfates. Lines should be kept vented at one end to avoid build-up of excess pressure.

For weaker strengths, 66° Bé and lower, PVC pipe has had limited success. For strengths from 54° to 66° Bé, lead pipe or lead-lined steel pipe may be used. On strengths below 54° Bé, hard lead and chemical lead provide good service at all temperatures.

For high temperatures, cast iron pipe gives good service but does not have the strength of Schedule-80 steel pipe and requires a superstructure. Ductile iron provides the strength of steel and the corrosion resistance of cast iron.

Rubber hose is not recommended for strong sulfuric acid; however, there are some special hoses that give satisfactory limited service without excessive carbonization (charring). There are also a few plastics, such as Hypalon, which give satisfactory service for weaker strengths of sulfuric acid.

Transfer of all oleums is carried out in steel pipes. Iron sulfate accumulates in the steel pipes as well as in the storage tanks. In order to avoid excessive plugging, lines should not be less than one inch in diameter.

The rate at which sulfuric acid is pumped is determined by the size of the pipe. In small steel lines up to two inches in diameter, the velocity should not exceed two feet per second. In lead or cast iron, the rate can be four feet per second. For intermittent service, these rates can be exceeded. High velocities increase erosion of pipe and decrease life of pipe.

Handling Electrolyte Sulfuric Acid

Special precautions must be taken when handling and storing electrolyte-quality sulfuric acid. It must meet the Federal specifications listed on page 321. Gravities less than 1.835 are usually shipped in glass carboys or polyethylene-lined drums. Bulk deliveries of 1.835 specific gravity electrolyte are made in baked phenolic-lined or lead-lined tank cars. Storage tanks are usually lined with the same material. Lead-lined wood tanks and steel-supported lead tanks have given satisfactory service.

Strong acid is usually diluted in lead-lined equipment, Karbate or Duriron. Chemical lead, PVC and glass are used for piping. Pumps, valves and gaskets may be the same as those used with commercial acid.

Electrolyte acid dilution data are found in Table XIII, page 86. Conversion data are found in Table XXV, page 274.

3. RESISTANCE OF CONSTRUCTION MATERIALS TO CORROSION BY SULFURIC ACID

Choice of Materials

The question of choice of steel, cast iron, lead or plastic for equipment handling sulfuric acid often arises in chemical plants because sulfuric acid is such a common chemical in use on a tonnage basis.

Table V gives a general picture of the possible uses of steel, cast iron and lead for pipelines for various sulfuric acid services. Table V does not cover special conditions, such as contamination of product.

Table VI recommends materials for equipment which handles sulfuric acid and oleum at ambient temperatures.

Table VII rates various materials of construction on their resistance to sulfuric acid and oleum in various environments.

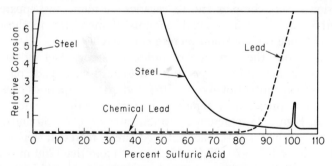

Fig. 22. Corrosion of steel and chemical lead in sulfuric acid at atmospheric temperatures. (*Fontana, "Corrosion", Copyright 1957.*)

Figure 22 illustrates the relative corrosion resistance of steel and lead to sulfuric acid at atmospheric temperatures (up to 95°F) over the complete concentration range including oleum. Corrosion rate decreases rapidly as the concentration is increased, as shown on the right-hand side of the figure.

51

Lead is susceptible to erosion-corrosion in strong acid, the rate of attack increasing rapidly with increasing concentration.

Lead-lined steel is tested for higher temperatures because steel provides mechanical support for the lead, which possesses low strength at these temperatures. Cast iron is not recommended for oleum service because of the danger of cracking the iron.

If concentrations of acid from 0 to 100% are handled, Duriron is the only commercial material obtainable at reasonable cost which resists 0 to 100% sulfuric acid at all temperatures including boiling.

Materials more resistant than steel or cast iron may be justified in cases where unusual aeration is involved. Careful consideration should be given to service conditions that may be unusual before making a final choice.

Figures 36 and 37, pp. 79–80, describe the areas of service, in terms of temperature and acid concentration, in which various metals and alloys exhibit satisfactory resistance to corrosion.

Corrosion of Steel: Temperatures and Concentrations

Ordinary carbon steel is widely used for the handling of sulfuric acid in concentrations over 70%. Storage tanks, pipelines, tank cars and shipping drums made of steel are very common for 78% (60° Bé), 93% (66° Bé), 98%, and stronger acids such as oleum. Pumps and valves are often made of alloys because of erosion-corrosion of steel. Much of the equipment in contact sulfuric acid plants is made of steel. Steel, however, is rapidly attacked by the more dilute sulfuric acids.

Corrosion is very complex and its vagaries are numerous; apparently insignificant variables, such as small amounts of impurities in the environment, can change the corrosion picture completely.

Figure 23 shows the corrosion of ordinary carbon steel by strong sulfuric acid as a function of temperature. Most tests were made on ordinary steel with carbon content of about 0.20% and exposure periods of 48 hours. Specimens were prepared by abrading the surface with 120 emery cloth.

Curves in Figure 23 represent corrosion rates of 5, 20, 50 and 200 mils per year. In other words, the outlined areas represent regions where corrosion rates of 0-5, 5-20, 20-50, 50-200 and more than 200 mils per year would be expected. Corrosion of steel by strong sulfuric acid is complicated because of the peculiar dips in the curves or the rapid increase in corrosion in the neighborhood of 100 to 101% acid. The narrowness of this range means that the acids must be carefully analyzed in order to obtain reliable results. Increased attack around 85% is more gradual and less difficult to establish.

Figure 23 shows that steel is not generally suitable for concentrations below about 65% at any temperature. Above 70% strength, steel can be

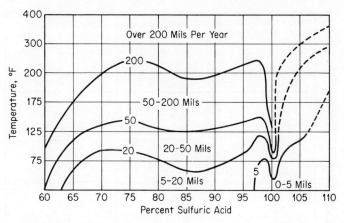

Fig. 23. Corrosion of carbon steel in strong sulfuric acid at various temperatures. (*Fontana, "Corrosion", Copyright 1957.*)

used, depending on the temperature involved. Steel is generally unsuitable if the temperature is above 175°F and the acid concentration is about 100%. Applications involving corrosion rates in the range 50 to 200 mils per year would involve relatively short life for steel and should be considered carefully; steel should be used only if the economics of the

(continued on page 64)

TABLE V. STEEL, CAST IRON, AND LEAD FOR PIPE LINES
HANDLING SULFURIC ACID[a]

Acid Concentration, %	Temperature		
	Atmospheric	35 to 80° C.	Over 80° C.[b]
70 and above	Lead	Lead	Lead or lead-lined steel
78 (60 Bé.)	Steel, cast iron, or lead	Steel, cast iron or lead	Cast iron, lead, or lead-lined steel
93 (66 Bé.)	Steel or cast iron	Steel or cast iron	Cast iron
98	Steel or cast iron	Steel or cast iron	Cast iron
104.5 and above	Steel	Steel	Steel
70 to 78[c]	Lead, steel, or cast iron	Lead, steel, or cast iron	Lead, lead-lined steel, or cast iron
70 to 100	Steel or cast iron	Steel or cast iron	Cast iron
70 to 120	Steel	Steel	Steel
98 to 100	Steel or cast iron	Steel or cast iron	Cast iron
100 to 104.5[d]	Steel	Steel	Steel
100 to 120	Steel	Steel	Steel

a See text for some precautions and limitations.

b High-silicon irons often used for pumps, evaporator tubes, etc. Also for lines at lower temperatures for 0 to 100% acid.

c Lower portion of table for acids with concentrations varying within range shown.

d 18-8 stainless steel preferred.

TABLE VI. RECOMMENDED EQUIPMENT FOR SATISFACTORY HANDLING OF SULFURIC ACID AND OLEUMS AT AMBIENT TEMPERATURES

GRADE AND STRENGTH OF SULFURIC ACID	STORAGE TANK	PIPE AND FITTINGS	VALVES	GASKETS	PUMPS	PUMP PACKINGS
Commercial (70–106%)	Heavy steel. Small tanks may be of epoxy resins or glass	Steel: Schedule 80 pipe, welding fittings & Series "15" welding flanges. Cast Iron: Heavy-wall C.I. pipe with integral or screwed flanges drilled to Series "15" templet or to old 125-lb. templet. Karbate. Glass	Durimet 20, and other Type 20 alloys, with Teflon packing and 150-lb flanges. Plug type, as above, with Teflon Sleeve	Teflon. Kel-F. Compressed asbestos. Blue African asbestos	Centrifugal type of Type 20 Alloys. All iron with Type 20 alloy impeller. Hi-Silicon cast iron	Packless or mechanical seals. Kel-F. Graphited lubricated blue African asbestos
Oleums (100-114.63%)	Heavy steel	Steel as above	Durimet 20, and other type 20 alloys with Teflon packing and 150-lb flanges	As above	Centrifugal type of Type 20 alloys	As above

TABLE VI. RECOMMENDED EQUIPMENT FOR SATISFACTORY HANDLING OF SULFURIC ACID AND OLEUMS AT AMBIENT TEMPERATURES

GRADE AND STRENGTH OF SULFURIC ACID	STORAGE TANK	PIPE AND FITTINGS	VALVES	GASKETS	PUMPS	PUMP PACKINGS
Electrolyte Sp. Gr. 1.835 93.19%	As above Steel, lined with baked phenolic (Heresite) Small tanks as above	Chemical lead pipe, 1/4" min. wall thickness, with 6% antimony lead 125-lb flanges or lap joint flanges Hi-Silicon cast iron pipe & fittings Pyrex Karbate	As above	As above	As above	As above
Chemically Pure (ACS Reagent)	Glass-lined steel	Pyrex glass Teflon-lined hose	Porcelain Y valves with Teflon discs and 150-lb flanges	Teflon envelope type	Glass-lined centrifugal type Diaphragm type with Teflon or Kel-F diaphragm	As above

(continued over)

TABLE VI. RECOMMENDED EQUIPMENT FOR SATISFACTORY HANDLING OF SULFURIC ACID AND OLEUMS AT AMBIENT TEMPERATURES

GRADE AND STRENGTH OF SULFURIC ACID	STORAGE TANK	PIPE AND FITTINGS	VALVES	GASKETS	PUMPS	PUMP PACKINGS
Electrolyte Sp. Gr. 1.270 to 1.706 (77.67%)	Steel or wood, chemical-lead-lined, or brick-lined Small tanks as above	Chemical lead pipe, 1/4" min. wall thickness, with 6% antimony lead 125-lb flanges or lap joint flanges Hi-Silicon cast iron pipe and fittings Rigid, unplasticized, normal-impact polyvinyl chloride (PVC) Schedule 80 pipe and fittings Pyrex Karbate	Durimet 20, and other Type 20 alloys, or Hi-Silicon cast iron, with Teflon packing and 150-lb flanges Plug type, of Type 20 alloys with Teflon sleeve & 150-lb flanges Saunders type with Penton lining and Teflon diaphragm 6% antimony lead with Teflon packing and 125-lb flanges	As above	Centrifugal type of Type 20 alloys Hi-Silicon cast iron	As above

TABLE VII. RESISTANCE OF CONSTRUCTIONAL MATERIALS TO SULFURIC ACID

No.	Material	Ratings	Exposure Conditions	Applications
		KEY		
1-3XX	Metals	Ratings are those of	° = deg. F	B, bodies of pumps
4XX	Carbon	materials manu–	% = concentration	and valves
5XX	Cement	facturers	Rm. = room temp.	I, impellers
6XX	Ceramics	A, good	Conc. = concentrated	V, valve trim
7XX	Plastics	F, fair	Dil. = dilute	P, piping
8XX	Rubber	V, varies depending	Sol.= solution	T, tanks
9XX	Wood	on conditions	L.= lined	S, shipping containers
		X, unsuitable		C, condensing surfaces
				H, heating surfaces
				D, ducts for fumes
				F, fans and blowers
				R, tower packing
		SULFURIC ACID		
3	Admiralty	V		
4	Admiralty	V	....	CH
6	Adnic	V	0.5-2.5%, 50%, 95%	
10-17	Aluminum	A	Fuming, rm.	S
		FX	Dil.; rm.	
19	Aloyco	A	All %; 70°	BV
		A	50% max.; boiling	BV
		A	50-93%; 150°	BV
		A	93% sulfuric to 65% oleum; 150°	BV
22	Ambraloy	V	....	CH
23	Ambraloy	V	....	CH
24	Ambraloy	V	....	CH
29-40	Ampco	A	To 10%; 212° max.	BIVPTCHDF
		V	10-75%; depends upon conditions	BIVPTCHDF
42	Antaciron	A	All conditions, with slurry, re-ducing or oxidizing	BIV
51	Berylco	A	Cold	
54	Brass	X		
61	Brass	X		
63	Brass	V	....	PCH
66	Bronze	V		
67	Bronze	A	Dil.; hot and cold	BIV
73	Bronze	V	....	VT
74	Bronze	V	....	V
75	Bronze	V	....	VP
76	Bronze	V		
77	Bronze	X		
81	CA-FA20	A	5% aerated and agitated; 70°	
		A	5% aerated and agitated; 176°	
		A	78% aerated and agitated; 176°	
		A	93% aerated and agitated; 70°	

*Reproduced from "Chemical Engineers' Handbook" by permission of CHEMICAL ENGINEER-ING and McGraw-Hill Book Co., Inc.

(continued over)

TABLE VII. RESISTANCE OF CONSTRUCTIONAL MATERIALS TO SULFURIC ACID (cont'd.)

No.	Material	Ratings	Exposure Conditions	Applications
82	CA-MM	A	5% aerated and agitated; 70°	
		F	5% aerated and agitated; 176°	
		X	73% aerated and agitated; 176°	
		F	93% aerated and agitated; 70°	
85	Cast iron	A	Over 77%	
86	Cast iron	A	75-95%, 98% fuming	
		X	To 75%	
86A	Cast iron	A	Over 90%	
87	Causul	A	Cold or hot to 60° Bé.; cold above 60° Bé.	B
88	Chlorimet	A	All % and temp. except hot over 80%	BIVCHF
89	Chlorimet	A	Dil. all temp.; conc. moderate temp.	BIVHF
		F	Intermediate %	BIVHF
111	Copper	V		
114	Copper	V	....	PTCHR
118	Copper	V	95%	
119	Corrosiron	A	25, 87, 95%; rm.; unagitated; c.p.	BIVPTCHDFR
123	Cupro-Ni	V	....	CH
124	Cupro-Ni	V	95%	
139	Durco	A	All % to 176°	BIVHF
		A	Under 45% to boil.	BIVHF
140	Durichlor	A	All % and temp.	BIVPCHFR
141	Durimet	A	All % to 176°	BIVCHF
		A	Under 25% boil.	BIVHF
		F	78% hot	BIVHF
142	Durimet	A	Under 10% boil; all % to 176° except near 60° Bé. (141 preferred)	BIVHF
143	Duriron	A	All % and temp.	BIVPHFR
148	Everdur	V	....	BIVR
149	Everdur	V	....	PTCHDR
150	Everdur	V	....	PCH
156	Gold	A	To boil.	
159	Hastelloy	A	Under 50%; to boil.	BIVPTCHDF
		A	Over 50%; to 160°	BIVPTCHDF
160	Hastelloy	A	Under 60%; to boil.	BIVPTCHDF
		A	Over 60%; to 160°	BIVPTCHDF
161	Hastelloy	A	Under 50%; to boil.	BIVPTCHDF
		A	Over 50%; to boil.	BIVPTCHDF
162	Hastelloy	A	All % to boil.	BIVP
163	Stellite	A	All %; rm. only	BIV
165	Stellite	A	All %; rm. only	BIV
184	Inconel	A	5%; 86°; unaerated	
		X	5%; 86°; aerated	
		X	19%; boil.	
185	Inc-clad	A	Conc.; 70°	BTSCH
191	Lead	A	....	PTH
193, 196, 200, 266	Lead	A	Under 96% to 60°; under 85% to 428°(No. 193, 248° max.)	BIPTSCHDF
216	Monel	A	5%; 86°; unaerated	BIVPTCHDF

TABLE VII. RESISTANCE OF CONSTRUCTIONAL MATERIALS TO SULFURIC ACID (cont'd.)

No.	Material	Ratings	Exposure Conditions	Applications
		F	5%; 86° ; aerated	
		A	19%; boil.	
		A	45, 60%; 140° ; unaerated	
		A	80%; 86°	
217	Monel-clad	A	Conc.; 70°	BTSCH
219	Muntz	X		
224	Nickel	A	5%; 86° ; unaerated	VPTH
		X	5%; 86° ; aerated	
		X	19%; boil.	
225	Ni-clad	A	Conc.; 70	BTSCH
226	Ni-silver	V		
231	Ni-Resist	A	5%; 86°; unaerated	BIVP
		X	5%; 86°; aerated	
		X	19%; boil.	
233	NS-5	A	Under 60° Bé; hot or cold	V
234	Olympic	V	95%	
235	Olympic	V	95%	
240	Platinum	A	To boil.	
242	Ir-Platinum	A	To boil.	
244	Rh-Platinum	A	To boil.	
245	Pyrasteel	V		
249	Resistac	A	66° Bé. max.	BIVCHF
270	304-clad	A	Conc.; 70°	BTSCH
271	316-clad	A	5%; 10%; fuming; 70°	BTSCH
274	430-clad	A	Conc.; 70°	BTSCH
275	St. 301	V	Conc.; rm.	
276	St. 302	V	Conc.; rm.; 60ᶜ Bé. min.; 180° max.	
		A	Diluted 1:20; 70°	
		X	Diluted 1:20; boil.	
		A	Diluted 1:10; 70°	
		X	Diluted 1:10; boil.	
		A	Diluted 1:1; 70°	
		X	Diluted 1:1; boil.	
		A	Conc.; 1:0; 70°	
		F	Conc.; 1:1; 212°	
		X	Conc.; 1:0; 300°	
		A	Fuming, 11% free SO_3; 212°	
		A	Fuming, 60% free SO_3; 70 , 160°	
278	St. 303	V	Conc.; rm.; 6ᴸ° Bé. min.; 180° max.	
279	St. 304	V	Conc.; rm.; 60° Bé. min.; 180° max.	
		A	5%; aerated and agitated; 70°	BIVP
		X	5%; aerated and agitated; 176°	
		X	78%; aerated and agitated; 176°	
		A	93%; aerated and agitated; 70°	BIVT
280	St. 308	V	Conc.; rm.; 60° Be. min.; 180° max.	
281	St. 309	V	Conc.; rm.; 60° Be. min.; 180° max.	
282	St. 310	V	Conc.; rm.; 60° Be. min.; 180° max.	
283	St. 316	V	Conc. or 15° Bé.; rm.	
		V	5% at 120° max.; 60° Bé. min. 200° max.	
		A	Diluted 1:20; 70°	(continued over)

TABLE VII. RESISTANCE OF CONSTRUCTIONAL MATERIALS TO SULFURIC ACID (cont'd.)

No.	Material	Ratings	Exposure Conditions	Applications
		F	Diluted 1:20; boil.	
		A	Diluted 1:10; 70°	
		X	Diluted 1:10; boil.	
		A	Diluted 1:1; 70°	
		X	Diluted 1:1; boil.	
		A	Conc., 1:0; 70°	
		F	Conc., 1:0; 212°	
		X	Conc., 1:0; 300°	
		A	Fuming 11% free SO3; 212°	
		A	Fuming 60% free SO3; 70°, 160°	
		A	5%; aerated and agitated, 176°,	BIVP
284	St. 317	V	Over 15° Bé.; rm.	
285	St. 321	V	Conc.; rm.	
		V	Over 60° Bé.; 180° F. max.	
286	St. 347	V	Conc.; rm.	
		V	Over 60° Bé.; 180° F. max.	
287	St. 403	V	Conc.; rm.	
288	St. 405	V	Conc.; rm.	
290	St. 410	V	Conc.; rm.	
		X	5%; aerated and agitated; 176°	
		X	78%; aerated and agitated; 176°	
		A	93%; aerated and agitated; 70°	BIVP
291	St. 414	V	Conc.; rm.	
292	St. 416	V	Conc.; rm.	
293	St. 418	V	Conc.; rm.	
294	St. 420	V	Conc.; rm.	
295	St. 430	V	Conc.; rm.	
		F	Diluted 1:10, 70°	
		X	Diluted 1:10, boil.	
		F	Conc. 1:0, 70°	
		X	Diluted 1:10, boil.	
		A	Conc. 1:0, 70°	
		F	Conc. 1:0, 212°	
		X	Conc. 1:0, 300°	
296	St. 430F	V	Conc.; rm.	
297	St. 431	V	Conc.; rm.	
298	St. 440A	V	Conc.; rm.	
300	St. 440C	V	Conc.; rm.	
301	St. 442	V	Conc.; rm.	
303	St. 446	V	Conc.; rm.	
316	St. CF-20	A	....	BIV
360A	Steel	A	Over 90%	
364	Stoody	A	10%; rm.; boil.	
365	Stoody	A	10%; rm.	
		X	10%; boil.	
367	Super Ni	V	....	PTCH
368	Tantalum	V	98% max.; 347° max. at 98%; avoid free SO3	H
369	Telnic	V	98% and under	
387	Stainless	X	All %	
388	Stainless	X	All %	
389	Stainless	A	Dilute; strong	

TABLE VII. RESISTANCE OF CONSTRUCTIONAL MATERIALS TO SULFURIC ACID (cont'd.)

No.	Material	Ratings	Exposure Conditions	Applications
		X	Medium	
390	Worthite	A	All %; 125°	BIV
		A	1-50%; aerated; 175°	BIV
		A	96-100%, aerated; 175°	BIV
		A	100-110%; 200°	BIV
		F	50-93%; aerated; 140°	BIV
392	Wyndaloy	A	Very dilute	
		V	Other %	
401	Karbate	V	96% max.; 338°max.	BIVPTCHD
402	Karbate	V	96% max.; 338°max.	BIVPTCHD
403	Kempruf	A	100% max. to boil.	PTDR
		A	115% max. to 158°	PTDR
404	Acheson	A	50% max.; to boil.	PTDR
500	Sul. cement	A	50% max.; 200° max.	PTD
501	Sul. cement	A	50% max.; 200° max.	PTD
502	Furan cement	A	50% max.; 360° max.	PTD
503	Furan cement	A	50% max.; 360° max.	PTD
504	Phen. cement	A	50% max.; 360° max.	PTD
505	Phen. cement	A	50% max.; 360° max.	PTD
506	Silicate cement	A	Strong sol. only; 1600° max.	PTD
507	Silicate cement	A	Strong sol. only; 1600° max.	PTD
508	Acichlor	V	Dilute and conc.; 300°	
510	Acitite	A	Dilute and conc.; 250°	
513	Asplit	A	All %; 350° max.	
514	Asplit-F	A	All %; 350° max.	
515	Basolit	A	Diluted; 200° max.	T
517	Carboline	A	50% max.	
518	C-Basolit	A	Diluted; 200° max.	T
521	Causplit	A	All %; 350° max.	
523	Duralon	F	Sp. gr. 1.5; 350° max.	BIPTCHDF
524	Durisite	F	Sp. gr. 1.5; 350° max.	BIPTCHDF
532	Lumnite	A	1% max.; 90° max.	TD
535	Nukem	A	....	T
536	Nukem	A	....	T
537	Pecomastic	A	Dilute and conc.; 300°	
538	Penchlor	A	All %; 750° max.	
539	Penchlor	A	All %; 750° max.	
540	Penchlor	A	All %; 500-2000°	
541	Pensalt	A	All %; 350° max.	
542	Permanite	V	Dil.; cold	TD
		X	Conc.; hot	
544	Plastite	F	175° max.	PTSD
545	P-Basolit	A	Dil.; 200° max.	T
554	Silastic	A	10-30%; (A.S.T.M. D-543-43)	
		X	Conc.; (A.S.T.M. D-543-43)	
556	Staminite	A	All %	T
559	Thiokol	X		
600	Acid brick	A	....	TDR
603, 612 615	Glass	A	....	THDR
604	Ceratherm	A	200-400°, depending on design	BIPTSCHDFR
606	Stoneware	A	All conditions	BIVPTCHDFR

(continued over)

TABLE VII. RESISTANCE OF CONSTRUCTIONAL MATERIALS TO SULFURIC ACID (cont'd.)

No.	Material	Ratings	Exposure Conditions	Applications
607	Glass-L	A	600° max.	PTCH
610	Stoneware	A	All %; any temp.	BIVPTCHDR
611	Porcelain	A	All % and temp.	BIPTDR
614	Glass-L	A	All %; 302° max.; agitation	BTCH
616	Pyrex	A		
617	Stoneware	A	140-160°	BIPTSCHDFR
618	Vitreo	A	1000° max.	
619	Vitreosil	A	....	PCH
621	Vycor	A		
700	Ace Saran	A	60%; 122°	P
704	DC Silicone	V		
706	Formica	F	25% max.; rm.	
707	Formica	F	25% max.; rm.	T
708	Formica	X	All %	
711	Haveg	V	75%; cold	BIVPTFDR
		V	50%; 300° max.	BIVPTFDR
718	Koroseal	A	50%; 150°	TD
		A	60%; 100°	TD
720	Lamicoid	X		
723	Nixon	A	3%	S
		F	30%	S
724	Nixon	A	3-30%	S
726	Nukemite	A	40%; rm.	PTSDF
727	Nylon	X	Conc.	
728	Nylon	X	Conc.	
729-732	Nylon	X		
733	Permanite	V	Dil.; cold	PVBDT
		X	Conc.; hot	
735	Polythene	X	Conc.; hot	
		V	Rm.	
736	Pyroflex	V	....	PTDCH
737	Resilon	F	175° max.	PTSD
740	Saran	F	77°	
741	Sealon	A	160° max.	BTPDF
742	Teflon	A	Rm.	VP
744, 745	Textolite	V	....	BI
746	Tygon	V	Dil. to med. conc.; 180° max.	BIPTSCHDF
800	Ace Hd. Rub	A	50%	BIVPTDF
801	Acidseal	A	50%; 150° max.	BIPTSDF
		A	60%; 100° max.	BIPTSDF
802	Acidseal	A	50%; 150° max.	BIPTDSF
		A	60%; 100° max.	BIPTSDF
805	Butyl	V	70%; 140° max.	
809	Fairprene	V		
814	G. E. Silicone	V	....	VPTDF
817	Heresite	A	50%; 122° max.	
836	Natural (S)	V		
837	Natural (H)	V		
838	GR-S (S)	V		
839	GR-S (H)	V		
840	GR-A (S)	V		

TABLE VII. RESISTANCE OF CONSTRUCTIONAL MATERIALS TO SULFURIC ACID (cont'd.)

No.	Material	Ratings	Exposure Conditions	Applications
841	GR-A (H)	V		
842	GR-M (S)	V		
843	GR-P (S)	X		
844	GR-I	V		
846	Saniprene	A	50%; 150° max.	BIPTDSF
		A	60%; 100° max.	BIPTDSF
848	Silastic	A	10–30%; (A.S.T.M. D-543-43)	
		X	Conc.; (A.S.T.M. D-543-43)	
849	Superflexite	A	50%; 150° max.	BIPTSDF
		A	60%; 100° max.	BIPTSDF
853	Thiokol	X	150° max.	
854	Thiokol	F	150° max.	PTSCDF
855	Triflex	A	50%; 150° max.	BIPTSDF
		A	60%; 100° max.	BIPTSDF
856	Vistanex	V	70%; 140° max.	
913	Redwood	A	5–12%; 36–190°; Falsewood L; steel pickle	T
		A	5–8% + dil. HNO_3; 36–90°; asphalt-L; explosives mfr.	T
		A	pH4.1; 36–80°; 17 years; plating works	T
		A	pH5.8; 36–80°; 20 years; plating works	T
		A	4–5%; 36–140°; 37 years; armor plate pickling	T
		A	3%; 36–90°; 7 years; plating works	T
		A	2% + 1.5% HCl; 40–180°; 21 years; chemical plant	T
		A	1.5%; 36–120°; 27 years; tannery	T
		A	1% + 1–5% $CuSo_4$; 36–170°; 13 years; chemical plant	T
		A	0.5% + dil. NaOH; 40–115°; 2 years; soap-specialties	T
		A	Dil.+ dil. HCl + dil. lead acetate; 40–150°; 13 years; paint	T
		A	Dil.; 60–200°; 2 years; petroleum refinery	T

situation demand the use of steel in spite of fairly frequent replacement. Steel shows comparatively high rates of corrosion around 100 to 101% acid.

Corrosion rates in acid strengths appreciably above 100% are quite low and steel is entirely satisfactory at moderate temperatures unless small amounts of contamination are undesirable.

In general, the effect of velocity, impingement or erosion-corrosion is to increase the rate of attack; the greater the static corrosion rate the more destructive the erosion-corrosion action. For example, static tests in sulfuric acid showing a pH of 3.5 give a corrosion rate of 40 mils per year. This same acid under conditions of high velocity shows an erosion-corrosion rate of 500 mils per year.

Tests in 95% acid, aerated and not aerated, at room temperature, showed little increase in rate of attack. Corrosion in dilute acid was so rapid that aeration effects were masked; practically identical corrosion rates (876 and 878 mils per year) were obtained in aerated and not aerated 3% sulfuric acid at room temperature.

The data for Figure 23 (page 53) were obtained on steel with the usual or normal microstructure (ferrite and pearlite).

In order to complete the picture shown by Figure 23, data on corrosion of steel by 0.005 to 50.0% sulfuric acid are listed in Table VIII. As is

TABLE VIII. CORROSION OF STEEL BY DILUTE SULFURIC ACID
AT ROOM TEMPERATURE

%H$_2$SO$_4$	Corrosion Rate, Mils per Year
0.005	8
0.05	15
0.5	120
1.0	200
3.0	875
5.0	1200
10.0	2300
50.0	1600

apparent in this table, dilute sulfuric acid, except for trace amounts, is very destructive to steel.

Corrosion of Lead: Temperatures and Concentrations

Lead resists all except the strongest sulfuric acid. Lead and steel are relatively cheap materials and one complements the other. If the acid is too strong for lead, steel will resist it; if too dilute for steel, lead can take over.

The curves in Figure 24 are less complex than those for steel because there are no dips in the curves.

Figure 24 does not show concentrations below 50% because the corrosion resistance of lead to dilute sulfuric acid is very good at temperatures including boiling.

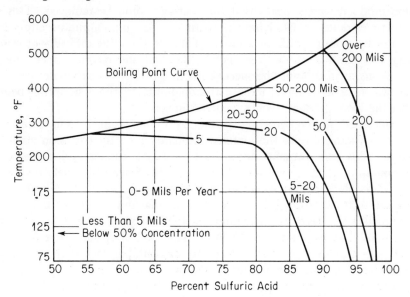

Fig. 24. Corrosion of chemical lead in strong sulfuric acid at various temperatures. (*Fontana, "Corrosion", Copyright 1957.*)

Lead depends for its corrosion resistance to sulfuric acid on the formation of a protective film, presumably lead sulfate. Solubility of lead sulfate increases as concentration of acid is increased in the stronger acid range, and, accordingly, corrosion increases. Figure 24 shows that as temperature and/or concentration is increased, corrosion resistance of lead decreases. Concentration of acid is an important factor. Lead dissolves quite rapidly in very strong acids—98% and above—at room temperature. Fuming acid attacks lead rapidly.

Corrosion resistance of lead to concentrated sulfuric acid at elevated temperatures is poor. Actually, none of the commercial metals and alloys is corrosion-resistant to hot, strong acid except high-silicon iron (Duriron), tantalum and noble metals. Occasionally, lead is used in strong acid at high temperatures with fairly frequent replacement because it is the economical material to use. When heat transfer is not a problem, lead is often protected by acid-proof brick. Steel tanks with intermediate lining of lead and inner lining of brick are common for handling hot, strong acid, as in concentrators, and also for equipment where abrasion or erosion is involved.

Corrosion Tests for Lead

Extent of corrosion should include all of the metal converted to corrosion product, which means that the coating should be removed. This is sometimes done by dissolving the coating in hot ammonium acetate solution or by scouring with an abrasive. There is, then, the difficulty of some attack or removal of the base metal. Standard and recommended procedure consists of rubbing the specimen with a rubber stopper under flowing tap water. This removes loose corrosion products, the assumption being that the loose products would come off in service.

Data used for constructing Figure 24 were obtained from corrosion tests on chemical lead, the material ordinarily used for corrosion applications. This lead contains approximately 0.06% copper and a specified minimum of other impurities. It is covered by American Society for Testing Materials (ASTM) specification B29-49 which calls for 0.04 to 0.08% copper; 0.002 to 0.02% silver; 0.001% zinc, maximum; 0.002% iron, maximum; 0.005% bismuth, maximum; 0.002% maximum total for arsenic, antimony and tin; and 99.90% lead. The ASTM specification for acid lead is essentially the same. High-purity or corroding lead is less resistant than chemical lead in hot acids in the range of concentrations shown in Figure 24. Pure lead has poorer mechanical properties than chemical lead.

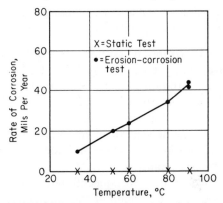

Fig. 25. Effect of high velocity on corrosion of hard lead in 10% sulfuric acid. (*Fontana, "Corrosion", Copyright 1957.*)

Data were obtained from simple immersion or static tests. Perhaps the most important factor not taken into account in static testing is the effect of velocity or erosion. Lead is a soft metal and easily abraded. Erosion or mechanical-wear effects remove the protective coating and the exposed lead is rapidly attacked. This is particularly true in the stronger acids or at the higher temperatures. Figure 25 shows the effect of high velocity, or erosion-corrosion, on hard lead in 10% sulfuric acid. (The "E-C," or erosion-corrosion, curve is based on a high-velocity test.)

Hard lead is often used when a material stronger than chemical lead is required, as in valves. Hard lead contains roughly 4 to 12% antimony. Creep strengths of hard or antimonial lead and chemical lead are about the same at 190° F.

Corrosion of Stainless Steel: Temperatures and Concentrations

Ordinary stainless steels are not often used for handling straight sulfuric acid. For dilute acids, lead is often preferred over the stainless steels. However, the stainless steels are sometimes used in process solutions containing sulfuric acid and other materials that decrease the rate of attack as compared to pure acid.

Three common stainless steels used in this manner are: 17% chromium steel, American Iron and Steel Institute Type No. 430; 18-8S, AISI Type No. 304, Alloy-Casting Institute designation CF-8; and 18-8SMo, Type 316, CF-8M. The AISI numbers are for wrought steels and the ACI designations for cast products. Corrosion resistances are essentially the same.

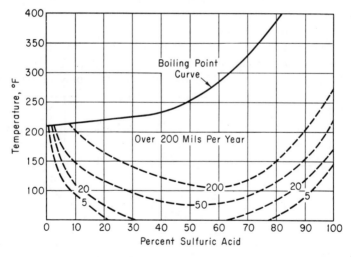

Fig. 26. Corrosion of 18-8SMo stainless steel in sulfuric acid at various temperatures. (*Fontana, "Corrosion", Copyright 1957.*)

Figure 26 shows a rough approximation of the corrosion of 18-8SMo by sulfuric acid in the range 0 to 100% as a function of temperature. The lines are isocorrosion lines for corrosion rates of 5, 20, 50 and 200 mils per year. Dotted lines represent approximations only.

18-8SMo may be used in dilute and strong sulfuric acids at room and moderate temperatures.

In most cases, 18-8S should not be considered as an alloy for straight sulfuric acid. The same is true for the 17% chromium alloy.

All three stainless steels show good resistance to fuming acids (over 100% strength). 18-8S and 17% chromium steels could be used and have been used for acid in a narrow range around 101% strength where steel shows a marked decrease in corrosion resistance.

Corrosion of Duriron (High-Silicon Iron): Temperatures and Concentrations

Duriron is a high-silicon cast iron containing approximately 14.5% silicon. It possesses the best all-around corrosion resistance, over the concentration range from 0 to 100% sulfuric acid, of all commercial metals and alloys. Duriron is very widely used today for sulfuric acid and many other applications.

The high-silicon irons are essentially cast iron with a high silicon content. Because of the high silicon content, there is much less carbon than in ordinary cast iron. High-silicon irons are available in cast form only.

Brittleness is Duriron's major drawback. It is susceptible to thermal and mechanical shock and must be handled with a reasonable degree of care in the foundry and in service.

High-silicon iron possesses inherent high hardness. For this reason, it is difficult to machine; shaping is usually best accomplished by grinding. Hardness, however, is an asset in that the alloy is abrasion-resistant and

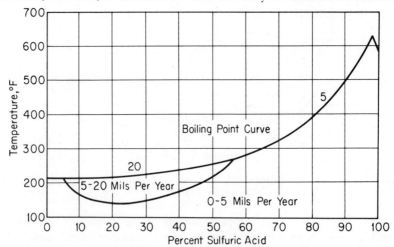

Fig. 27. Corrosion of Duriron in sulfuric acid at various temperatures. (*Fontana, "Corrosion", Copyright 1957.*)

also resistant to erosion-corrosion. Many plant acid slurries cannot be handled by other materials.

Figure 27 shows corrosion of Duriron by sulfuric acid in concentrations from 0 to 100% as a function of temperature. This alloy is not recommended for service in oleum or acid over 100% strength because of the cracking tendency of cast irons in these acids.

Curves in this figure are isocorrosion lines for corrosion rates of 5 to 20 mils per year. These lines indicate regions where corrosion rates of less than 5, and between 5 and 20 mils, per year would be expected. Duriron possesses good corrosion resistance to sulfuric acid at all temperatures including boiling. Corrosion resistance to the stronger acids is excellent and corrosion rates in even high-boiling-point acids are often less than 5 mils per year. Duriron is the only commercial material (except glass and certain precious metals) that shows this excellent corrosion resistance in the range 55 to 100% acid. This is one reason why sulfuric acid concentrators of all types are equipped with Duriron heating tubes.

Corrosion resistance of high-silicon iron in the lower concentrations is good, but not excellent, for this range. Less than 5 mils is considered excellent and less than 20 mils per year is considered good in evaluating corrosion data.

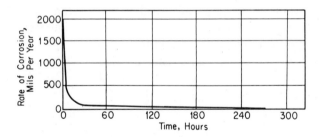

Fig. 28. Corrosion of Duriron in boiling 30% sulfuric acid as a function of exposure time. (*Fontana, "Corrosion", Copyright 1957.*)

Other uses for high-silicon irons in sulfuric acid and sulfuric acid-containing process liquors and slurries are: rayon baths, fertilizer plants, chamber and contact acid plants, pickling solutions, fume exhaust fans, laboratory and plant waste. In fact, this material is in use in practically all processes involving sulfuric acid. High-silicon iron is perhaps the only material capable of withstanding attack by sulfuric acid in combination with erosion or wear caused by solids in suspensions. Equipment involved includes pumps, valves, heat exchangers, jets, spargers, fans, small tanks, tank outlets, nozzles, pipe and fittings, anodes, sinks, bubble caps and tower sections. In spite of its limited mechanical properties, as compared to common metals and alloys, high-silicon iron is one of the main materials of construction for handling sulfuric acid.

The high-silicon irons sometimes show very rapid rates of attack for short times after initial exposure. A durable passive surface quickly develops, however, and the material then shows good corrosion resistance and performance. Figure 28 shows corrosion versus time in boiling 30% sulfuric acid and is a good example of this effect. The unusual character of this passivity effect is that it operates under either oxidizing or reducing conditions.

Corrosion of Durimet 20: Temperatures and Concentrations

Durimet 20 (cast alloy) or Carpenter Stainless 20 (wrought form) is marketed under such trade names as Aloyco 20 and Esco 20. Sometimes, the designation is FA-20. The number 20 always designates the alloy.

Durimet 20 is a low-carbon austenitic alloy containing nickel, chromium, molybdenum and copper as the main alloying elements for corrosion resistance. Three per cent copper in the alloy is essential for good corrosion resistance to sulfuric acid. Nickel content provides a good base for resistance to acid. Chromium provides good resistance to oxidizing conditions such as the presence of strong sulfuric and nitric acid. Molybdenum increases resistance to sulfuric acid and to pitting.

The alloy differs from lead and steel in that it can be used over the entire concentration range of zero to 100%. Corrosion resistance of this alloy to oleum or fuming sulfuric acid is good.

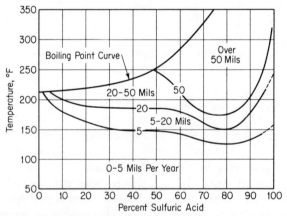

Fig. 29. Corrosion of Durimet 20 in sulfuric acid at various temperatures. (*Fontana, "Corrosion", Copyright 1957.*)

Figure 29 shows Durimet 20 possesses excellent (less than 5 mils per year) corrosion resistance over the entire concentration range at temperatures up to 125°F or 50°C, and it possesses good resistance (less than 20 mils per year) to 150°F. Higher temperatures can be used with more dilute and with strong acids. The dips (increased corrosion) in the curves occur around 78% or 66° Bé sulfuric acid. Corresponding dips in the curves for steel occur around 85% sulfuric acid at considerably lower temperatures. Durimet 20 is generally unsuitable at high temperatures in the range of roughly 50 to 90% acid, as shown in Figure 29.

Durimet 20 sometimes exhibits what is known as borderline passivity in sulfuric acid. Passivity usually implies low rates of corrosion or almost complete immunity to attack.

Corrosion of Durimet 20 by sulfuric acid can often be reduced through additives that act as inhibitors—for example, the presence of small amounts of ferric sulfate or of copper sulfate in sulfuric acid often reduces the corrosion rate. Major uses for Durimet 20 in sulfuric acid are in pumps and valves.

Corrosion of Chlorimet 2 (High Ni-Mo Alloy): Temperature and Concentrations

Chlorimet 2 is made up of two parts nickel and one part molybdenum. Its outstanding characteristic is good corrosion resistance to hot, intermediate concentrations of sulfuric acid. It is probably the only commercial material, aside from the high-silicon irons and lead, which has this property.

Chlorimet 2 is somewhat similar to Hastelloy B, and for most applications the corrosion resistance of Hastelloy B and Chlorimet 2 are practically equivalent. Chlorimet 2 is available in cast form only. Hastelloy B is available cast and wrought.

Both Chlorimet and Hastelloy B are relatively low-carbon, nickel-base alloys containing molybdenum as the chief alloying element. Rolled alloy shows better mechanical properties than the cast material.

Both are high-strength ductile alloys as far as corrosion applications are concerned. Machinability is not too good but machining is readily performed after a little experience. A quench-annealing heat treatment, which consists of heating to above 2000°F followed by quenching in water, produces optimum corrosion resistance.

Figure 30 pictures corrosion resistance of Chlorimet 2 to sulfuric acid from 0 to 100% concentration as a function of temperature.

The curves in Figure 30 are isocorrosion lines for corrosion rates of 5, 20, 50 and 200 mils per year. These curves indicate the regions where corrosion rates of less than 5, between 5 and 20, between 20 and 50, between 50 and 200, and over 200 mils per year would be expected. Data are rather sparse for the hot or more concentrated acids.

Fig. 30 shows the good corrosion resistance (less than 20 mils per year) of Chlorimet 2 to hot acid, including boiling, in the intermediate concentration ranges of about 10 to 60% acid. Corrosion resistance is good also in stronger acid up to about 250°F. Corrosion increases rapidly in the strong acids as the temperature is increased.

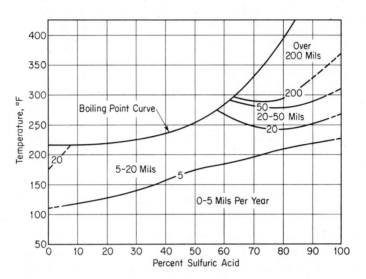

Fig. 30. Corrosion of Chlorimet 2 in sulfuric acid at various temperatures. (*Fontana, "Corrosion", Copyright 1957.*)

An interesting point in connection with this alloy concerns dilute acid at temperatures above 175°F. This is shown by the dotted 20-mil line in the left-hand half of the figure. Corrosion is relatively rapid in this area. Accordingly, Chlorimet 2 is not used for hot acids of less than 10% strength. This point was also established by relatively poor performance of equipment in dilute sulfuric acid process solutions. Less expensive chromium-bearing alloys such as Durimet 20, Chlorimet 3 and Hastelloy C do much better under these conditions.

Chlorimet 2 does not contain chromium and is not suitable for acids containing oxidizing agents. Highly aerated solutions could also be destructive. Cupric and ferric chlorides and sulfates increase corrosion of this alloy.

Corrosion of Chlorimet 3 (High Ni-Mo-Cr Alloy): Temperatures and Concentrations

Chlorimet 3 is a high–nickel alloy consisting of nickel base with high molybdenum and chromium content. Total nickel, molybdenum and chromium content is about 96%. Iron content is around 3% or less.

Chlorimet 3 is a high-strength and ductile alloy somewhat similar to Hastelloy C. For most applications corrosion resistance of Chlorimet 3 and Hastelloy C are practically equivalent. Machining is readily performed after a little experience. Best corrosion resistance is achieved by heating at temperatures of 2000°F or above, followed by quenching in water.

Chlorimet 3 is available in cast form only.

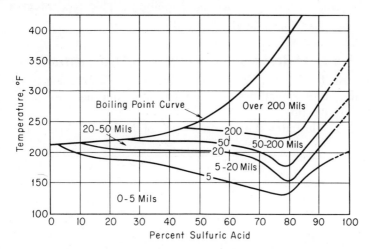

Fig. 31. Corrosion of Chlorimet 3 in sulfuric acid at various temperatures. (*Fontana, "Corrosion", Copyright 1957.*)

Figure 31 pictures corrosion of Chlorimet 3 by sulfuric acid in concentrations from 0 to 100% as a function of temperature. Corrosion resistance to oleum or fuming sulfuric acid is good.

Curves in this figure are isocorrosion lines for corrosion rates of 5, 20, 50 and 200 mils per year. Lines (extreme right-hand) for concentrations of 95 to 100% are dotted because of insufficient data.

Figure 31 shows that Chlorimet 3 possesses excellent corrosion resistance (corrosion rate of less than 5 mils per year) for most concentrations from 0 to 100% at temperatures up to about 150°F. Dips (increased corrosion) in the curves occur around 80% concentration. Aside from the dip portion, Chlorimet 3 shows good resistance (less than 20 mils per year) to all concentrations of sulfuric acid up to about 200°F.

Corrosion resistance in hot dilute acid is particularly good. This is the region where Chlorimet 3 finds many applications in the chemical industry, particularly for handling high-temperature rayon baths used in the manufacture of high-strength rayon. Chlorimet 3 is used in pumps, valves, agitators, orifices, and other equipment where lead fails because of erosion-corrosion.

Chlorimet 3 is also used for handling sulfuric acid containing additional ingredients in solution which accelerate attack on other metals and alloys. High alloy content provides insurance against acceleration of corrosion by other factors such as velocity and impurities. Chlorimet 3 is superior to many other alloys as far as pitting is concerned.

Presence of 18% chromium in Chlorimet 3 makes it a stainless alloy and good for oxidizing or aerated conditions. This type of alloy also possesses good strength at high temperatures.

Corrosion of Ni-Resist: Temperatures and Concentrations

Ni-Resist Type 1 is a high-nickel, gray cast iron containing copper and chromium. It is sometimes used for handling sulfuric acid, particularly dilute concentrations.

Figure 32 illustrates the corrosion rate of Ni-Resist Type 1 by deaer-

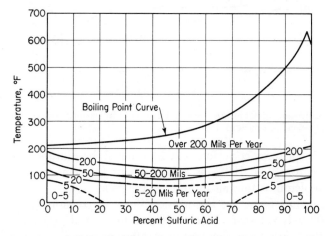

Fig. 32. Corrosion of Ni-Resist Type 1 in sulfuric acid at various temperatures. (*Fontana, "Corrosion", Copyright 1957.*)

ated sulfuric acid as a function of temperature. It shows Ni-Resist Type 1 can be used in some cases for all concentrations of sulfuric acid at the lower temperatures. However, corrosion increases rapidly with temperature as shown by the chart. This material finds application in the unaerated dilute acids where it is markedly superior to ordinary cast iron. The latter is rapidly attacked by sulfuric acid in all concentrations below approximately 60%. Superiority of the alloyed iron decreases considerably in the concentrated acid.

Ni-Resist Type 1 contains 5.50 to 7.50% copper and is often referred to as copper-bearing Ni-Resist. It is the Ni-Resist type used most often for sulfuric acid applications.

Ordinary gray cast iron shows a tendency to crack in oleum or fuming sulfuric acid. Ni-Resist Type 3 is sometimes used in fuming acids because it is resistant to cracking.

In very hot concentrated acid, all Ni-Resists (except Type 5) show higher corrosion rates than ordinary unalloyed gray cast iron, presumably because of the chromium content. However, corrosion of ordinary iron is also high under these conditions.

Corrosion of Copper Under Non-oxidizing Conditions

Copper and copper-base alloys are not widely used in straight sulfuric acid services, probably because of the increase in corrosion when aeration and other oxidizing ingredients are present in the environment. Some of these materials, however, show good corrosion resistance in the more dilute sulfuric acids under reducing conditions.

Principal or basic materials are straight copper, brass (copper-zinc), tin bronze (copper-tin), cupro-nickel (copper-nickel), silicon bronze (copper-silicon) and aluminum bronze (copper-aluminum). However, a wide variety of alloys are produced including copper, aluminum, tin, zinc, silicon, nickel, lead, iron, tellurium, arsenic, phosphorus, antimony, beryllium and manganese.

TABLE IX. CORROSION OF COPPER BY
SULFURIC ACID

H_2SO_4 %	Temp., °F.	Corrosion Rate, Mils/Year	
		Aerated	Nonaerated
6	Room	150	4 (H_2 flushed)
20	Room	130	6 (H_2 flushed)
5	Room	......	12
5	200	......	19
10	Room	......	8
10	200	......	24
20	Room	......	4
20	200	......	17
10	100	......	7
10	100	900[a]	...

[a] 5% potassium dichromate added to acid.

Table IX shows some corrosion data on copper in dilute sulfuric acids. This table shows the increased corrosion when oxygen or air is bubbled through 6 and 20% acid as compared to bubbling hydrogen; the increase in the rate of corrosion when the temperature is raised to 200°F; and the rapid increase in corrosion when an oxidizing agent such as potassium dichromate is added to the acid. Copper and most of its alloys are susceptible to water-line or liquid-line attack because of the effects of air just above the liquid in these areas and the concentration cells developed.

Corrosion rates in dilute acid are usually low in the absence of oxidizing conditions.

Except for red brass, which is frequently used with refinery sludge, brass is not often used for sulfuric acid services. Dezincification, or the selective removal of zinc from the copper base, often occurs in dilute acids. Although corrosion rates for brass may be quite low in the absence of oxidizing conditions, the alloy loses most of its strength when dezincification occurs.

In general, copper-tin alloys show better corrosion resistance to sulfuric acid than copper and brass. Tin increases resistance to water-line attack. Tin bronzes, however, are rapidly attacked by acids over 60% concentration and at temperatures above 175°F.

The copper silicon alloys or silicon bronzes, such as Everdur, are sometimes used where high strength is required. Examples are bolts, nuts, tie rods and other hardware. Table X shows the results of corrosion tests

TABLE X. CORROSION OF 3% SILICON
BRONZE BY SULFURIC ACID

H_2SO_4, %	Temp., °F.	Corrosion Rate, Mils/ Year
3	77	3
10	77	2
25	77	2
70	77	1
3	158	7
10	158	6
25	158	4
70	158	1

in nonaerated solutions containing 3 to 70% sulfuric acid. Warm and aerated 10% sulfuric acid corrodes this alloy at rates as high as 200 mils per year.

The cupro-nickels show better corrosion resistance than brass and are roughly equal to the bronzes in sulfuric acid.

The aluminum-copper alloys or the aluminum bronzes are probably used more extensively than the other copper alloys for sulfuric acid services. These alloys with 5 to 15% aluminum are strong, show better resistance to erosion-corrosion, and less marked effects of aeration.

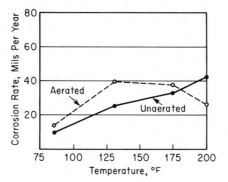

Fig. 33. Corrosion of 10% aluminum bronze in 5% sulfuric acid at a velocity of 15.5 ft./min. (*Fontana, "Corrosion", Copyright 1957.*)

Figure 33 shows corrosion of a 10% aluminum bronze by 5% sulfuric acid as a function of temperature. The acid was flowing past the specimen at a velocity of 15.5 feet per minute. Silicon bronze (Everdur) tested under identical conditions shows much higher corrosion rates in both the unaerated and air-saturated conditions.

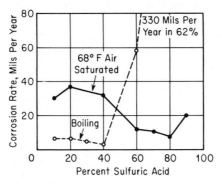

Fig. 34. Corrosion of 8% aluminum bronze in sulfuric acid at room temperature and boiling. (*Fontana, "Corrosion", Copyright 1957.*)

Figure 34 shows corrosion of an 8% aluminum bronze by sulfuric acid of various concentrations at room temperature and boiling. These tests were run under static conditions.

Ampco alloys are aluminum bronzes containing some iron and small amounts of nickel. Table XI lists corrosion data on several Ampco alloys in sulfuric acid with no aeration under static conditions.

TABLE XI. CORROSION OF AMPCO ALLOYS BY
STATIC NONAERATED SULFURIC ACID

Material*	H2SO4, %	Temp., °F	Corrosion Rate, Mils/ Year
Ampco A3 (10% Al)	0.5	90	2
	1.0	90	2
	2.0	90	2
	5.0	90	2
Ampco 16 (10% Al)	10	72	4
Ampco 12 (11% Al)	10	85	1
Ampco 16	35	72	2
	35	194	45
	50	75	3
Ampco 18	50	185	8
	65	185	3
	75	185	4
	78	120	4
Ampco 8 (7% Al)	78	120	5

* These alloys contain some iron and small amounts of nickel—i.e., Ampco 8: 7% Al, 2% Fe, 0.35% Ni, balance copper. Ampco 18: 10.5% Al, 4% Fe, 0.35% Ni, balance copper.

Stability of Orlon

Orlon is a highly oriented yarn of polymerized acrylonitrile. The fiber is a light material and exhibits good mechanical properties of strength, fatigue resistance and elastic recovery.

Orlon exhibits good resistance to most acid salts.

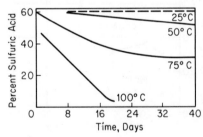

Fig. 35. Stability of Orlon in sulfuric acid at various temperatures. (*Fontana, "Corrosion", Copyright 1957.*)

Figure 35 shows the resistance of Orlon to sulfuric acid in concentrations up to 60% for temperatures up to 100°C. The dotted line shows the maximum concentrations and times investigated. No deterioration of Orlon was observed after 64 days in 60% sulfuric acid at 25°C or in 35% acid below 65°C, but the material was attacked by 35% sulfuric acid after six days at 100°C and after 25 days at 75°C.

Orlon yellows after prolonged exposure at 110°C and shows a sticking temperature of 250°C. It has 0 to 2.5% shrinkage in water at 100° C; 0.9 to 2.0% moisture regain at 60% relative humidity; and 2 to 3% absorption when soaked in water. The resistance to microorganisms, marine bacteria, insects, mildew, soils and sunlight is reported as excellent. Orlon has been rated nonhazardous in toxicological investigations.

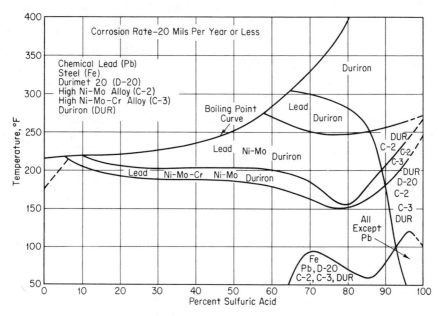

Fig. 36. Corrosion of six metals and alloys in sulfuric acid at various temperatures. (*Fontana, "Corrosion", Copyright 1957.*)

Some of the suggested uses for Orlon in corrosion applications are as follows: pneumatic filtration (dust collection bags); heavy and lightweight filter press cloths for handling acids; lamination; electrical insulation; diaphragm fabric; belting and hose for handling chemicals; plant window screens; and protective work clothing.

Wool has shown good performance as a material for dust collection bags, but it is not a material generally suitable for temperatures over 200° F, especially in the presence of sulfur dioxide and other acid gases. Orlon dust bags have been used satisfactorily for filtration of acid fumes and dust at temperatures in the neighborhood of 275–300°F.

Orlon fiber is of special interest for filter cloths handling acids at elevated temperatures. More common cloths often show excessive shrinkage and/or attack in acids at temperatures above atmospheric.

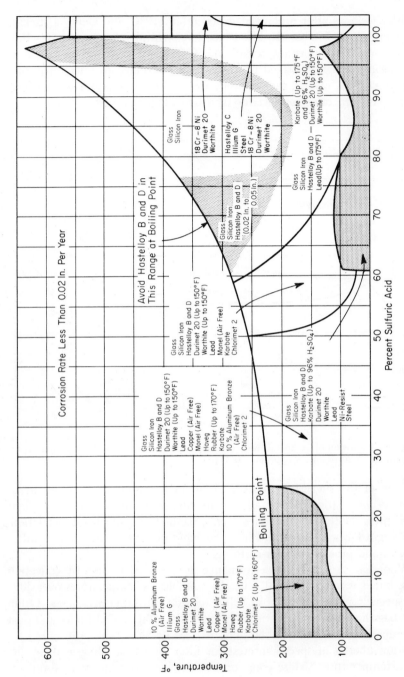

Fig. 37. Corrosion of materials in sulfuric acid at various temperatures. (*Courtesy Shell Development Company.*)

4. TYPICAL CALCULATIONS FOR SULFURIC ACID

Basic Factors

Sulfuric acid, as it is used in industry today, ranges from very dilute solutions to a strength as high as 114.63%. Sulfuric acid in any strength over 100% contains free sulfur trioxide which causes the acid to vaporize and classifies it as a fuming acid. Sulfuric acid of any strength under 100% is a nonfuming acid.

The following basic factors derived from molecular structure are employed in common sulfuric acid calculations:

Ratio of SO_3 to 100% H_2SO_4

$$\frac{SO_3}{H_2SO_4} = \frac{80.06}{98.076} = 0.8163$$

That is, 100% H_2SO_4 contains 81.63% SO_3.

Ratio of water to 100% H_2SO_4

$$\frac{H_2O}{H_2SO_4} = \frac{18.016}{98.076} = 0.1837$$

100% H_2SO_4 contains 18.37% water.

Ratio of 100% H_2SO_4 to SO_3

$$\frac{H_2SO_4}{SO_3} = \frac{98.076}{80.06} = 1.225$$

Pure SO_3 has an equivalent acidity of 122.5%

81

Applying these basic factors, the following can be determined for non-fuming sulfuric acid (that is, sulfuric acid with less than 100% strength).

1. $\%SO_3 = \%H_2SO_4 \times 0.8163$ or $\%H_2SO_4 \div 1.225$

(See Table XXII, p. 261,
for various values.)

2. $\%H_2SO_4 = \%SO_3 \times 1.225$ or $\% SO_3 \div 0.8163$

3. % Free Water $= 100 - \% H_2SO_4$

4. % Combined $H_2O = \% H_2SO_4 \times 0.1837$

5. % Total Water $= \%$ Free Water plus % Combined Water

(See Table XXII, p. 261,
for various values.)

For fuming sulfuric acid strengths above 100%, the factors apply as follows:

1. Total Water $=$ Combined Water (no free water in fuming acid)
   $= \%$ actual $H_2SO_4 \times 0.1837$
   or $= \%$ equivalent $H_2SO_4 \times 0.1837 - (\%$ equivalent $H_2SO_4 - 100)$

(See Table XXII, p. 261,
for various values.)

2. % Actual $H_2SO_4 = \%$ Combined $H_2O \div 0.1837$
   $= 100\%$ less % Free SO_3

3. Equivalent % $H_2SO_4 = \%$ Total $SO_3 \div 0.8163$
   $= \%$ Total $SO_3 \times 1.225$

4. % Combined $SO_3 = \%$ Actual $H_2SO_4 \times 0.8163$ (use steps 1 & 2)

5. % Free $SO_3 = 100\% - \%$ Actual H_2SO_4 (use steps 1 & 2)

6. Total $SO_3 = \%$ Combined SO_3 plus % Free SO_3

Determination of Strength

Determination of Weight of Sulfuric Acid

1. *Weight, pounds per cubic foot*
   Obtain specific gravity at $\frac{60°F}{60°F}$ from Table XXII, p. 261, and multiply by weight of water at 60°F (62.37 lbs/cu. ft.)

2. *Weight, pounds per gallon*

Obtain specific gravity at $\frac{60°F}{60°F}$ from Table XXII, p. 261, and multiply by weight of water at 60°F (8.337 lbs./gal.)

Determination of Equivalent Per Cent Strength

60° Bé (77.67% H_2SO_4) is

$$\frac{77.67\%}{93.19\%} \times 100 = 83.35\% \text{ of } 66° \text{ Bé}$$

Calculating Weight of Sulfuric Acid

Shipping weight or inventory weight can be accurately calculated if the volume, specific gravity and strength are known. If strength is determined by titration, the temperature need not be known at the time specific gravity is taken. If, however, tables are used to determine the acidity from specific gravity, temperature must be taken along with the specific gravity reading and specific gravity, as well as volume, corrected to 60°F.

(1) Determination of weight when strength is determined by titration: Sp. Gr. × 8.337 × Volume in Gallons = Number of Pounds "as is." Pounds "as is" × % Acidity = Number of Pounds 100%.

(2) Determination of weight by tables: Gravity is corrected to 60°F in order to obtain strength; from this point, the above formula (1) applies.

True Acidity

Spent acids recovered from various petrochemical and petroleum operations vary in acidity from 60 to 92%; the carbon content varies from 0.3 to 50.0%. The characteristics of the acid depend on the sulfuric acid content and the water content (true acidity). Titratable acidity on a total weight basis is not the determining factor.

Example: Determine the true acidity of a spent alkylation sulfuric acid having the following analysis:

H_2SO_4 .... 85.0%
H_2O 6.0%
Hydrocarbons 9.0%

$$\text{True Acidity} = \frac{\text{Titratable Acidity}}{\text{Titratable Acidity} + \text{Water}}$$

$$= \frac{85.0}{85.0 + 6}$$

$$= 93.4\%$$

True acidity for various percentages of acidity and free water is determined from Fig. 38.

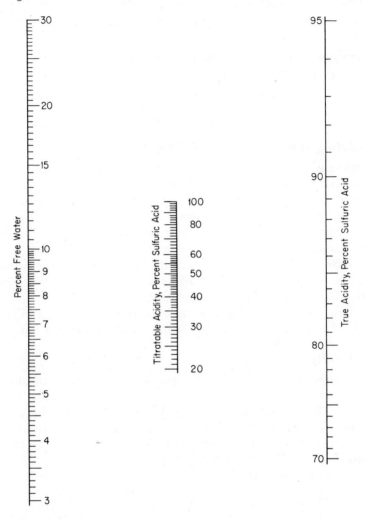

Fig. 38. Determination of true acidity of sulfuric acid.

Determining Approximate Acidity of Sulfuric Acid by Dilution (Specific Gravity Test)

Approximate acidity of sulfuric acid up to 93% can be determined by taking specific gravity. For strengths ranging from 93 to 100%, specific gravity does not determine a near approximation of acidity. If strong acid is diluted to a strength below 93%, specific gravity can then be used to indicate acidity.

Specific Gravity Test of Dilute Mixture. Equal volumes (usually 50 ml) of water and acid are mixed thoroughly and cooled. Specific gravity and temperature are taken. Specific gravity is corrected to 60°F. (Table

TABLE XII. TEMPERATURE CORRECTION TABLE
(for use with Sulfuric Acid Dilution Test
to adjust specific gravity to 60° F)

Temp °F.	Sub-tract	Temp. °F.	Add	Temp. °F.	Add
30	.0135	62	.0009	92	.0144
32	.0126	64	.0018	94	.0153
34	.0117	66	.0027	96	.0162
36	.0108	68	.0036	98	.0171
38	.0099	70	.0045	100	.0180
40	.0090	72	.0054	102	.0189
42	.0081	74	.0063	104	.0198
44	.0072	76	.0072	106	.0207
46	.0063	78	.0081	108	.0216
48	.0054	80	.0090	110	.0225
50	.0045	82	.0099	112	.0234
52	.0036	84	.0108	114	.0243
54	.0027	86	.0117	116	.0252
56	.0018	88	.0126	118	.0261
58	.0009	90	.0135	120	.0270

XII above lists temperature corrections.) Acidity of strong acid is calculated from corrected specific gravity of diluted solution. Let:

$$A = \text{\% Strong acid}$$
$$B = \text{\% Mixture}$$
$$C_a = \text{Volume of acid}$$
$$C_c = \text{Volume of water}$$
$$D = \text{Sp Gr water at } 60°F$$
$$E = \text{Sp Gr acid at } 60°F$$

Then:

$$\frac{A \times C_a \times E}{C_c \times D + C_a \times E} = B$$

Because equal volumes are mixed, the equation becomes:

$$\frac{A \times E}{D + E} = B$$

TABLE XIII DETERMINING ACID STRENGTH BY DILUTION (Specific Gravity Test)

Sp Gr at 60° F	%H2SO4 Before Dilution	Sp Gr at 60° F	%H2SO4 Before Dilution	Sp Gr at 60° F	%H2SO4 Before Dilution	Sp Gr at 60° F	%H2SO4 Before Dilution
1.5034	92.75	1.5196	95.00	1.5345	97.02	1.5493	99.10
1.5055	93.05	1.5200	95.06	1.5354	97.14	1.5501	99.22
1.5061	93.20	1.5209	95.18	1.5363	97.26	1.5509	99.35
1.5064	93.22	1.5218	95.30	1.5372	97.38	1.5518	99.47
1.5072	93.35	1.5227	95.43	1.5381	97.51	1.5526	99.59
1.5081	93.47	1.5237	95.55	1.5389	97.63	1.5534	99.71
1.5089	93.59	1.5247	95.67	1.5398	97.75	1.5542	99.84
1.5099	93.71	1.5256	95.79	1.5408	97.88	1.5551	99.96
1.5108	93.83	1.5264	95.92	1.5417	98.00	1.5554	100.00
1.5117	93.96	1.5271	96.00	1.5424	98.12	1.5563	100.09
1.5120	94.00	1.5273	96.04	1.5431	98.24	1.5577	100.21
1.5127	94.08	1.5283	96.16	1.5439	98.37	1.5590	100.33
1.5137	94.20	1.5291	96.28	1.5449	98.49	1.5604	100.45
1.5147	94.32	1.5301	96.41	1.5458	98.61	1.5616	100.58
1.5156	94.45	1.5310	96.53	1.5467	98.73	1.5628	100.70
1.5164	94.57	1.5319	96.65	1.5475	98.85	1.5639	100.82
1.5173	94.69	1.5328	96.77	1.5484	98.98	1.5652	100.94
1.5183	94.81	1.5336	96.90	1.5485	99.00	1.5664	101.07
1.5192	94.94	1.5343	97.00				

Values in Table XIII above were calculated for use with the dilution test. As previously noted, corrected specific gravity of diluted mixture indicates acidity of the strong acid before dilution.

Suppose equal volumes of strong acid and water are mixed and cooled to 60°F: hydrometer reads 1.512. From Table XIII, the acidity of the strong acid is 94.0%. As a check, the acidity of the mixture is calculated as follows:

Using equation above

$$\frac{94.0 \times 1.8381}{1.000 + 1.8381} = 60.88\%$$

from Table XXII, page 261, 60.88% acid has a specific gravity (by interpolation) of 1.512.

Hydrogen Ion Values of Sulfuric vs. Muriatic Acid

% Hydrogen ion in 100% sulfuric acid:

$$\frac{2H}{H_2SO_4} \times 100\% = \frac{2.016}{98.08} \times 100\% = 2.055\%$$

% Hydrogen ion in 20° Bé (31.45%) muriatic acid:

$$\frac{H}{HCl} \times 0.3145 \times 100\% = \frac{1.008 \times 0.3145}{36.47} \times 100\% = 0.869\%$$

One ton of 100% H_2SO_4 contains 41.1 lbs of hydrogen ions; one ton 20° Bé HCl, 17.4 lbs hydrogen ions.

One ton of 100% H_2SO_4 is equivalent to 2.36 tons of 20° Bé HCl; one ton 98% H_2SO_4 to 2.31 tons 20° Bé HCl; and one ton 93.19% H_2SO_4 to 2.20 tons 20° Bé HCl.

Dilution of Acid

Diluting and Blending Sulfuric Acid to Obtain Required Consumption Strength

Let A = Strength by weight of strong acid (SA)
B = Strength by weight of weak acid (WA)
C = Strength by weight of desired acid (DA)
X = Quantity of SA to be used
Y = Quantity of WA or Water (0%) to be used
Z = X + Y = Quantity of DA required

Basic Equation:

$$AX + BY = C (X + Y)$$

Derivations:

(1) Quantity of SA required $X = \dfrac{Y (C - B)}{(A - C)}$

(2) If diluent is 0%, equation becomes $X = Y \dfrac{(C)}{(A - C)}$

(3) Quantity of WA to be used $Y = X \dfrac{(A - C)}{(C - B)}$

(4) If diluent is 0% equation becomes $Y = X \left(\dfrac{A}{C} - 1\right)$

(5) Quantity of DA $Z = \dfrac{AX + BY}{C}$

(6) If diluent is 0% equation becomes $Z = \dfrac{AX}{C}$

Example: Dilution with water.

1. Find amount of 66° Bé (93.19%) sulfuric acid produced when 100 pounds of 98% acid is cut with water. Apply equation (6).

$$Z = \frac{AX}{C}$$

Amount 93.19% produced $= \dfrac{0.98 \times 100}{0.9319} = 105.16$ lbs

Amount water added: $Y = X \left(\dfrac{A}{C} - 1 \right)$

$$= 100 \left(\frac{0.98}{0.9319} - 1 \right)$$

$$= 5.16 \text{ lbs}$$

Rectangle Method

The rectangle method applies the foregoing algebraic equations diagrammatically and provides a quick and accurate means of determining quantities involved for diluting or blending sulfuric acid.

Constructing Rectangle. Draw a rectangle with two intersecting diagonals. Write the percentage of the stronger solution in the upper left-hand corner, the percentage of the weaker solution (percentage is zero when diluting with water) in the lower left-hand corner, and the percentage of the desired solution at the intersection of the diagonals. Subtract the percentages on each diagonal; in each case, the smaller from the larger. Write the differences at the right-hand end of the same diagonals. The difference in the upper right-hand corner indicates the relative weight of the solution whose concentration is given in the upper left-hand corner and the difference in the lower right-hand corner indicates the relative weight of the solution whose concentration is in the lower left-hand corner.

Example 1. In the acidulation of phosphate rock, 60° Bé (77.67%) sulfuric acid is usually diluted with water to 50° Bé (62.18%) sulfuric acid and mixed with phosphate rock. The rectangle with water as 0% sulfuric acid is set up in the following manner:

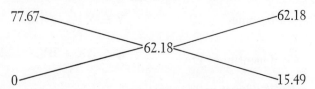

Thus, 62.18 pounds of 60° Bé (77.67%) sulfuric acid and 15.49 pounds of water are required to make 77.67 pounds of 50° Bé (62.18%) sulfuric acid. If quantities to produce a hundred pounds of 50° Bé acid are required, ratios are used.

$$60° \text{ Bé acid} = \frac{62.18}{62.18 + 15.49} \times 100 = 80.06 \text{ lbs}$$

$$\text{Water} = \frac{15.49}{62.18 + 15.49} \times 100 = 19.94 \text{ lbs}$$

$$\text{Total} \qquad \qquad 100.00 \text{ lbs}$$

Example 2. In some refinery processes, spent sulfuric acid is blended with fuming acid to obtain the required strength for reprocessing. If 104.5% acid is used to raise the strength of 87% acid to 98%, then from the rectangle:

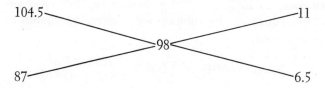

Thus, 11 pounds of 104.5% added to 6.5 pounds of 87% acid will make 17.5 pounds of 98% acid.

This method can be used for mixing calculations when two solutions are similar or one is water.

Mixing On Volume Basis

In some cases, consumers blend or dilute on a volume basis; that is, gallons of strong acid are mixed with gallons of water or weak acid to obtain a certain volume of a desired strength. The applicable equations are:

$$\text{Gals SA} =$$

$$(1) \quad \frac{\text{Gals DA} \times \text{Sp Gr DA} \times \text{C} - \text{Gals WA} \times \text{Sp Gr WA} \times \text{B}}{\text{Sp Gr SA} \times \text{A}}$$

If diluting with water the equation becomes:

$$\text{Gallons SA} = \text{Gals DA} \times \frac{\text{Sp Gr DA} \times \text{C}}{\text{Sp Gr SA} \times \text{A}}$$

$$(2) \quad \text{Gallons WA} = \text{Gals DA} \times \text{Sp Gr DA} \frac{\left(1 - \frac{\text{C}}{\text{A}}\right)}{\text{Sp Gr WA}}$$

If diluting with water the equation becomes:

$$\text{Gallons } H_2O = \text{Gal DA} \times \text{Sp Gr DA}\left(1 - \frac{C}{A}\right)$$

or

$$(3) \quad \text{Gallons WA} = \text{Gals SA} \times \frac{\text{Sp Gr SA } (A - C)}{\text{Sp Gr WA } (C - B)}$$

If diluting with water the equation becomes:

$$\text{Gallons } H_2O = \text{Gals SA} \times \text{Sp Gr SA}\left(\frac{A}{C} - 1\right)$$

Example 1. In pickling, 66° Bé (93.19%) sulfuric acid is usually diluted with water to 15%. If 1,000 gallons of the 15% acid are required, the use of the equation (1), diluting with water, determines the acid requirement in gallons.

$$\text{Gallons 66° Bé} = 1,000 \times \frac{1.1064 \times 0.15}{1.835 \times 0.9319}$$

$$= 97 \text{ gals 66° Bé sulfuric acid}$$

The use of equation (2), diluting with water, determines the water requirement in gallons.

$$\text{Gallons } H_2O = 1,000 \times 1.1064\left(1 - \frac{0.15}{0.9319}\right)$$

$$= 928.3 \text{ gals } H_2O$$

Total gallons of acid and water exceed 1,000, but this is accommodated by shrinkage on mixing.

Example 2. If 100 gallons of 98% acid are blended with 70% acid to produce 91% acid for fortification, and quantities are to be determined by equation (3):

$$\text{Gallons 70%} = 100 \times \frac{1.8437 \ (0.98 - 0.91)}{1.6153 \ (0.91 - 0.70)}$$

$$= 38.0 \text{ gals}$$

$$\text{Gallons 91%} = \frac{100 \times 1.8437 + 38.0 \times 1.6153}{1.8259}$$

$$= 134.6 \text{ gals}$$

Mixing causes a shrinkage of 3.4 gallons.

TABLE XIV. BLENDING SULFURIC ACID

Tons of 98% Sulfuric Acid Required to Produce One Ton of Desired Strength

DESIRED STRENGTH %

STRENGTH WEAK ACID %	60	62	64	66	68	70	72	74	76	77.67	78	80	82	84	86	88	90	92	93.19	94	96	98
60	0	.053	.105	.158	.211	.263	.316	.368	.421	.465	.474	.526	.579	.632	.684	.736	.789	.842	.873	.895	.947	1.00
62		0	.056	.111	.167	.222	.278	.333	.389	.435	.444	.500	.555	.611	.667	.722	.778	.833	.866	.888	.944	1.00
64			0	.0588	.118	.176	.235	.294	.353	.402	.412	.471	.529	.588	.647	.706	.765	.824	.859	.882	.941	1.00
66				0	.0625	.125	.188	.250	.313	.365	.375	.438	.500	.563	.625	.688	.750	.813	.850	.875	.938	1.00
68					0	.0667	.133	.200	.267	.322	.333	.400	.467	.533	.600	.667	.733	.800	.840	.867	.933	1.00
70						0	.071	.143	.214	.274	.286	.357	.429	.500	.571	.643	.714	.786	.828	.857	.929	1.00
72							0	.077	.154	.218	.231	.308	.385	.462	.538	.615	.692	.769	.815	.846	.923	1.00
74								0	.083	.153	.167	.250	.333	.417	.500	.583	.667	.750	.800	.833	.917	1.00
76									0	.076	.091	.182	.273	.364	.455	.545	.636	.727	.781	.818	.909	1.00
77.67										0	.016	.115	.213	.311	.410	.508	.606	.705	.763	.803	.902	1.00
78											0	.100	.200	.300	.400	.500	.600	.700	.760	.800	.900	1.00
80												0	.111	.222	.333	.444	.556	.666	.733	.778	.889	1.00
82													0	.125	.250	.375	.500	.625	.699	.750	.875	1.00
84														0	.143	.286	.428	.571	.656	.714	.857	1.00
86															0	.167	.333	.500	.599	.667	.833	1.00
88																0	.200	.400	.519	.600	.800	1.00
90																	0	.250	.399	.500	.750	1.00
92																		0	.198	.333	.667	1.00
93.19																			0	.168	.584	1.00
94																				0	.500	1.00
96																					0	1.00
98																						0

CALCULATIONS FOR TABLE:

Let: x — tons 98% to be used
a — strength of weak acid
y — tons of weak acid
b — strength of mixed acid
l — tons of mixed acid

Then: $98 x + a.y = b.l$
$x + y = l$
$98 x + a (l - x) = b$
$$x = \frac{(b - a)}{(98 - a)}$$

"Numbers" indicate tons of 98% acid which when mixed with one minus "the number" of tons of weak acid will produce one ton of the desired strength acid.

EXAMPLE: To produce 1 ton of 66% acid, add 0.158 tons 98% acid to (1−0.158) or 0.842 tons 60% acid.

TABLE XV. MIXING TABLE FOR ELECTROLYTE ACID

Electrolyte Desired			Gallons of 1.823 Sp. Gr. (93.19%) And Water To Make 1000 Gallons Of Desired Specific Gravity	
Specific Gravity @80° F	Percent H_2SO_4	Lbs. Per Gallon @80° F	Acid	Water
1.250	34.28	10.39	252	790
1.255	34.88	10.43	258	785
1.260	35.47	10.48	263	780
1.265	36.06	10.52	269	775
1.270	36.65	10.56	274	770
1.275	37.23	10.60	279	765
1.280	37.82	10.64	285	760
1.285	38.39	10.68	290	755
1.290	38.98	10.73	296	750
1.295	39.55	10.77	302	745
1.300	40.11	10.81	307	740
1.310	41.25	10.89	318	730
1.320	42.38	10.97	329	720
1.325	42.93	11.02	335	714
1.330	43.49	11.06	340	709
1.340	44.58	11.14	352	699
1.350	45.66	11.22	363	689
1.360	46.73	11.31	374	678
1.365	47.26	11.35	380	673
1.370	47.79	11.39	385	668
1.375	48.31	11.43	391	662
1.380	48.83	11.47	397	657
1.385	49.35	11.51	402	652
1.390	49.86	11.56	408	646
1.395	50.38	11.60	414	641
1.400	50.89	11.64	419	636
1.410	51.90	11.72	431	625
1.420	52.90	11.81	442	614
1.425	53.40	11.85	448	608
1.430	53.90	11.89	454	603
1.440	54.98	11.97	466	591
1.450	55.95	12.06	478	579
1.460	56.90	12.14	489	569
1.470	57.85	12.22	500	558
1.475	58.32	12.26	506	552
1.480	58.79	12.30	512	546
1.490	59.71	12.39	524	535
1.500	60.63	12.47	535	524
1.510	61.55	12.55	547	513
1.520	62.46	12.64	559	501
1.525	62.90	12.68	564	496
1.530	63.35	12.72	570	490
1.540	64.24	12.80	582	478
1.550	65.12	12.89	594	467
1.560	66.00	12.97	606	455
1.570	66.89	13.05	618	443
1.575	67.34	13.09	624	437
1.580	67.83	13.14	631	430
1.590	68.71	13.22	643	418
1.600	69.57	13.30	655	406

(cont'd)

TABLE XV   MIXING TABLE FOR ELECTROLYTE ACID (cont'd.)

Electrolyte Desired			Gallons of 1.823 Sp. Gr. (93.19%) And Water To Make 1000 Gallons Of Desired Specific Gravity	
Specific Gravity @80° F	Percent H2SO4	Lbs. Per Gallon @80° F	Acid	Water
1.610	70.41	13.39	667	393
1.620	71.27	13.47	679	381
1.625	71.69	13.51	685	375
1.630	72.11	13.55	691	369
1.640	72.95	13.64	704	356
1.650	73.81	13.72	716	343
1.660	74.64	13.80	729	330
1.670	75.48	13.88	742	317
1.675	75.91	13.93	748	311
1.680	76.33	13.97	755	304
1.690	77.18	14.05	768	290
1.700	78.31	14.13	783	272
1.710	78.99	14.22	795	260
1.720	79.86	14.30	808	246
1.725	80.32	14.34	815	238
1.730	80.77	14.38	822	231
1.740	81.69	14.47	837	215
1.750	82.65	14.55	851	198
1.760	83.62	14.63	866	181
1.770	84.70	14.72	883	161
1.775	85.23	14.76	890	152
1.780	85.76	14.80	898	142
1.790	87.01	14.88	916	119
1.800	88.43	14.97	937	92
1.810	90.70	15.05		
1.820	92.12	15.13		
1.823	93.19	15.16		
1.830	95.20	15.21		

Blending Acids of Different Strengths

Table XIV gives the amount of 98% sulfuric acid to blend with weaker strengths to produce a mixture of any intermediate strength. Table XV gives dilution data for electrolyte acid.

Figure 39 shows the proportions of acids of different strengths which can be blended to produce a desired acid of a particular strength.

Draw a line which connects the desired strength of blended acid (e.g. 90%) with the strength of weaker acid available (e.g. 80%) and intersects the Index Line W.

Draw another line which connects the strength of strong acid available (e.g. 98%) with the strength of weak acid and intersects the Index Line S.

Now connect the points of intersection on Index Lines W and S. The intersection of this line with the tilted scale indicates the proportions of

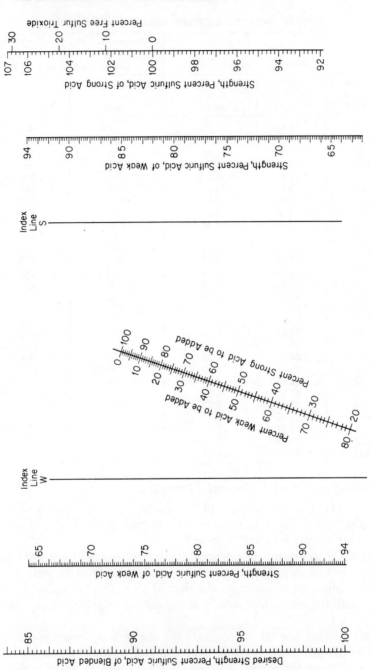

Fig. 39. Nomograph for use in blending sulfuric acids of different strengths to produce an acid of desired strength.

strong (56%) acids and weak (44%) acids to be blended to produce the acid of desired strength (90%).

Dilution with Water

Figure 40 shows the proportions of water and sulfuric acid required to obtain a desired strength of acid.

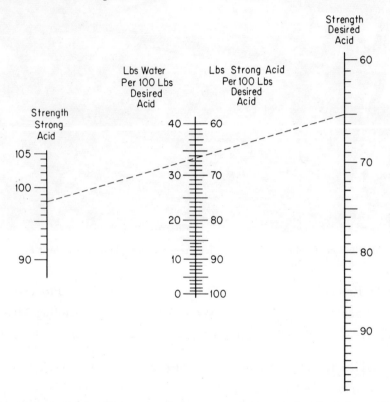

Fig. 40. Dilution of sulfuric acid with water to produce an acid of desired strength.

Heat Evolved During Dilution and Blending

Considerable heat may be evolved, with an accompanying temperature rise, when sulfuric acid is diluted with weaker acid or with water. Heat evolution can be estimated from Figure 4, p. 15, and Table II, p. 16. Precise values may be calculated as follows:

H = enthalpy or heat of solution
$\overline{H}$ = corresponding partial molal enthalpy
n = number of mols

Acid Dilution: Cooling coils at Stauffer's regeneration plant control heat evolution during acid dilution.

Reactants   Products

Strong Acid   Weak Acid   Resulting Mixture

$(n_{H_2O}\overline{H}_1 + n_{SO_3}\overline{H}_2) + (n_{H_2O}\overline{H}_1 + n_{SO_3}\overline{H}_2) + \Delta H = (n_{H_2O}\overline{H}_1 + n_{SO_3}\overline{H}_2)$

ΔH = Resulting Mixture minus Strong Acid minus Weak Acid

Example 1. 100 lbs of an oleum solution containing 104.5% Equiv. H_2SO_4 is to be diluted with 85.0% H_2SO_4 to make 90.0% H_2SO_4. How much heat is evolved? What is the temperature rise of the mixture? Assume the two acids are the same initial temperature before being mixed.

104.5%   5.0%   See pages 88 and 89 for other examples of the
        90.0%   rectangle method for dilution and concentration
85.0%   14.5%   of sulfuric acid to form solutions of any desired
                            strength.

$$\frac{14.5}{5.0} \times 100 = 290 \text{ lbs } 85.0\% \ H_2SO_4 \text{ added to}$$
100 lbs of 104.5% to form
390 lbs of 90.0% H_2SO_4

$$\frac{290 \times .3062}{18} = 4.933 \text{ lb mols } H_2O \text{ in } 290$$
$$\text{lbs } 85.0\% \ H_2SO_4$$

$$\frac{290 \times .6938}{80} = 2.515 \text{ lb mols } SO_3 \text{ in } 290$$
lbs of 85.0% H_2SO_4

	Lb Mols H_2O	Lb Mols SO_3
100 lbs 104.5% =	.8167	1.0663
290 lbs 85.0% =	4.9330	2.5150
390 lbs 90.0% =	5.7497	3.5813

STRONG ACID   WEAK ACID

$-(.8167 \times 32,160) - (1.0663 \times 6820) - (4.933 \times 8,758) - (2.515 \times 32,566) + \Delta H =$

RESULTING MIXTURE

$- (5.7497 \times 10,713) - (3.5813 \times 29,034)$

$\Delta H = - 6936 \text{ BTU Evolved}$

$$\frac{6936}{.45 \times 390} = 39.5°F \text{ Rise in temp. of the mixture}$$

Example 2. 100 lbs of 98.0% sulfuric acid is to be diluted with pure water to make a 93.19% solution of sulfuric acid in water. How much heat is evolved?

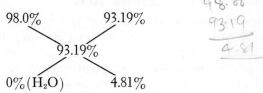

$$\frac{4.81}{93.19} \times 100 = 5.16 \text{ lbs } H_2O \text{ added to } 100 \text{ lbs of } 98.0\% \text{ to make}$$
$$105.16 \text{ lbs } 93.19\% \ H_2SO_4$$

$$\frac{5.16}{18} = 0.2867 \text{ lb mols of } H_2O$$

	Lb Mols H_2O	Lb Mols SO_3
100 lbs 98.0% H_2SO_4 =	1.1111	1.0000
5.16 lbs H_2O =	.2867	0
105.16 lbs 93.19% H_2SO_4 =	1.3978	1.0000

STRONG ACID

$$\Delta H - (1.1111 \times 15{,}950) - (1.0000 \times 22{,}420)$$

WATER

$$- (0.2867 \times 0) =$$

RESULTING MIXTURE

$$- (1.3978 \times 12{,}300) - (1.0000 \times 26{,}600)$$

$$\Delta H = - 3650 \text{ BTU evolved}$$

See Tables XXXV, page 294, and XXXVI, pages 295 and 296, for calculated values.

Strengthening Acid

Concentration of Sulfuric Acid

Heat Requirements. The curve[1] in Fig. 41 shows heat required to bring sulfuric acid of various strengths from any temperature to its boiling point. The curve[1] in Fig. 42 shows heat required to concentrate sulfuric acid of various strengths at its boiling point to 98.5% acid.

The following example[1] will illustrate the usefulness of these curves:

"Suppose 60 deg. Bé sulfuric acid at atmospheric temperature is being concentrated in open pans, with no fume recovery, to 66 deg. Bé, there being required 500 lb. coal, of 13,000 B.t.u. per lb., per ton of finished acid. The recovery is known to amount to 96 per cent. What is the thermal efficiency of the apparatus?

"The per cent H_2SO_4 in 60 deg. Bé acid is 77.7; in 66 deg. Bé acid, 93.2. One ton of finished acid thus contains $2{,}000 \times 0.932 = 1{,}864$ lb. H_2SO_4, which requires $500 \times 13{,}000 = 6{,}500{,}000$ B.t.u., or 3,487 B.t.u. per lb. H_2SO_4. One lb. H_2SO_4 in the finished acid corresponds to $1 \div 0.96 = 1.042$ lb. H_2SO_4 in the original acid. To heat 1.042 lb. H_2SO_4 as 77.7 per cent acid from atmospheric temperature 20 deg. C., to boiling, requires, from Fig. 40, 194 B.t.u. $\times$ 1.042 = 202 B.t.u. To concentrate 1 lb. H_2SO_4 from 77.7 per cent, and boiling temperature, to 93.2 per cent, requires, from Fig. 41, 465 − 122 = 343 B.t.u. To concentrate 0.042 lb.

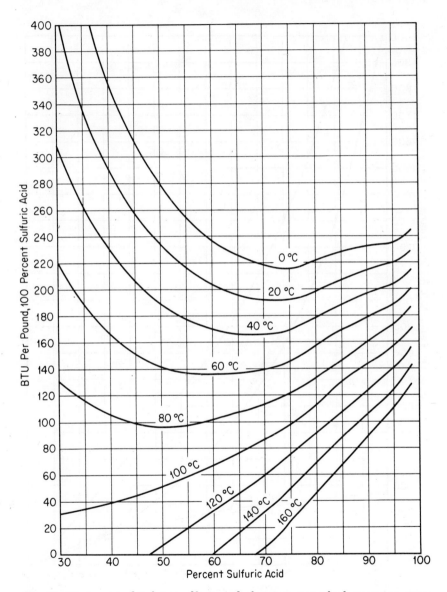

Fig. 41. Heat required to bring sulfuric acid of various strengths from various temperatures to boiling.

H_2SO_4 from 77.7 per cent to 98.5 per cent—i.e., completely—requires, from Fig. 41, 465 B.t.u. $\times$ 0.042 = 20 B.t.u., exclusive of the heat required to volatilize the H_2SO_4 itself. This would be 0.042 $\times$ 220 = 9 B.t.u. The total theoretical heat required is, hence, per lb. finished H_2SO_4:

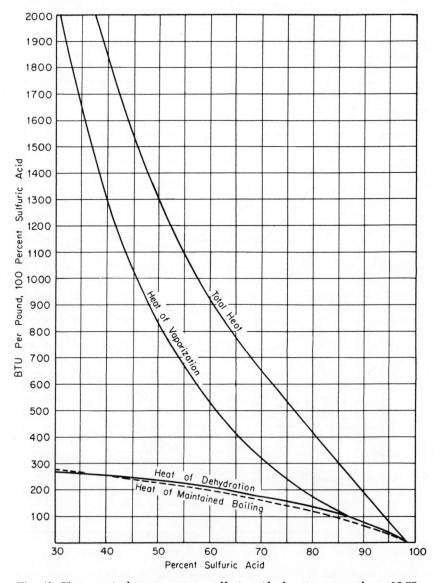

Fig. 42. Heat required to concentrate sulfuric acid of various strengths to 98.5%.

	B.t.u.
Sensible heat, H_s	202
Total heat, H_t	343
Heat in H_2SO_4 lost by evaporation	9
Total heat of this lost H_2SO_4	20
Total Theoretical	574
Actually used	3,487

Theoretical thermal efficiency is $574 \div 3,487 = 16.5$ per cent."

[1] Zeisberg, F. C., "Thermal Considerations in Sulphuric Acid Concentration," Vol. 27, No. 1, *Chemical and Metallurgical Engineering*.

Fortification of Sulfuric Acid

In many petrochemical processes, strong sulfuric acid is recovered after catalysis and concentrated to a usable spent acid. This acid, probably containing some carbonaceous matter, has an acidity ranging from 70 to 92%. It can be fortified to original strength with sulfur trioxide.

Figures 43 and 44 illustrate typical spent acid cycles followed in petroleum refineries and petrochemical plants.

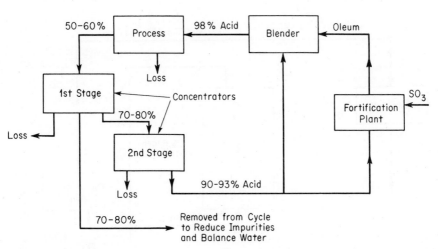

Fig. 43. Spent acid recovery cycle for a petrochemical process.

To determine the amount of strong acid produced by the addition of sulfur trioxide to a weak acid, water content of the weak acid should be assumed constant and the same as that of the strong fortified acid. Neglecting any carbonaceous matter in the weak acid or atmospheric moisture collected in production of sulfur trioxide, the following applies:

Example: Determine how much 98% acid is produced when 80% spent acid is fortified by adding SO_3.
From Table XXII, p. 261, the total water percentages are:
80% acid — 34.70%
98% acid — 20.00%

> Water Content Weak Acid = Water Content Strong Acid
> Let X = Amount of Weak Acid (WA)
>   Y = Amount of Strong Acid (SA)
> % H_2O(WA) × X = %H_2O(SA) × Y

Thus, the fortification ratio—units of strong acid produced when SO_3 is added to one unit of weak acid—becomes:

$$\frac{X}{Y} = \frac{\% \ H_2O(WA)}{\% \ H_2O(SA)}$$

The fortification ratio becomes $\frac{0.3470}{0.2000} = 1.735$

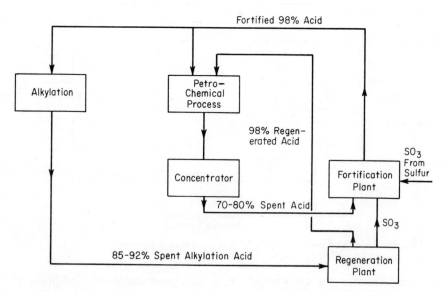

Fig. 44. Spent acid recovery cycle for a petroleum refinery-chemical plant.

Thus, the following can be derived:

Basis	80% H_2SO_4 (Tons)	+	SO_3 (Tons)	→	98% H_2SO_4 (Tons)
As Is	1.000		0.735		1.735
As Is	1.360		1.000		2.360
As Is	0.576		0.424		1.000
100%	0.800		0.900		1.700
100%	1.000		1.125		2.125
100%	0.889		1.000		1.889
100%	0.471		0.529		1.000

The Fortification ratios nomograph, Figure 45, is based upon the calcu-

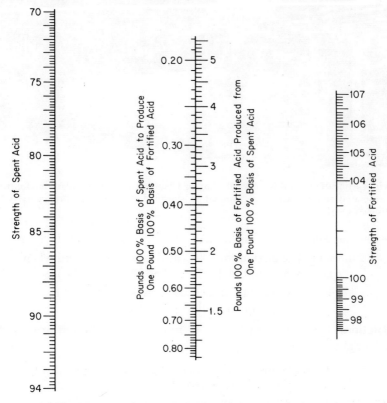

Fig. 45. Fortification ratios for spent sulfuric acids.

lations for the fortifications of sulfuric acid as set out under Calculations, page 102. (The carbon content of the spent acid is neglected and the water content of the spent remains constant.) Ratios for various strengths of spent and fortified acid can be quickly determined.

Acid Fortification: In this tower at Stauffer Chemical Company's plant in Houston, regenerated sulfuric acids are brought to specified strengths by fortification with sulfur trioxide.

Example: Suppose 80% spent acid is fortified to 98% acid.

Find (1) The amount of 100% acid as 98% produced when one pound of 100% acid as 80% is fortified.

(2) The amount of 100% acid as 80% required to produce one ton 100% as 98% acid.

Solution: Draw a line on Figure 45 from 80% on the left axis to 98% on the right axis and then read.

(1) 2.125 lbs. of 100% as 98% produced per lb. of 100% as 80% fortified.

(2) .470 lbs. of 100% as 80% required to produce one lb. 100% acid as 98%.

Fortification Ratios for a wide range of spent sulfuric acids are found in Table XVI, opposite.

TABLE XVI. FORTIFICATION RATIOS OF SPENT SULFURIC ACIDS

	Acid Fortified	Ratios—Units of fortified acid per unit weak acid			
Percent H_2SO_4	Percent Total Water	93.19% Ratio	98% Ratio	104.5% Ratio	109% Ratio
50	59.19	2.474	2.960	4.027	5.371
51	58.37	2.439	2.919	3.971	5.296
52	57.55	2.405	2.878	3.915	5.222
53	56.74	2.371	2.837	3.860	5.149
54	55.92	2.337	2.796	3.804	5.074
55	55.10	2.303	2.755	3.748	5.000
56	54.29	2.269	2.715	3.693	4.926
57	53.47	2.235	2.674	3.638	4.852
58	52.65	2.200	2.633	3.582	4.777
59	51.84	2.166	2.592	3.527	4.704
60	51.02	2.132	2.551	3.471	4.630
61	50.21	2.098	2.511	3.416	4.556
62	49.39	2.064	2.470	3.360	4.482
63	48.57	2.030	2.429	3.304	4.407
64	47.76	1.996	2.388	3.249	4.334
65	46.94	1.962	2.347	3.193	4.259
66	46.12	1.927	2.306	3.138	4.185
67	45.31	1.894	2.266	3.082	4.111
68	44.49	1.859	2.225	3.027	4.037
69	43.68	1.825	2.184	2.972	3.964
70	42.86	1.791	2.143	2.916	3.889
71	42.04	1.757	2.102	2.860	3.815
72	41.23	1.723	2.062	2.805	3.741
73	40.41	1.689	2.021	2.749	3.667
74	39.59	1.654	1.980	2.693	3.592
75	38.78	1.621	1.939	2.638	3.519
76	37.96	1.586	1.898	2.582	3.444
77	37.14	1.552	1.857	2.527	3.370
77.67	36.60	1.530	1.830	2.490	3.321
78	36.33	1.518	1.817	2.472	3.297
79	35.51	1.484	1.776	2.416	3.222
80	34.70	1.450	1.735	2.361	3.149
81	33.88	1.416	1.694	2.305	3.074
82	33.06	1.382	1.653	2.249	3.000
83	32.25	1.348	1.613	2.194	2.926
84	31.43	1.313	1.572	2.138	2.852
85	30.61	1.279	1.531	2.082	2.778
86	29.80	1.245	1.490	2.027	2.704
87	28.98	1.211	1.449	1.971	2.630
88	28.17	1.177	1.409	1.916	2.556
89	27.35	1.143	1.368	1.861	2.482
90	26.53	1.109	1.327	1.805	2.407
91	25.72	1.075	1.286	1.750	2.334
92	24.90	1.041	1.245	1.694	2.259
93	24.08	1.006	1.204	1.638	2.185
93.19	23.93	1.000	1.197	1.628	2.171
94	23.27		1.164	1.583	2.112
95	22.45		1.123	1.527	2.037
96	21.64		1.082	1.472	1.964
97	20.82		1.041	1.416	1.889
98	20.00		1.000	1.361	1.815
99	19.19			1.305	1.741
100	18.37			1.250	1.667
101	17.55			1.194	1.592
102	16.74			1.139	1.519
103	15.92			1.083	1.445
104	15.10			1.027	1.370
104.5	14.70			1.000	1.334
105	14.29				1.297
106	13.47				1.222
107	12.66				1.149
108	11.84				1.074
109	11.02				1.000

Example: If one ton 80% spent acid is fortified with SO_3 to 98%, reading under the 98% ratio column 1.735 tons 98% acid will be produced and .735 tons of SO_3 consumed. This table is calculated on "As Is" weights and does not include the moisture taken up in fortifying from the drying tower.

Total water = the chemically combined water plus the free water.

Simplified Water Balance for Fortification

Spent acid from some petrochemical processes is returned to the acid producer for fortification to its original required process strength. The consumer retains ownership of the weak acid and must take back all the strong acid made from the spent acid. That is, total water put into the fortification cycle must equal the total water out. The purpose of Figure 46 is to rapidly estimate the water put in the absorbing tower and the equivalent amount of strong acid that will be produced.

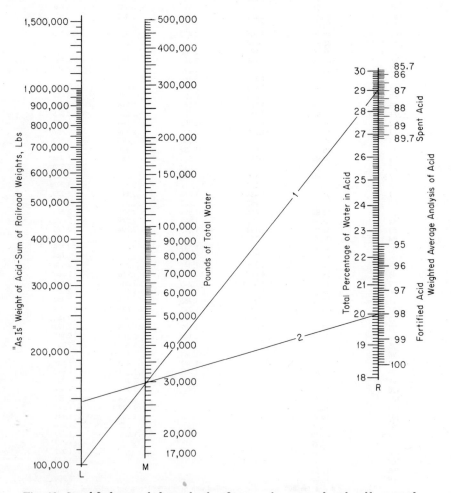

Fig. 46. Simplified water balance for fortification of spent acid with sulfur trioxide.

Example: One tank car of 87% spent acid weighing 100,000 pounds is fortified to 98.0%. Determine pounds of total water fed to the absorbing tower and the amount of 98% acid produced.

Solution: Draw line on Figure 46 from weight (L axis) to acidity of spent (R axis). Connect the intersecting point weight of water (middle axis) with the strength of the strong acid (R axis) and extend line to the L axis and read 144,900 pounds of strong acid produced.

(The nomograph neglects carbon content of spent acid.)

Stripping Acid

Stripping Oleum

Stripping sulfur trioxide from oleum is the reverse of fortification. The amount of sulfur trioxide that will be produced by this method can be calculated from the water content ratios or from the sulfur trioxide content.

Example: Determine the amount of SO_3 produced when 65% oleum (114.63% H_2SO_4) is stripped down to 20% oleum (104.5% H_2SO_4). From Table XXIII, p. 269.

65% oleum contains 6.43% H_2O; 93.57% SO_3
20% oleum contains 14.70% H_2O; 85.30% SO_3

$$\text{Tons 20\% oleum} = \frac{0.0643}{.1470} = 0.4375; \text{ so that:}$$

	65% Oleum (Tons)	SO₃ Produced (Tons)	20% Oleum Produced (Tons)
"As is"	1.000	0.5625	0.4375
"100% H₂SO₄"	1.1463	0.6891	0.4572

The following formula can also be used.

$$\text{Weight } SO_3 = \frac{\% \text{ Oleum in Strong Oleum} - \% \text{ Oleum in Stripped Oleum}}{100 - \% \text{ Oleum in Stripped Oleum}}$$

$$= \frac{65 - 20}{100 - 20} = 0.5625 \text{ ton/ton 65\% Oleum Stripped to 20\%}$$

Producing Sulfur Trioxide from Oleum

A new service making pure sulfur trioxide (either liquid or gaseous) is now available from some sulfuric acid suppliers. The supplier company ships, say, 65% oleum (114.63%), sulfur trioxide is distilled off, and lean 20% oleum is returned to the supplier company for fortification.

Sulfur trioxide vapor is produced by feeding the 65% oleum to a vaporizer similar to a fin tube boiler. The source of heat (600°F) can be hot gases or oil. The oleum is outside the tubes.

Operating pressure and exit oleum strength are selected; this determines temperature. The temperature is controlled to obtain the desired gas pressure in the boiler. (See equation below.)

The rate of sulfur trioxide production is proportional to the strong-oleum feed for a given lean-oleum strength. Every ton of 65% oleum will produce 0.5625 ton of sulfur trioxide and 0.4375 ton of 20% oleum.

The 20% oleum is removed by pump or gravity through an interior standpipe in order to maintain the proper level in the boiler. The standpipe is connected to a loop seal to maintain the boiler pressure.

Sulfur trioxide vapor is taken off the vapor space of the oleum boiler. The take-off is baffled to avoid oleum entrainment. The sulfur trioxide delivery line is steam-traced to avoid sulfur trioxide freezing.

Calculations for Producing Sulfur Trioxide from Oleum*

Vapor pressure equation:

$$\text{Log P psia} = A - \frac{B}{T\,(°\text{Rankin})}$$

TABLE OF CONSTANTS

% Free SO_3	A	B
10	6.90759	4643.32
20	7.26678	4595.47
22	7.41716	4642.67
24	7.47747	4627.15
26	7.69956	4726.77
28	7.80480	4738.68
30	8.14453	4916.56
60	7.98324	4155.71
65	7.74284	3906.90
70	7.89732	3899.19

* Adapted from Trans. Faraday Soc., Volume 36, pp. 345–356 (1940) by Miles, Niblock and Wilson.

This equation is the basis for the following boiling-temperature values for stripping 65% oleum at a pressure of 15 psig:

% SO$_3$ in Lean Oleum	Boiling Point, °C. at 15 psig	Available SO$_3$ as Weight % of Input
20	333	56.25
22	321	55.13
24	311	53.95
26	299	52.70
28	288	51.39
30	277	50.00

Generation of Anhydrous Hydrogen Chloride Gas

Sulfuric acid's great affinity for water makes it possible to evolve hydrogen chloride gas by mixing sulfuric acid and muriatic acid.

Example: Anhydrous hydrogen chloride gas is produced by adding 20° Bé (31.45% HCl) muriatic acid to 98% sulfuric acid until the strength of the sulfuric acid is reduced to 75%.

1. How much strong sulfuric acid (in pounds) is required to produce one pound of anhydrous hydrogen chloride on a yield of 90%?

2. How many pounds of 20° Bé muriatic acid are required to produce one pound of anhydrous hydrogen chloride on a yield of 90%?

3. How many pounds of weak sulfuric acid is produced?
Thus:

$$\text{Lbs Anhydrous HCl} = \text{Lbs Muriatic Acid (MA)} \times \% \text{ HCl} \times \text{Yield} =$$

$$\text{Lbs Sulfuric Acid} \left(\frac{\text{Initial } \%}{\text{Final } \%} - 1 \right) \frac{\% \text{ HCl (in MA)}}{\% \text{ H}_2\text{O (in MA)}} \times \text{Yield}$$

Solution 1

$$\text{Lbs H}_2\text{SO}_4 = \text{Lbs Anhydrous HCl} \times \frac{\% \text{ H}_2\text{O (in MA)}}{\% \text{ HCl (in MA)}} \times \frac{\text{Final } \% \text{ H}_2\text{SO}_4}{(\text{Initial} - \text{Final } \% \text{ H}_2\text{SO}_4)}$$

$$= 1 \times \frac{68.55}{31.45} \times \frac{75.00}{98.00 - 75.00}$$

$$= 7.11 \text{ lbs}$$

Solution 2

$$\text{Lbs Muriatic Acid} = \frac{\text{Lbs Anhydrous HCl}}{\% \text{ HCl (in MA)} \times \text{Yield}}$$

$$= \frac{1}{0.3145 \times 0.9}$$

$$= 3.53 \text{ lbs}$$

Solution 3

$$\text{Lbs Weak Acid} = \text{Lbs Strong } H_2SO_4 \frac{(\text{Initial } \%)}{(\text{Final } \%)}$$

$$= 7.11 \times \frac{(98.0)}{(75.0)}$$

$$= 9.29 \text{ lbs}$$

Material Balance

Pounds Weak H_2SO_4 plus Pounds Anhydrous HCl = Pounds Strong H_2SO_4 plus Pounds Muriatic Acid minus Loss in Generation:

$$9.29 + 1.00 = 7.11 + 3.53 - 0.35$$
$$10.29 = 10.29$$

Acid Transfer

Pressure Required to Unload Sulfuric Acid

Air pressure can be used to unload sulfuric acid if the acid is within the range of 60° Bé to 65% oleum and has been shipped by tank car or tank truck. The amount of pressure required depends on the height the acid must be lifted.

Example: Over-all height from the end of the deep line in a tank car to the discharge line at the opening of the tank is 25 feet. Find the pressure required to unload a tank car of 66° Bé sulfuric acid. The air pressure required is:

$$\text{Lbs/Sq In.} = \text{Height (Ft.)} \times \text{Lbs } H_2SO_4/\text{Cu Ft} \times \frac{1}{144 \text{ Sq In./Sq Ft}}$$

$$= 25 \times \frac{114.47}{144}$$

$$= 19.9 \text{ psig}$$

Various pressures are shown on Table III, p. 30.

Price and Freight Equivalents

In many cases, sulfuric acid is shipped at strengths other than the strength on which price and freight are based.

Example: Price is $23.95 per ton; basis is 100% H_2SO_4 and 66° Bé (93.19%) sulfuric acid shipped to a destination where the freight rate is $4 per net ton. Find the delivered cost on "as is" and 100% basis.

The 100% price multiplied by the acidity will give the "as is" price. The freight rate divided by the acidity will give the 100% freight equivalent. Thus:

	Price per ton	
	Basis 100%	Basis 93.19%
Price f.o.b. shipping point	$23.95 × 0.9319 = $22.32	
Freight to destination: $\dfrac{\$4.00}{0.9319} = \$4.29$	4.29 × 0.9319 = 4.00	
Delivered cost	$28.24	$26.32

Price and freight equivalents are given in Tables XX and XXI, respectively, on pp. 230 and 260.

Friction Problem

Example: Commercial sulfuric acid is pumped from tank A (Fig. 47) to tank B through 9,444 feet of all-welded Schedule 80 six-inch pipe. There are nineteen 90-degree ells in the pipeline. What are friction, static and actual pressures within the pipe?

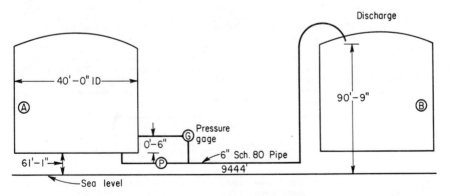

Fig. 47. Illustration for Friction Problem above.

TABLE XVII. FRICTION VALUES FOR WEAK ACID

Showing loss of head* (expressed in feet of acid) in LEAD PIPE (s) when passing 52° and 60° Bé sulfuric acid (at 20° C) at the rates shown.

Gal. per Min.	52° Bé Sulfuric Acid (Visc.=9.2 Cp-Sp. Gr.=1.56) Friction per 100 feet					60° Bé Sulfuric Acid (Vis. 17.2 Cp.-Sp. Gr. 1.70) Friction per 100 feet				
	1½ Inch	2 Inch	2½ Inch	3 Inch	4 Inch	1½ Inch	2 Inch	2½ Inch	3 Inch	4 Inch
5	0.80					1.00				
10	2.10	0.50				2.50	0.70			
15	4.00	1.00				5.00	1.35			
20	6.70	1.70	0.50			8.00	2.20	0.70		
25	9.90	2.55	0.80			11.60	3.20	1.00		
30	13.65	3.50	1.10			16.00	4.30	1.40		
35	17.70	4.65	1.45	0.80		21.25	5.70	1.85	1.00	
40	22.50	5.90	1.90	0.90		27.50	7.10	2.40	1.20	
45	28.00	7.30	2.35	1.05			8.70	2.90	1.40	
50		8.90	2.90	1.20			10.30	3.50	1.60	
60		12.10	4.00	1.65			14.10	4.70	2.10	
75		18.00	5.90	2.40			21.20	6.90	3.00	
80		20.00	6.60	2.75	0.70		23.60	7.70	3.40	0.85
90		24.60	8.15	3.40	0.90		29.00	9.55	4.10	1.10
100		30.00	9.90	4.20	1.10			11.50	5.00	1.30
125			14.70	6.20	1.55			17.30	7.50	1.90
150			19.70	8.50	2.20			23.20	10.20	2.65
175			25.10	11.20	2.85			31.00	13.60	3.40
200				14.30	3.60				16.90	4.30
250				20.40	5.35				25.10	6.45
300				28.00	6.30					8.90
350					9.40					11.70
400					12.00					14.60
450					14.65					18.00
500					17.80					21.50
550					21.60					25.45
600					25.80					29.70

*SAFETY FACTOR: This table includes a safety factor of 20% to cover irregularities due to joints, and condition of pipe surface.

PIPE ENDS: The friction in lead pipe bends can only be approximated, as much depends upon the uniformity of the radii to which they are bent; buckling; and contractions. For 90° bends free from buckling or contractions, the friction may be estimated as being equal to that found in a straight pipe of the same diameter, the length of which is "K" pipe diameters long. The Values of "K" are as follows.

(w) $\frac{R}{D}$	0.1	1.0	2.0	5.0	10.0
K	30.0	18.0	7.5	6.0	7.0

(w) D = Diameter of pipe in inches.
R = Radius of bend in inches measured to center of channel.
(y) For strong acid see Table XVIII.
(z) Pipe sizes shown on this page are exact internal diameters.

Data:

Start time: 9:50 a.m.; gage tank A (depth of acid measured from the bottom): 10 feet 5¾ inches; Acid: 98% H_2SO_4; Specific Gravity: 1.822 at 100° F.

Finish time: 11:04 a.m.; gage tank A (depth of acid measured from bottom): 8 feet 7 inches. There is no significant change in acid or temperature. Pressure-gage reading, at location shown on Figure 47, is 97 pounds per square inch. Compute expected pressure-gage reading from Charles S. Lewis friction-flow data in Tables XVII and XVIII.

Solution:

(a) Volume of acid pumped

$$(40)^2 \ \frac{\pi}{4} \ (10'5\tfrac{3}{4}'' - 8'7'') =$$

$$(40)^2 \ \frac{\pi}{4} \ (1.896') = 2383 \text{ cu ft}$$

(b) Time of run
$$9:50 \text{ to } 11:04 = 1 \text{ hr and } 14 \text{ min, or } 74 \text{ min}$$

(c) Area of pipe section
Six-inch Schedule 80 pipe is 5.761 in. (inside diameter)

$$\frac{5.761 \text{ in.}}{12} = 0.48 \text{ ft}$$

$$\text{Area} = 0.48^2 \ \frac{\pi}{4} = 0.181 \text{ sq ft}$$

(d) Linear velocity of acid in pipe during run
$$\frac{2383 \text{ cu. ft.}}{(74 \text{ min.}) \ (60 \text{ sec./min.}) \ (0.181 \text{ sq. ft.})} = 2.96 \text{ ft per sec}$$

(e) Volume pumped per minute
$$\frac{2381}{74 \text{ min.}} \text{ cu. ft. } (7.48 \text{ gal./cu. ft.}) = 241 \text{ gals per min}$$

(f) Static head from center of pressure gage to discharge of pipe in tank B
$$(90 \text{ ft-9 in.}) - [(61 \text{ ft-1 in.}) + (0 \text{ ft-6 in.})] = 29 \text{ ft-2 in.}$$
$$29 \text{ ft-2in.} = 29.17 \text{ ft.}$$
$$\text{Specific gravity } H_2SO_4 = 1.822$$
$$\text{Pressure of acid} = 0.4335 \text{ psi/ft.}$$

(Cont'd on page 117)

TABLE XVIII. FRICTION VALUES FOR STRONG ACID

Showing loss of head* (expressed in feet of acid) in commercial IRON PIPE AND ELBOWS when passing 60° (z) Bé Sulfuric Acid (at 20° C) at the rates shown. 60° Bé H_2SO_4 (Visc. 17.2 Cp.-Sp. Gr. 1.70)

Gal. per Min.	Frict. 100' Pipe	Frict. per Elbow	Frict. 100' Pipe	Frict. per Elbow	Frict. 100' Pipe	Frict. per Elbow	Frict. 100' Pipe	Frict. per Elbow	Frict. 100' Pipe	Frict. per Elbow
	1½" Pipe		2" Pipe							
5	1.00	0.040								
10	2.20	0.088	0.60	0.031	2½" Pipe					
15	4.30	0.173	1.20	0.062						
20	7.20	0.290	2.00	0.114	0.90	0.056				
25	10.40	0.418	3.00	0.156	1.20	0.074	3" Pipe			
30	14.00	0.564	4.10	0.207	1.70	0.105				
35	18.30	0.736	5.30	0.275	2.40	0.148	0.80	0.061		
40	23.10	0.930	6.80	0.353	3.00	0.185	1.20	0.092		
45	28.30	1.140	8.20	0.425	3.60	0.222	1.40	0.107		
50			9.90	0.513	4.40	0.272	1.60	0.122	4" Pipe	
60			13.60	0.705	6.10	0.377	2.10	0.161		
75			20.20	1.045	8.85	0.547	2.90	0.222		
80			22.60	1.170	9.80	0.606	3.30	0.253	1.00	0.100
90			28.00	1.450	11.90	0.735	4.10	0.312	1.20	0.121
100					14.40	0.890	4.90	0.375	1.50	0.151
125					21.30	1.318	7.20	0.552	2.10	0.212
150					28.80	1.780	10.10	0.843	2.90	0.292
175							13.20	1.010	3.80	0.383
200							16.50	1.262	4.80	0.484
250							24.40	1.870	7.10	0.715
300									9.60	0.967
350									12.60	1.270
400									16.00	1.610
450									19.70	1.980
500									23.70	2.385
550									28.00	2.820

*SAFETY FACTOR: This table includes a safety factor of 20% to cover irregularities due to joints, condition of pipe surface, and age.

(y) For weak acid see Table XVII.

(z) For 66° Bé, sulfuric acid, add 5% to above friction values. The viscosity of 66° Bé. sulfuric acid is 20 centipoises and the specific gravity is 1.84 at 20° C.

TABLE XVIII.   FRICTION VALUES FOR STRONG ACID (cont'd.)

Showing loss of head* (expressed in feet of acid) in CAST IRON PIPE AND ELBOWS when passing 60° (z) Bé Sulfuric Acid (at 20° C) at the rates shown.
66° Bé H₂SO₄ (Visc. 7 cps. Sp. Gr. 1.80)

Gal. per Min.	Frict. 100' Pipe	Frict. per Elbow	Frict. 100' Pipe	Frict. per Elbow	Frict. 100' Pipe	Frict. per Elbow	Frict. 100' Pipe	Frict. per Elbow
	3" Pipe							
30	0.528	0.040						
35	0.702	0.053						
40	0.888	0.067	4' Pipe					
45	1.092	0.082						
50	1.323	0.100	0.335	0.034				
60	1.795	0.134	0.470	0.047				
70	2.360	0.177	0.603	0.061				
80	2.990	0.224	0.753	0.076				
90	3.675	0.275	0.940	0.094				
100	4.325	0.324	1.120	0.112	6" Pipe			
125	6.540	0.490	1.660	0.166				
150	9.000	0.675	2.280	0.228	0.331	0.050		
175	11.700	0.876	3.025	0.303	0.440	0.066	8" Pipe	
200	14.520	1.087	3.775	0.378	0.544	0.082		
250			5.620	0.562	0.846	0.127	0.208	0.042
300			7.690	0.769	1.170	0.176	0.289	0.058
350			10.320	1.032	1.513	0.228	0.378	0.076
400			13.050	1.305	1.860	0.280	0.475	0.095
450			16.200	1.620	2.330	0.350	0.593	0.119
500			19.700	1.970	2.761	0.415	0.721	0.145
600					3.940	0.592	0.988	0.198
700					5.250	0.789	1.290	0.258
800					6.500	0.975	1.670	0.334
900					8.100	1.215	2.065	0.414
1000					9.730	1.460	2.510	0.500
1250							3.700	0.740
1500							5.170	1.035
1750							6.810	1.360
2000							8.760	1.750

*   SAFETY FACTOR: This table includes a safety factor of 20% to cover irregularities due to joints, condition of pipe surface, and age.

(z) For 98% Sulfuric Acid, add 5% to above friction values. The viscosity of 98% Sulfuric Acid is 7.9 cps. and the Specific Gravity is 1.83 at 60° C.

(continued over)

TABLE XVIII. FRICTION VALUES FOR STRONG ACID (cont'd.)

Showing loss of head* (expressed in feet of acid) in
EXTRA HEAVY IRON PIPE AND ELBOWS when passing
66° Bé Sulfuric Acid (at 20° C) at the rates shown.
66° Bé H_2SO_4 (Visc. 20.0 Cp.-Sp. Gr.=1.84)

Gal. per Min.	Frict. 100' Pipe	Frict. per Elbow	Frict. 100' Pipe	Frict. per Elbow	Frict. 100' Pipe	Frict. per Elbow	Frict. 100' Pipe	Frict. per Elbow
	3" Pipe							
30	0.84	0.061						
35	1.11	0.081						
40	1.39	0.102	4" Pipe					
45	1.69	0.124						
50	1.99	0.145	0.64	0.006				
60	2.74	0.200	0.80	0.075				
70	3.56	0.260	1.00	0.096				
80	4.55	0.332	1.25	0.120				
90	5.63	0.411	1.48	0.142				
100	6.75	0.493	1.80	0.172	6" Pipe			
125	10.10	0.803	2.69	0.257				
150	13.50	0.985	3.70	0.354	0.58	0.084		
175	17.80	1.30	4.82	0.461	0.74	0.107		
200	22.60	1.65	5.82	0.557	0.90	0.130		
250			8.80	0.842	1.31	0.189	8" Pipe	
300			12.09	1.164	1.73	0.249	0.465	0.089
350			15.90	1.520	2.45	0.353	0.600	0.114
400			20.19	1.930	2.85	0.410	0.756	0.144
450			25.25	2.410	3.28	0.472	0.830	0.158
500			30.35	2.900	4.22	0.608	1.120	0.213
600					5.90	0.850	1.560	0.297
700					7.33	1.057	2.040	0.389
800					9.75	1.403	2.580	0.492
900					11.95	1.720	3.040	0.580
1000					14.30	2.060	3.850	0.733
1250							5.750	1.095
1500							7.770	1.480
1750							10.380	1.978
2000							13.150	2.510

*SAFETY FACTOR: This table includes a safety factor of 20% to cover
irregularities due to joints, condition of pipe surface, and age.

Thus: (1.822) (29.17) (0.4335 psi./ft.) = 23.05 lbs per sq in.
(g) Pressure drop from friction of flow
      Fanning flow formula is:

$$P = \frac{(0.323) \ (f) \ (L) \ (s) \ (v^2)}{D}$$

f = Friction factor
L = Length of pipe in feet (including allow-
      ance for bends, enlargements, contrac-
      tions, etc.)
s = Specific gravity of liquid
v = Average linear velocity in pipe in feet
      per second
z = Viscosity in centipoises (rel. to H_2O at 68°F)

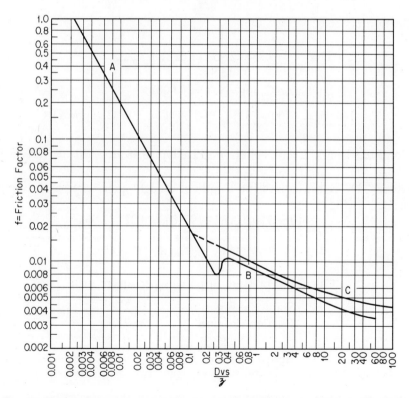

Fig. 48. Factors for use in computing friction through pipes and fittings. Curve A gives values for smooth and rough pipe; B, for smooth tubes only; C, for commercial wrought iron pipe. (*Courtesy Chas. S. Lewis & Company.*)

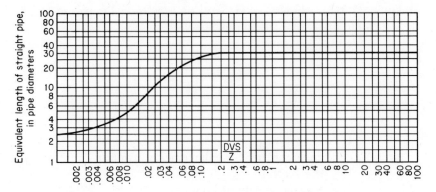

Fig. 49. Length of straight pipe (expressed as pipe diameters) which is equivalent to an elbow in terms of friction offered. (*Courtesy Chas. S. Lewis & Company.*)

Friction factor is:

$$\frac{Dvs}{z} = \frac{(5.76)\ (2.96)\ (1.822)}{13.8} = 2.25$$

From Curve C, Fig. 48: f = 0.0082

$$100^\circ\ F = (100 - 32)\ \frac{5}{9} = 37.8^\circ\ C = 38^\circ\ C\ (approx)$$

Corrected length L = 9,444 ft. + (19 ells) (0.48 ft.) (30) = 9,717.6 ft.

where "30" is the equivalent length of straight pipe, expressed as pipe diameters (Fig. 49).

$$P = \frac{(0.323)\ (0.0082)\ (9718)\ (1.822)\ (2.96)^2}{5.76}$$

71.5 lbs. per sq in.

Calculated pressure in pounds per square inch:

Static Pressure	=	23.0
Friction Pressure	=	71.5
Total		94.5
Actual Pressure		97.0

5. RECOVERY OF SULFURIC ACID

Sulfuric acid is sometimes consumed and appears as an integral part of the finished product or by-product. This occurs in the production of ammonium sulfate, aluminum sulfate, sodium sulfate and superphosphate. It also takes place in water treating, ore leaching, steel pickling and the wet process for the manufacture of phosphoric acid. In other processes, where sulfuric acid is used as a dehydrating agent, carrying agent or catalyst, there can be acid recovery in the form of spent acid.

Spent acids are recoverable from both inorganic and organic processes. In the drying of chlorine gas, for example, acid is recovered from an inorganic process. Organic processes yielding acid include refining of petroleum products, manufacture of petrochemicals and scrubbing of organic chemicals.

Characteristics of Spent Acid

Although "spent sulfuric acid" or "spent acid" are terms commonly applied to the acid residue from a petrochemical or refining process, the terms are actually misnomers. A more correct name would be "recovered acid" because the sulfate radical is not consumed as in spent acid from inorganic waste such as pickle liquor. Because the composition of the recovered acid is mainly sulfuric acid (sometimes as high as 92%), the reactive characteristics of the acid (that is, true acidities) are similar to virgin sulfuric acid when compared by acidity-water ratios.

Some types of spent acid are referred to as sludge. These are the more viscous types having low acid and high hydrocarbon content. Sludges often cannot be utilized economically as such or as a raw material for virgin sulfuric acid manufacture. If this is the case, they are dumped or burned for fuel.

In the process industries, reclaimed sulfuric acid falls into two categories. The first, spent sulfuric acid, refers to an acid with carbon and other impurities totaling less than one per cent. The acid can be used as such or fortified to its original strength and reused in its original process.

119

Its value is almost that of the virgin acid less freight and handling charges. The second, sludge, includes spent alkylation sulfuric acid and the heavy types of reclaimed acid and is usually regenerated into new acid. Its value is that of a raw material and depends upon the following.

1. *Viscosity.* Extremely viscous (nonfluid) sludge cannot be transported for other uses or regeneration.
2. *General Stability.* This is usually measured by determining the stratification occurring during long storage.
3. *Compatibility.* Capability of producing a stable fluid mixture when blended with other reclaimed acids.

About the only generalization that can be made about refinery acid sludges is that they contain sulfuric acid, hydrocarbons and water. Acidity may range from 90% to as low as 20%. Small amounts of inorganic ash may be present, as well as compounds of sodium, magnesium, lead, calcium, nickel, vanadium, iron, chromium and others. Inorganic ash usually amounts to less than 0.10%.

The exact nature of hydrocarbons in sludges is not known. The general type of hydrocarbon depends upon the nature of the process from which the sludge is derived. Sulfate esters, degradation products from treated stock and various sulfonic acids are present. Color indicates that some free carbon is also present.

Sludge Handling

Sludges from the manufacture of petroleum products are mixtures of sulfuric acid, hydrocarbon and water. The nature of the hydrocarbon fraction depends upon the process from which the acid was recovered. The only reaction that can occur is:

$$H_2SO_4 + CH_X \rightarrow 2H_2O + SO_2 + CH_{X-2}$$

Thus, the acid is reduced to sulfur dioxide. As this reaction proceeds further, carbon is formed as a product and the sludge "cokes up." The reaction is accelerated by any increase in temperature so it is imperative to control temperature carefully at all times.

If two sludges with different acid-to-water ratios are mixed, there will be a rise in temperature because of the heat of dilution effect. In blending acid sludges which may range from highly viscous materials to a fluidity comparable to virgin acid, it is important to know beforehand the effect of temperature for the particular blend. At least one sample batch should be made. All blending should be done in the absence of atmospheric moisture.

A stability factor is associated with each blended sludge. Stability is generally measured by determining the stratification which occurs upon standing for a reasonably long period of time. In most cases, it is necessary to recirculate sludges continuously to prevent separation.

Exclusion of atmospheric moisture becomes especially important when sludges are recirculated. Strong sulfuric acid tends to absorb water vapor from the atmosphere. When water vapor is so absorbed, an almost negligible heat of dilution occurring at the surface is enough to accelerate the decomposition reaction. The result is the formation of a thin surface film of carbonaceous material which increases in thickness as time passes. This layer is difficult to disperse.

The accelerating effect of temperature in the decomposition reaction is evidenced by the considerable amounts of sulfur dioxide evolved when sludge blends are heated. Coolers must generally be used to prevent excessive loss of sulfur dioxide.

All spent acid and sludges are shipped in tank trucks, tank cars, barges or pipelines and are subject to the same regulations and precautions as commercial acid.

Types of Recovered Sulfuric Acids

Spent Sodium Acid:

Clear brown acid recovered from the manufacture of antiknock fluids. Approximate analysis:

Acidity	82–90.00%
Free Chlorine	0.41%
Ash	0.25%

Used for superphosphate manufacture.

Spent Chlorine Acid:

Clear acid, colorless to dark brown, returned from the drying of chlorine gas. Approximate analysis:

Acidity	88–92.00%
Free Chlorine (max.)	0.50%
Ash	0.10%

Used for fertilizer manufacture or fortified to 98% with SO_3 for re-use in chlorine production.

Spent Alcohol Acid:

Dark, opaque acid recovered from the manufacture of ethyl or isopropyl alcohol. A small amount of suspended carbonaceous matter gives this acid a dark color, but the acid is of good quality and can be substituted for virgin acid if percentages of acid, carbon and ash in the acid approximate the following:

Acidity	65.0–85.0%
Carbon/Hydro-	
carbons	0.3– 0.5%
Ash	0.2– 0.4%

When fortified, the acid has about the same viscosity as virgin acid and can be used by refineries for general treating and alkylation processes or returned to the alcohol plant for further use.

Spent Butadiene Acid:

When properly separated from hydrocarbons, the color of this acid varies from straw to black. Although its acidity is below that of 60° Bé, it can be shipped in plain steel tank cars because it contains a native inhibitor. Approximate analysis:

Acidity	65.0–75.0%
Carbon/Hydro-	
carbons	0.3– 0.5%
Ash	0.1– 0.2%

Used to acidulate sea water in the manufacture of bromine, or fortified for fertilizer manufacture.

Spent Benzol Sludge Acid:

A light sludge acid resulting from the purification of benzene. Approximate analysis:

Acidity	60.0–70.0%
Carbon/Hydro-	
carbons	10.0–20.0%
Ash	0.05–0.1%

Blends with other sludge acids for burning in regeneration units.

Spent DDT Acid:

A brown-to-black acid containing various amounts of chloral and chlorobenzene from the manufacture of DDT. Approximate analysis:

Acidity	70.0–80.0%
Carbon/Hydro-carbons	3.0–21.0%
Ash	0.05–0.1%

Used to manufacture fertilizers.

Recovered Refinery Acid and Alkylation Sludge Acid:

In refineries, light-oil acid sludges are hydrolyzed to an acid concentration of 30%. This causes the hydrocarbon to separate and rise to the top. After separation, the 30% acid is used to hydrolyze the spent alkylation acid. The acid thus produced is about 60% in concentration and settles to the bottom of the mixture. Hydrocarbons are removed from the upper layer. The 60% acid is then sent to concentrators and raised to approximately 85% acidity. This 85% acid is described as "recovered refinery acid." Approximate analysis:

Recovered

Acidity	85.0–90.0%
Carbon/Hydro-carbons	1.0– 3.0%
Ash	0.3– 0.7%

Sludge

Acidity	85.0–90.0%
Carbon/Hydro-carbons	4.0–10.0%
Ash	0.1– 0.3%

Recovered. Fortified and returned to refineries.

Sludge. Burned in production of virgin acid or used for manufacturing fertilizers.

In newer units the spent alkylation acid is recovered directly from the reactor and has the following analysis:

Acidity	87.0–92.0%
Carbon/Hydro-carbons	4.0– 8.0%
Ash	0.1– 0.3%

This is ideal for regeneration. Without regeneration, it can be used in fertilizer manufacture if air pollution is not a problem.

Spent Tall Oil Sludge Acid:

Heavy, viscous light-brown-to-black acid from the purification of tall oil. Approximate analysis:

Acidity	27.0–31.0%
Carbon/Hydro-	
carbons	40.0–45.0%
Ash	0.1– 0.2%

Unstable. Usually regenerated.

Spent Dimethyl Ether:

Dark, opaque acid. Approximate analysis:

Acidity	80.0–85.0%
Carbon/Hydro-	
carbons	1.0– 2.0%
Ash	0.5– 1.0%

Usually regenerated.

Spent Caprolactam Acid Sludge Acid:

Dark, mahogany-colored acid. Approximate analysis:

Acidity	50.0–55.0%
Carbon/Hydro-	
carbons	12.0–15.0%
Ash	1.0– 2.0%

Has good characteristics for regeneration.

Spent Naphtha Acid Sludge Acid:

Dark, viscous sludge; stable and fluid. Approximate analysis:

Acidity	52.0–57.0%
Carbon/Hydro-	
carbons	14.0–30.0%
Ash	10.0–13.0%

Blended for regeneration.

Spent Lube Oil Acid Sludge Acid:

Black, highly viscous material. Must be kept away from atmospheric moisture. Approximate analysis:

Acidity	25.0–35.0%
Carbon/Hydro-carbons	40.0–65.0%
Ash	1.0– 2.0%

Blended for regeneration.

Sulfonation Sludges:

Black, viscous material. Approximate analysis:

Acidity	45.0–75.0%
Carbon/Hydro-carbons	25.0–50.0%
Ash	1.0– 2.0%

Blended for regeneration.

Spent Acetylene Acid:

Recovered from the purification of acetylene; similar to spent benzene. Approximate analysis:

Acidity	85.0–90.0%
Carbon/Hydro-carbons	3.0– 4.0%
Ash	0.05–0.1%

Usually regenerated.

Asphalt Sludges:

Black; highly viscous, but fluid. Approximate analysis:

Acidity	55.0–60.0%
Carbon/Hydro-carbons	34.0–38.0%
Ash	0.0– 0.1%

Blended for regeneration.

Acid Regeneration: Spent acid is burned in this combustion chamber at Houston plant of Stauffer Chemical Company.

Pollution Control in Acid Recovery

Differences in storage and handling properties between some spent acids and heavy sludges can be easily seen by comparing flow properties of spent alkylation acid with a viscosity of 20 centipoise and lubricating oil sludge with a viscosity of several thousand poise. Heavy sludges are generally mixed with lighter sludge acids to produce a blend with a middle-range viscosity.

A troublesome characteristic of acid sludge is its tendency to evolve sulfur dioxide. A slight rise in temperature or a little stirring can cause this reaction. Reduction of sulfuric acid by the hydrocarbons present in the mixture causes the sulfur dioxide evolution.

Mixing of one sludge with another can be the signal for copious sulfur dioxide evolution, particularly if the sludges have different acid-water ratios. In this instance, the reaction is from the heat effect of mixing different strengths of sulfuric acid.

Many sludges form a coke layer on exposed surfaces because of absorption of water from the atmosphere with a consequent heat-of-dilution effect and sulfur dioxide evolution at the surface. The end product of the reaction is a heavy coke. Layers can form in a storage tank over a long period of time or in an open tank in a matter of hours. A not uncommon sight in refineries is hydrolysis equipment choked by a mass of coke.

There are, on the other hand, a great many easy-to-handle sludges. These usually contain considerable amounts of water so that the oxidizing power of the acid is lessened by dilution. The heavy sludges are usually those containing less than 5 to 10% water.

To summarize: Refinery acid sludges are relatively unstable mixtures of sulfuric acid, hydrocarbons and water. They are highly variable in composition, fluidity and behavior. Although increases in temperature of these sludges promote evolution of sulfur dioxide, heat must often be applied to the heavier sludges to increase fluidity so that they can be processed.

The tendency of sludges to evolve sulfur dioxide with its attendant noxious fumes, in addition to the enormous quantity in which sludges are necessarily produced by the petroleum industry, makes these materials worthy subjects for the application of pollution control measures.

Unloading Spent Alkylation Acid

Spent alkylation acid can be unloaded from tank cars into storage tanks by applying air pressure to the tank car. When the tank car is empty of acid, the compressed air begins to blow through into the storage tanks. At this point the unloading line is at once closed off and the flow of compressed air to the tank is stopped. The compressed air remaining in the tank car is then vented to the atmosphere.

The American Conference of Government Industrial Hygienists in 1950 adopted 10 ppm as the maximum concentration of sulfur dioxide to which a workman can be exposed for eight hours a day, but this gas becomes very annoying at concentrations considerably below this. Tests made in Stauffer Chemical Company laboratories have indicated that concentrations as low as 1 ppm can be detected by sensitive individuals. It is important to avoid ground-level concentrations of the magnitude reached when a tank car full of compressed vapors is vented to the atmosphere.

A tower was modified to eliminate air pollution during the unloading of tank cars of spent alkylation acid. Acid was unloaded into one of three storage tanks. Vapor spaces of these tanks were connected by an eight-inch line to a tower constructed of lead-lined wood and packed with two-inch partition rings. A solution of sodium carbonate was circulated over the tower through plastic lines. This equipment, however, generates a liquid effluent that may cause other disposal problems.

An improved system calls for replacement of the scrubber. The manifold connecting the three storage tanks is extended to cover two additional storage tanks. One end of the manifold ties into the exit stack of the regeneration unit; the other end of the manifold connects with two flame arresters in parallel and then passes on to make a connection with the suction side of the main gas blower of a standard sulfuric acid plant. In this way, a continuous stream of dry stack gas is pulled through the vapor spaces of the storage tanks and into the blower where the sulfur dioxide content can be used in acid manufacture. Because all storage tanks are under a slight vacuum, all gage openings in these tanks are covered by a weighted lid, preventing entrance of moist air and subsequent excessive corrosion of equipment. Surges of air from tank car unloadings are also handled by this system.

Aluminum elements of the flame arresters in this system do not give as good service as elements made of 316 stainless steel.

Unloading and Storing Heavy Sludge

Heavy lube oil sludges are frequently blended with spent alkylation acid before being fed to a regeneration plant. Preliminary tests of one blend, plus the fact that the sludge had to be heated to produce the blend, warned one chemical company that considerable precautions would be required to prevent air pollution when unloading or storing this material. The material was to be shipped by barge as well as by tank car so it was necessary to plan an extension of the venting system to cover barge unloading.

Construction of the new venting system was carried out while the plant was being built.

The system consists of three branches. One branch includes a flexible eight-inch hose connected to the vapor space by submerged pumps located in the barge itself. Air pressure in the vapor space is used to speed unloading. When the barge is empty of acid the air line and acid unloading line are shut off and the valve in the vent line is opened to draw off the vapors in the barge. Booster blowers promote flow in the long eight-inch steel line. These blowers, made of nonplasticized polyvinyl chloride with a Teflon seal, have a capacity of 1,535 cfm with a two-inch water differential.

Vapor mixture passes through the eight-inch steel line and enters process gas stream in a regeneration unit. Filters and flame arresters are provided. The installation previously described had no filters and frequent cleaning of the flame arresters was necessary because of accumulations of iron sulfate. The filters, similar to those supplied in industrial air conditioning equipment, are made of glass fiber and are easier to clean, and need cleaning less frequently, than flame arresters.

In addition to servicing the barge–unloading equipment, this branch of the vent system provides coverage for eight sludge storage tanks. Here again the gage openings of the tanks are closed with a weighted lid to prevent entrance of atmospheric air. For emergency use, an eight-inch auxiliary vent line leads to the exit stack of the regeneration unit. This line is normally blanked off because it is more desirable to vent the gases into the regeneration unit where they are made into sulfuric acid.

The second branch of the system connects with the barge vent line and leads to the suction side of a second acid plant. An auxiliary blower, filters and flame arrester are provided. This line, generally valved off, is used if the operator directing the barge unloading feels that more capacity is required. Water manometers are located at points throughout the venting system to make sure the entire system is under a slight vacuum at all times. When no barges or tank cars are being unloaded the unloading connections are closed to prevent entrance of atmospheric air.

The third branch of the system ties into the second branch and consists of the system described earlier with several improvements. Filters have been added upstream of the flame arrester and an additional vent line has been run for tank car unloading so that air from tank cars is now passed directly to the blower of the acid plant. Previously, as described, this air had been vented through the acid unloading line to the storage tanks. With the new line an operator need only close off the air and turn a single cock to vent the tank-car air into the acid-plant blower. The new line also connects directly to the exit stack of the acid plant so that the gases can be satisfactorily drawn away in case the acid plant is shut down.

Flame arresters are necessary because of the hydrocarbons present in the vapors. Filters are cleaned when readings of water monometers indicate an excessive pressure drop.

Piping in the vent system is entirely of steel. One short section of the piping originally made of plastic-lined steel pipe failed when an unusually active sludge boiled up into a portion of the line and dissolved the plastic lining.

6. MAJOR USES OF SULFURIC ACID

Pickling

Acid Bath

The cleaning of iron by pickling in sulfuric acid is the commonest, quickest and most generally satisfactory method of removing scale and preparing surfaces for painting, galvanizing or enameling.

Concentration of acid in the bath is extremely important for successful pickling. Proper concentration in a given instance depends on variables such as temperature used, material being pickled and length of time available. Activity of a sulfuric acid pickling bath reaches its maximum at approximately 20 to 25% sulfuric acid by weight. Increasing acid concentration beyond this point produces a proportional decrease in activity. Varying percentages of acid speed or slow operations within wide limits.

Best practice is not to use more than 8 or 10% sulfuric acid by weight. Beyond this point, appreciable quantities of acid are lost or time is wasted in exhausting the bath. A concentration of 5 or 6% by weight will clean average work in 30 to 60 minutes, depending on the temperature. It is more economical to operate with a low than with a high percentage of acid. The bath can be reinforced as needed.

Agitation is necessary, especially during preparation for fortification. Sulfuric acid, nearly twice as heavy as water, forms a bottom layer which does not readily mix with the bath water unless the bath is stirred. Agitation also eliminates the danger that all the acid might suddenly combine with the water and, evolving heat, cause splattering of acid and water.

Agitation may be either mechanical or by a jet of compressed air or by steam. Vigorous action at one end of a bath and little at another part should be avoided.

Different parts of a tank can vary as much as 3 or 4% in acid concentration for adequately mixed samples. The bath, once mixed, forms a true solution which does not separate on standing.

Operation of Bath

The rate of any pickling operation is increased by raising the bath temperature. Sulfuric acid at 190°F has a solution rate 100 times greater than its solution rate at room temperature.

Temperatures between 170 and 190°F are generally satisfactory for short-time cycles. With certain steels, such as many with high carbon and high alloy content, temperatures between 140 and 150°F are most satisfactory. When a manufacturer is using relatively high temperatures, consideration should be given to such possibilities as overpickling, breaking down inhibitors at high temperatures or evaporating the adhering film of pickling solution before the material reaches the rinse tank. If the latter occurs, oxidation will appear as brown spots or stains on the surface.

Oxides usually considered in the pickling of iron and steel are of three common varieties: ferric oxide (Fe_2O_3), which contains the most oxygen; Fe_3O_4, which is intermediate in oxygen content; and FeO, which is the leanest and closest in structure to the metal. FeO is the most difficult to dissolve and causes the most difficulties in pickling heat-treated bars. Upon slow cooling, however, FeO will disintegrate around 110°F (43°C) into Fe and Fe_3O_4 or Fe_2O_3 alone.

An old theory of pickling is that steel pickles away from under the scale. A study of the reactions involved, combined with characteristics of the oxides, accounts for this apparent pickling of the scale on the underside.

$$
\begin{array}{llll}
(1) & Fe & + H_2SO_4 = & FeSO_4 & + H_2\uparrow \\
(2) & FeO & + H_2SO_4 = & FeSO_4 & + H_2O \\
(3) & Fe_3O_4 + 4H_2SO_4 = & Fe_2(SO_4)_3 + FeSO_4 + 4H_2O \\
(4) & Fe_2O_3 + 3H_2SO_4 = & Fe_2(SO_4)_3 + 3H_2O
\end{array}
$$

In equation (1), iron is being pickled: the products are ferrous sulfate with hydrogen. In equation (2), the by-product is water; there is no hydrogen by-product. In equations (3) and (4) there is no hydrogen by-product, but the higher oxides are converted to ferrous and ferric sulfate. From these reactions, it can be concluded that when hydrogen bubbles to the top of a pickling bath, metal is being attacked.

When a bath has been in use for some time, accumulation of ferrous sulfate (copperas) becomes a problem, and, although acid concentration remains constant and temperature is increased, the bath becomes too sluggish for economical operation. When specific gravity reaches 1.17, sluggishness becomes noticeable; when specific gravity is 1.25, the bath should be dumped. When specific gravity approaches the limit, it is customary to discontinue addition of acid and to operate at as high a temperature as possible. This is called "killing" the bath.

Cleaning Pickled Steel

Cleaning and washing pickled metal is an important part of the operation. In order to avoid rust, cleaning must be done as soon as possible after removing the metal from the pickling bath. Pickled steel requiring only ordinary cleaning can be effectively washed by rinsing thoroughly in running water. Cleaning is then finished by thoroughly blowing off the metal with steam. If a tank is used, the tank should be supplied with an adequate quantity of running water and regularly cleaned of sediment collecting on the bottom.

The last traces of acid are extremely difficult to wash off and the slightest trace increases tendency to rust. An alkaline bath after the water rinse remedies this situation. The alkaline bath should be composed of ½% caustic soda and ¾% trisodium phosphate (by weight) heated to a high temperature. The high temperature assures rapid drying after removal. Alkalinity of the bath must be constantly checked; small amounts of acid carried over can quickly neutralize the solution. An alkali tank should be kept free of sediment by frequent cleaning.

A bath of 2 to 4% muriatic acid after the sulfuric acid bath is sometimes employed to facilitate cleaning.

Traces of muriatic acid evaporate after the water wash.

Pickling Inhibitors

Pickling inhibitors are organic compounds added in very small quantities to the pickle bath for the purpose of confining action to scale and reducing the volume of hydrogen gas evolved. Confining the action to scale saves acid and prevents overpickling of some areas and consequent underpickling of others. Reduction of hydrogen evolution is desirable because: (1) undue quantities of hydrogen tend to weaken the iron by occlusion in cracks (hydrogen embrittlement) and (2) vigorous evolution of gas causes trapping of acid particles and formation of a corrosive mist hazardous for workmen and damaging to adjacent equipment.

Pickling Defects

Certain defects making their appearance during pickling are often blamed upon improper operation of the pickling cycle or upon faulty steel. Many of these, however, are the result of previous operations, such as rolling, forging or heat-treating. Some of the main defects correctly associated with pickling are as follows:

Overpickling. Overpickling is the result of holding the material in the pickle bath longer than the time required for optimum results. The effect is a loss of weight and size of material along with the presence of porosity and roughening of the entire surface.

Pickle Pitting. Pitting is caused by localized electrolytic action between the scale and the clean metal and occurs when scale has been removed from small areas before pickling. Pitting is characterized by patchwork pitted areas of irregular shape, frequently aligned longitudinally. Pits are generally of two types: those uniform in depth (formed in an inhibited bath) and those irregular in depth (uninhibited bath).

Pits are sometimes caused by overpickling, but this rarely occurs. They can also originate in the rolling process from rolled-in scale or refractories at which points pickling action is intensified.

Hydrogen Embrittlement. When hydrogen ions are evolved on exposed metal surfaces because of direct acid attack, nascent hydrogen can diffuse into the steel instead of linking to form molecules that appear as gas bubbles. This embrittlement can be removed by aging for a few days at room temperature or by soaking immediately in boiling water. Inhibitors aid in minimizing the initial action.

Blisters. During pickling of sheet and strip steel, hydrogen, absorbed by the steel, may diffuse into lamellar or plate-like nonmetallic inclusions and cavities where it is catalytically converted by the amorphous iron into molecular hydrogen. The gas thus formed cannot escape and eventually builds up a pressure which ruptures the steel along planes of weakness produced by the inclusions. This is confirmed empirically by observing that blisters never occur in thoroughly killed steels because the inclusions, though numerous, do not contain free ferrous oxide. Blisters seldom occur in strongly oxidized steels because strong rimming action has almost completely cleansed the steel of inclusions.

Analysis of Bath

Apparatus. Necessary apparatus includes: standard one normal-strength (1N.) sodium hydroxide solution; methyl orange indicator; 50-cc burette and suitable stand; 250-cc Erlenmeyer flask; 10-cc pipette; hydrometer (range 1.000 to 1.300 specific gravity); hydrometer cylinder; copper dipper (generally 3 inches in diameter and 12 inches long).

Procedure: Take a large sample from the bath with the copper dipper. Pour sample into the hydrometer cylinder and determine specific gravity. By means of pipette, transfer exactly 10 cc into the flask; dilute with pure water, five or six times the sample volume; and add 4 or 5 drops of methyl orange indicator. Fill the burette with 1N. sodium hydroxide solution, being careful to avoid any dilution of the standard solution. Run sodium

TABLE XIX. ACID PERCENTAGES OF PICKLING SOLUTIONS

Baumé	Specific Gravity	.5 %	1.0 %	1.5 %	2.0 %	2.5 %	3.0 %	3.5 %	4.0 %	4.5 %	5.0 %	5.5 %	6.0 %	6.5 %	7.0 %	7.5 %	Factor
							CUBIC CENTIMETERS OF NORMAL SODIUM HYDROXIDE USED										
3.5	1.025	0.2	0.5	0.7	1.0	1.2	1.4	1.7	1.9	2.2	2.4	2.6	2.9	3.1	3.4	3.6	0.0512
6.8	1.050	0.2	0.5	0.7	1.0	1.2	1.4	1.6	1.9	2.1	2.3	2.6	2.8	3.0	3.3	3.5	0.0524
10.1	1.075	0.2	0.5	0.7	0.9	1.1	1.4	1.6	1:8	2.1	2.3	2.5	2.7	3.0	3.2	3.4	0.0539
13.2	1.100	0.2	0.5	0.7	0.9	1.1	1.3	1.6	1.8	2.0	2.2	2.5	2.7	2.9	3.1	3.4	0.0554
16.1	1.125	0.2	0.5	0.7	0.9	1.1	1.3	1.5	1.7	2.0	2.2	2.4	2.6	2.8	3.1	3.3	0.0566
18.9	1.150	0.2	0.4	0.6	0.9	1.1	1.3	1.5	1.7	1.9	2.1	2.3	2.6	2.8	3.0	3.2	0.0579
21.6	1.175	0.2	0.4	0.6	0.8	1.1	1.3	1.5	1.7	1.9	2.1	2.3	2.6	2.7	2.9	3.1	0.0593
24.2	1.200	0.2	0.4	0.6	0.8	1.0	1.2	1.4	1.6	1.8	2.0	2.2	2.5	2.7	2.9	3.1	0.0607
26.6	1.225	0.2	0.4	0.6	0.8	1.0	1.2	1.4	1.6	1.8	2.0	2.2	2.4	2.6	2.8	3.0	0.0620
29.0	1.250	0.2	0.4	0.6	0.8	1.0	1.2	1.4	1.6	1.8	2.0	2.2	2.4	2.6	2.7	2.9	0.0634
31.3	1.275	0.2	0.4	0.6	0.8	1.0	1.2	1.4	1.5	1.7	1.9	2.1	2.3	2.5	2.7	2.9	0.0650
33.5	1.300	0.2	0.4	0.6	0.8	1.0	1.1	1.3	1.5	1.7	1.9	2.1	2.3	2.5	2.6	2.8	0.0666
35.6	1.325	0.2	0.4	0.6	0.7	0.9	1.1	1.3	1.5	1.7	1.9	2.0	2.2	2.4	2.6	2.8	0.0680
37.6	1.350	0.2	0.4	0.6	0.7	0.9	1.1	1.3	1.5	1.6	1.8	2.0	2.2	2.4	2.5	2.7	0.0695

Baumé	Specific Gravity	8.0 %	8.5 %	9.0 %	9.5 %	10.0 %	10.5 %	11.0 %	11.5 %	12.0 %	12.5 %	13.0 %	13.5 %	14.0 %	14.5 %	15.0 %	Factor
							CUBIC CENTIMETERS OF NORMAL SODIUM HYDROXIDE USED										
6.8	1.050	3.8	4.0	4.2	4.4	4.7	5.0	5.1	5.4	5.6	5.8	6.1	6.3	6.5	6.8	7.0	0.0524
10.1	1.075	3.6	3.9	4.1	4.3	4.6	4.8	5.0	5.2	5.5	5.7	5.9	6.2	6.4	6.6	6.8	0.0539
13.2	1.100	3.6	3.8	4.0	4.2	4.5	4.7	4.9	5.1	5.4	5.6	5.8	6.0	6.2	6.5	6.7	0.0554
16.1	1.125	3.5	3.7	3.9	4.1	4.4	4.6	4.8	5.0	5.2	5.5	5.7	5.9	6.1	6.3	6.5	0.0566
18.9	1.150	3.4	3.6	3.8	4.0	4.3	4.5	4.7	4.9	5.1	5.3	5.5	5.8	6.0	6.2	6.4	0.0579
21.6	1.175	3.3	3.5	3.8	4.0	4.2	4.4	4.6	4.8	5.0	5.2	5.4	5.6	5.8	6.0	6.3	0.0593
24.2	1.200	3.3	3.5	3.7	3.9	4.1	4.3	4.5	4.7	4.9	5.1	5.3	5.5	5.7	5.9	6.1	0.0607
26.6	1.225	3.2	3.4	3.6	3.8	4.1	4.2	4.4	4.6	4.8	5.0	5.2	5.4	5.6	5.8	6.0	0.0620
29.0	1.250	3.1	3.3	3.5	3.7	3.9	4.1	4.3	4.5	4.7	4.9	5.1	5.3	5.5	5.7	5.9	0.0634
31.3	1.275	3.1	3.3	3.5	3.7	3.9	4.1	4.2	4.4	4.6	4.8	5.0	5.2	5.3	5.6	5.8	0.0650
33.5	1.300	3.0	3.2	3.4	3.6	3.8	4.0	4.2	4.3	4.5	4.7	4.9	5.1	5.3	5.5	5.7	0.0666
35.6	1.325	3.0	3.1	3.3	3.5	3.7	3.9	4.1	4.3	4.4	4.6	4.8	5.0	5.2	5.4	5.6	0.0680
37.6	1.350	2.9	3.1	3.3	3.5	3.6	3.8	4.0	4.2	4.4	4.5	4.7	4.9	5.1	5.3	5.5	0.0695

Baumé	Specific Gravity	15.5 %	16.0 %	16.5 %	17.0 %	17.5 %	18.0 %	18.5 %	19.0 %	19.5 %	20.0 %	20.5 %	21.0 %	21.5 %	22.0 %	22.5 %	Factor
							CUBIC CENTIMETERS OF NORMAL SODIUM HYDROXIDE USED										
6.8	1.050	7.3	7.5	7.7	7.9	8.2	8.4	8.6	8.8	9.1	9.3	9.6	9.8	10.0	10.3	10.5	0.0524
10.1	1.075	7.1	7.3	7.5	7.7	8.0	8.2	8.4	8.6	8.9	9.1	9.4	9.6	9.8	10.0	10.2	0.0539
13.2	1.100	7.0	7.1	7.4	7.6	7.8	8.0	8.2	8.5	8.7	8.9	9.1	9.4	9.6	9.8	10.0	0.0554
16.1	1.125	6.9	7.0	7.2	7.4	7.6	7.8	8.0	8.3	8.5	8.7	8.9	9.2	9.4	9.6	9.8	0.0566
18.9	1.150	6.6	6.8	7.0	7.2	7.4	7.7	7.9	8.1	8.3	8.5	8.7	8.9	9.2	9.4	9.6	0.0579
21.6	1.175	6.6	6.7	6.9	7.1	7.3	7.5	7.7	7.9	8.1	8.3	8.5	8.8	9.0	9.2	9.4	0.0593
24.2	1.200	6.4	6.5	6.7	6.9	7.1	7.3	7.5	7.7	8.0	8.2	8.4	8.6	8.8	9.0	9.2	0.0607
26.6	1.225	6.2	6.4	6.6	6.8	7.0	7.2	7.4	7.6	7.8	8.0	8.2	8.4	8.6	8.8	9.0	0.0620
29.0	1.250	6.0	6.3	6.5	6.7	6.8	7.0	7.2	7.4	7.6	7.8	8.0	8.2	8.4	8.6	8.8	0.0634
31.3	1.275	6.0	6.1	6.3	6.5	6.7	6.9	7.1	7.3	7.5	7.7	7.9	8.1	8.3	8.5	8.6	0.0650
33.5	1.300	5.8	6.0	6.2	6.4	6.6	6.8	7.0	7.2	7.3	7.5	7.7	7.9	8.1	8.3	8.5	0.0666
35.6	1.325	5.7	5.9	6.1	6.3	6.5	6.6	6.8	7.0	7.2	7.4	7.6	7.8	8.0	8.1	8.3	0.0680
37.6	1.350	5.6	5.8	6.0	6.2	6.3	6.5	6.7	6.9	7.1	7.3	7.4	7.6	7.8	8.0	8.2	0.0695

hydroxide from burette to flask and swirl flask. The end point is reached when the solution in the flask turns from red to yellow. Using Table XIX, locate on the top line the number corresponding to the burette reading. Follow down this column to a point opposite the number in the specific gravity column which corresponds to the hydrometer reading. The value in this square gives percent by weight of sulfuric acid present in the pickling bath.

Example

Specific gravity of bath 1.050
Burette reading 12.5
Per cent sulfuric acid by weight 5.8

Formula for Fortifying Sulfuric Bath

(% Acid desired — % Acid present) × Cubic feet of solution × Factor
= Gallons of acid to be added.

Determine by titration the strength of the acid in the bath.

Subtract this value from the strength desired and multiply the difference by the cubic feet of solution already in the bath. From Table XIX, locate the factor corresponding to the present specific gravity of the bath. This factor times the aforementioned product gives gallons of 66° Bé to be added.

Example

Per cent acid desired in bath 7.5
Per cent acid now in bath 5.8
Difference 1.7
Cubic feet of solution 200
Factor (specific gravity: 1.050) 0.0524

1.7 × 200 × 0.0524 = 17.8 gallons or approximately one-third of a 50-gallon drum.

Sulfuric Acid Treatment of Alkali Soils

Sulfuric acid for correction of alkali in soil is not a new idea. Elemental sulfur, applied to a soil and disked under, gradually converts to sulfuric acid under bacterial action. This, however, requires considerable time. Sulfuric acid does the same job almost overnight.

When a soil exhibits a pH value above 7.6, plant roots generally have trouble absorbing nitrate and phosphate and, consequently, do not thrive. Acidifying treatment is advisable, sometimes essential.

Types of Soil

Mildly alkaline soils are usually designated "white alkali." The term "black alkali" comes from the dark brown to black color of soils containing excessive amounts of alkali. Soil organic matter or humus, soluble in alkali, creates the black color rather than the alkali itself. Alkali salts are white.

Black Alkali Soils. Black alkali soils develop either from the use of irrigation water containing a high proportion of sodium salt or from too much sodium salt in the soil or soil solution. Sodium salts are generally very soluble and very active chemically. Thus, they react with some of the soil minerals, notable calcium carbonate and the clay minerals (silicates), to form sodium carbonate and sodium clay. These are the active chemicals of black alkali. When black alkali soil is wet, these chemicals react with water to form the very caustic salt known as lye.

There are three main reasons why black alkali reduces the productive capacity of a soil and should be corrected. Excess alkalinity (1) tends to destroy plant roots, (2) creates an unfavorable mechanical condition in the soil and (3) seriously disturbs the normal nutritional balance of the crop.

In addition to neutralizing the soil, sulfuric acid retains or fixes the organic matter in the soil and frequently flocculates the soil.

Neutralization of black alkali soil takes place in this way:

1. Sulfuric acid reacts with sodium carbonate to form sodium sulfate, a neutral salt, which is leached out of the soil in the drainage water.
2. Sulfuric acid reacts with calcium carbonate, present in practically all black alkali soils, to form calcium bicarbonate and calcium sulfate. Both these calcium salts are sufficiently soluble in water to displace the sodium during the leaching operation and, at the same time, flocculate the soil enough to increase the rate of downward water movement.

White Alkali Soils. The usual white alkali salts are sulfates and chlorides. Most white alkali soils can be reclaimed by leaching if good water is available for leaching operations. However, leaching can be simplified and accelerated if a soil corrective such as sulfuric acid is used along with the leaching.

Application of sulfuric acid to white alkali soils should be lighter than for black alkali soils because there is no caustic alkali to neutralize. The principal purpose of the acid is to accelerate leaching and prevent the development of black alkali during leaching operations.

Flocculating Soils. Preliminary experiments indicate that, like soil sulfur, sulfuric acid flocculates certain heavy, tight soils and will allow more and quicker water penetration. A simple test can determine whether or not a hard adobe soil can be made more flocculent by the application of sulfuric acid. Place about a spoonful of soil in each of two glass containers (fruit jars will do) and half fill with water. Add a little sulfuric acid to one jar and shake both jars well (until all the soil is in suspension). Allow the soil to settle. If the soil in the acid jar settles faster, an application of sulfuric acid will be beneficial.

Acid Application

Dispersion of Sulfuric Acid. If too little sulfuric acid is used, there may be spots of alkali left untreated. If too much acid is used there should be no serious consequences, other than the greater cost of acid, because the extra acid merely seeps deeper into the soil and neutralizes alkali further down. After an acre of land having strongly alkaline spots is completely flooded with acidified irrigation water, the acid will tend to gravitate toward alkaline spots where it will react. As long as the irrigation water stands above the ground, the sulfuric acid will continue to react with the alkali, until either all the acid has been used up in neutralization or the water has seeped into the soil so that the acid can no longer move about chemically.

In order to arrive at the amount of acid which is to be applied per acre, an estimate should be made of the approximate average pH of the soil to be treated. Anywhere from a few hundred pounds of sulfuric acid to as much as 600 pounds, occasionally even more, may be needed per acre. Those soils having few spots of black alkali per acre need less acid than the soils where whole sections are barren. It may be quite difficult to determine the exact amount of acid necessary.

Acid should be added to the water during the whole time that it is flowing onto the land so that an even, dilute dispersion is assured. In order to bring about a calibrated flow of sulfuric acid from drums to irrigation water, pipe caps have been developed with measured orifices which, when fitted into the ¾-inch bung in the head of the sulfuric acid drum, will allow the acid to flow out at a timed rate.

There are two relatively easy methods for accomplishing calibrated dispersion. These are straight-line flow and two-foot-drop flow. (See Figures 50 and 51.)

Straight-Line Flow. In straight-line flow, a ½- to ¾-inch bushing is attached to the ¾-inch bung in the drum. Leading out is a ½-inch black iron water pipe with a ½-inch black iron valve for control. This extends over the irrigation water and ends with a ½-inch pipe cap drilled for the proper orifice.

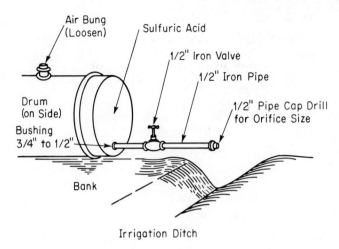

Fig. 50. Straight-line flow setup for soil dispersion of sulfuric acid.

If this ½-inch pipe cap is drilled with a $\frac{9}{32}$-inch drill, a 55-gallon drum will empty through this hole in approximately one hour. Drilled with a $\frac{3}{16}$-inch drill, it will empty in two hours. Drilled with a $\frac{9}{64}$-inch drill, it will empty in four hours. These intervals are subject to slight variations because pressure at the orifice gradually lessens as the head is lowered, causing the acid to flow out more and more slowly as the drum is emptied. This is the simplest distribution method. (Drum must be tilted in order to be completely emptied.)

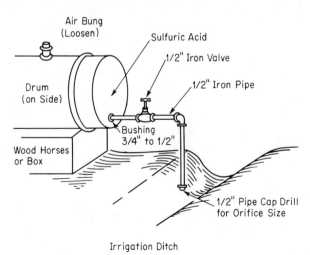

Fig. 51. Two-foot drop flow setup for soil dispersion of sulfuric acid.

Two-Foot-Drop Flow. The most satisfactory method for dispersing the concentrated sulfuric acid from the drum with an even flow, accurately calibrated and timed, is the two-foot-drop flow. The drum or drums should be elevated on platforms or mounds so that they may sit either horizontally or slightly tilted toward the bung and at least two feet above the surface of the irrigation water in the ditch. The drum should again be fitted with ½- to ¾-inch bushing, a short length of ½-inch pipe, a ½-inch valve and a length of ½-inch pipe long enough to reach out over the water. There is, then, a ½-inch 90-degree elbow and a two-foot length of pipe straight downward ending with a drilled pipe cap just over the surface of the water. This drilled pipe cap can be any distance over the water as long as there is a minimum two-foot drop. The drop minimizes the change in pressure caused by the diminishing head as the drum empties, and allows for a very even rate of flow whether the drum is full or empty.

When the height of the bung is approximately 24 inches above the orifice in the pipe cap, a $^{13}\!/_{64}$-inch hole will allow the drum to empty in just about one hour. The drum will be approximately half empty in 30 minutes and one-quarter empty in 15 minutes because the flow is uniform. The $^{9}\!/_{64}$-inch hole will empty the drum in two hours, a $^{3}\!/_{32}$-inch hole will empty the drum in four hours. The additional pressure of the two-foot drop will tend to keep the orifice clean of foreign particles which might otherwise obstruct the flow. Any variation in acid velocity because of temperature change is of no consequence because of the additional pressure.

By using either of these methods of emptying the acid drums, proper quantities of acid can be distributed over predetermined acreage in close enough proportion to obtain good results and reasonable assurance that the acidified water is quite dilute.

Sulfuric acid normally tends to stratify in layers when added to water because it is twice as heavy as water and, if not mixed properly, will be more concentrated in the lower level than on the top. Dropping small quantities of acid into an actively moving water stream eliminates the possibility of this stratifying in concentrated layers and assures even dispersion of small amounts of acid throughout the water.

Any method of introducing sulfuric acid to water is satisfactory as long as it is remembered that sulfuric acid has a great affinity for water and, for this reason, must always be added to water, rather than adding water to it. The containers in which acid is shipped should never be used for any other purpose because of danger of chemical reaction.

Direct Application of Concentrated Acid. Experiments are under way in the direct application of concentrated sulfuric acid from drum to alkaline spots or areas. Direct application may be necessary when irrigation water is not readily available in quantity, or when a field has growing crops which might be affected by general flooding.

Superphosphates

Superphosphates are produced by reacting ground phosphate rock with sulfuric acid, phosphoric acid or a mixture of both acids. The highest grade possible when pure fluor apatite is acidulated with sulfuric acid alone is 24 percent superphosphate. All grades containing 24 percent or less phosphoric oxide (P_2O_5) are known as single, ordinary or normal superphosphate. Grades from 24 to 41 percent phosphoric oxide are made from mixtures of sulfuric and phosphoric acid and are known as enriched superphosphate. Grades above 42 percent are made from phosphoric acid and are called triple superphosphate.

Single, Normal or Ordinary Superphosphate

Single superphosphate, primarily monocalcium salt of phosphoric acid, is produced by adding 50 to 55° Bé sulfuric acid to ground (100-mesh) phosphate rock of 76 to 78% $3Ca_3(PO_4)_2 \cdot CaF_2$—principally fluorapatite —in a cast iron revolving pan mixer. After a mixing of one to three minutes, the mixture is moved promptly to a den. The move to the den is made promptly in order to avoid "setting up" of the mixture. For the reaction to continue to completion, the acidulated rock is left in the den six to twenty-four hours. Temperature is usually about 100°C so that all gaseous products escape leaving a dry porous substance.

From the den the superphosphate is transferred to the storage pile where it is allowed to cure from four to sixteen weeks. After curing, the superphosphate is ground and mixed to grade, and then screened and bagged for shipment. This is the batch process. Single superphosphate is also made by the continuous process known as the Broadfield (Figure 52) and Sackett Super-Flow process; most ordinary phosphate, however, is made by the batch process.

The principal chemical reactions are:

$$Ca_3(PO_4)_2 + 2H_2SO_4 + 4H_2O \rightarrow CaH_4(PO_4)_2 + 2(CaSO_4 2H_2O)$$
$$\text{(Monocalcium} \qquad \text{(Gypsum)}$$
$$\text{phosphate)}$$
$$CaF_2 + H_2SO_4 \rightarrow CaSO_4 + 2HF$$
$$4HF + SiO_2 \rightarrow SiF_4 + 2H_2O$$
$$3SiF_4 + 2H_2O \rightarrow SiO_2 + 2H_2SiF_6$$

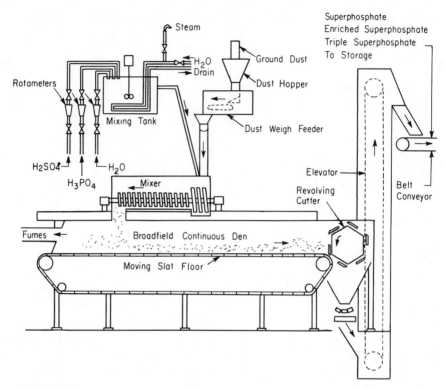

Fig. 52. Broadfield unit for continuous production of superphosphate.

The following is a more probable expression of the main reaction:

$$2(CaF)Ca_4(PO_4)_3 + 7H_2SO_4 + 3H_2O \rightarrow$$

(Phosphate rock)

$$3CaH_4(PO_4)_2 H_2O + 2HF + 7CaSO_4$$

(Monocalcium   (Anhydrite)
phosphate)

Triple Superphosphate

Phosphoric instead of sulfuric acid is used to decompose the phosphate rock in the production of triple superphosphate. Sulfuric acid is used as the intermediary in the production of phosphoric acid by the commonly used wet process.

Triple superphosphate is made from both electric-furnace phosphoric acid and wet-process phosphoric acid. Wet-process phosphoric acid is relatively dilute and contains substantial amounts of impurities. Electric furnace phosphoric acid is concentrated and almost free from contaminants.

The principal reaction occurring in a wet-process phosphoric acid production unit is the reaction between tricalcium phosphate and sulfuric acid to produce phosphoric acid and insoluble calcium sulfate:

$$Ca_3(PO_4)_2 + 3H_2SO_4 \rightarrow 3CaSO_4 + 2H_3PO_4$$

In addition there are various side reactions, such as the reaction between calcium fluoride, sulfuric acid and water to produce gypsum and hydrofluoric acid, and the reaction between hydrofluoric acid and silica to produce hydrofluosilicic acid and water.

The principal reaction occurring in the triple superphosphate unit involves the phosphate rock or tricalcium phosphate and phosphoric acid to produce monocalcium phosphate:

$$Ca_3(PO_4)_2 + 4H_3PO_4 + 3H_2O \rightarrow 3CaH_4(PO_4)_2 H_2O$$

Procedure for Wet Process. Weighed phosphate rock is discharged by gravity into one of three premixers.

Sulfuric acid at 66° Bé is pumped from storage tanks in the acid area directly to the phosphoric acid building. For a normal rock feed rate of 340 tons per day per train, approximately 20 gallons per minute of sulfuric acid are required.

In the mixing heads, sulfuric acid is combined with "return" acid. Return acid (filtrate from the washing of gypsum in a subsequent step) contains approximately 18 to 20% phosphorus pentoxide. The mixing heads discharge into the feed launders of the premixers.

The phosphate rock-sulfuric acid reaction takes place in a series of six tanks on each line.

A very large volume of slurry is recirculated through 10-inch rubber-lined pipes from the third agitator back to the first premixer. A large recirculation rate is an essential part of the process.

The reaction between phosphate rock and sulfuric acid is exothermic. To maintain the reaction at the optimum temperature of 70 to 75°C, excess heat is removed by blowing a large quantity of low-pressure air through the slurry in each reaction tank.

Slurry from the last agitator is pumped to any or all of five traveling pan vacuum filters.

The filter cake, which consists primarily of gypsum, is washed first with weak phosphoric acid and then with hot water.

The phosphoric acid filtrate, containing approximately 32% phosphorus pentoxide, is concentrated in a vacuum-type evaporator.

The evaporated acid (at 39% phosphorus pentoxide) is then pumped to the triple superphosphate unit.

The evaporated 39% acid is pumped into the first of the acidulators where it is mixed with ground phosphate rock.

The slurry leaving the acidulator goes by gravity to a blunger.

The blungers discharge by gravity directly into an oil-fired, direct-heat, co-current rotary dryer. The dryer discharge moves by way of conveyor, elevator, and classifying screens to storage bins for undersize, product, and oversize.

The granulated triple superphosphate goes out in bags or bulk.

Sulfuric Acid Treatment of Boiler Feed Water

Acid treatment of a boiler feed water involves, by one method, the addition of dilute sulfuric acid to the feed water either before or after the softener, the flow of acid being proportional to the flow of feed water.

In a second widely used method, acid treatment is effectively accomplished with the passage of a certain percentage of the feed water through carbonaceous zeolite, operating in the hydrogen cycle. The effluent of such a softener is acidic in nature and, when mixed with the remaining portion of the feed water, results in alkalinity reduction very similar to the direct addition of acid to the water.

Use or Purpose

Reduction of the natural alkalinity of the feed water is often desirable for the following reasons:

To reduce boiler-water alkalinity.

To increase the sulfate-carbonate ratio.

To permit zeolite softening of raw water containing carbonate (CO_3^{--}) or hydroxyl (OH^-) alkalinity.

To reduce the carbon dioxide content of the steam produced by the boiler.

To convert calcium bicarbonate to calcium sulfate in the make-up water for cooling water systems.

When direct addition of acid to boiler feed water is considered, sulfuric acid, almost without exception, is the acid selected for this task because of its availability and low cost. Also, when sulfate-carbonate ratios are important, sulfuric acid is preferred for its sulfate content.

Sulfuric acid reacts with the natural alkalinity of water, whether in the form of bicarbonate, carbonate, hydroxyl or any combination of these ions. The acid releases carbon dioxide gas from bicarbonates and carbonates present and forms water after neutralizing hydroxyl ions. The various reactions which take place may be summarized as follows:

$$H_2SO_4 + 2NaHCO_3 \rightarrow Na_2SO_4 + 2H_2O + 2CO_2$$

sulfuric + sodium → sodium + water + carbon
acid   bicarbonate   sulfate   dioxide

$$H_2SO_4 + Na_2CO_3 \rightarrow Na_2SO_4 + H_2O + CO_2$$
sulfuric + sodium → sodium + water + carbon
acid   carbonate   sulfate   dioxide

$$H_2SO_4 + 2NaOH \rightarrow Na_2SO_4 + 2H_2O$$
sulfuric + sodium → sodium + water
acid   hydroxide   sulfate

Acid treatment of feed water with zeolite effluent forms sodium sulfate and carbonic acid. The water thus treated is then passed through an aeration chamber or degasifier where carbon dioxide gas is liberated. The pH of the acid-treated and decarbonated water depends on the residual alkalinity and the carbon dioxide. Free carbon dioxide will normally be 10 ppm or less with efficient decarbonation.

Each additional ppm of sulfuric acid reduces total alkalinity, expressed as calcium carbonate, by 1.02 ppm. Conversely, 0.96 ppm of sulfate is added to the water for each ppm reduction in total alkalinity. Hence, very little reduction in total dissolved solids is achieved by this form of acid treatment.

Regeneration of Hydrogen Zeolite by Sulfuric Acid

Hydrogen zeolite is the name given to a group of non-siliceous organic materials, either natural or synthetic, which have the property, when operated in the acid cycle, to exchange hydrogen for cations of calcium, magnesium, sodium, etc. Upon exhaustion of the hydrogen zeolite bed, it is regenerated with acid.

When water containing calcium, magnesium and sodium ions is passed through a hydrogen zeolite these ions are exchanged for hydrogen, and the bicarbonate, sulfate, nitrate and chloride radicals are converted to their respective acids: carbonic acid (H_2CO_3), sulfuric acid (H_2SO_4), nitric acid (HNO_3) and hydrochloric acid (HCl), as is shown by the following equations:

$$1 \quad \begin{matrix} Ca \\ Mg \\ Na_2 \end{matrix} (HCO_3)_2 + H_2Z \rightarrow \begin{matrix} Ca \\ Mg \\ Na_2 \end{matrix} (Z) + 2H_2CO_3$$

$$2 \quad \begin{matrix} Ca \\ Mg \\ Na_2 \end{matrix} (SO_4) + H_2Z \rightarrow \begin{matrix} Ca \\ Mg \\ Na_2 \end{matrix} (Z) + H_2SO_4$$

$$3 \quad \begin{matrix} Ca \\ Mg \\ Na_2 \end{matrix} (Cl_2) + H_2Z \rightarrow \begin{matrix} Ca \\ Mg \\ Na_2 \end{matrix} (Z) + 2HCl$$

When the hydrogen zeolite becomes exhausted it is backwashed and re-generated with acid. After rinsing, the bed is again ready for use. Sulfuric acid is generally used for this regeneration process because of its low cost.

The following equations illustrate the reactions which take place when sulfuric acid is used for regeneration:

$$4 \quad \begin{matrix} Ca \\ Mg \\ Na_2 \end{matrix} (Z) + H_2SO_4 = H_2Z + \begin{matrix} Ca \\ Mg \\ Na_2 \end{matrix} SO_4$$

From reaction (1) it is evident that all of the bicarbonates are converted into carbonic acid (H_2CO_3). This gas is very unstable in water solution and can easily be removed by aeration or degasification. However, sulfuric, nitric and hydrochloric acids cannot be removed by this method. These acids must be neutralized to prevent severe acidic corrosion of the metal in the system.

7. ANALYSIS OF SULFURIC ACID

Preparation and Standardization of Reference Standard Sulfuric Acid Solution

Scope

This procedure provides a method for preparing a stable reference sulfuric acid solution which may be standardized and employed as a reliable acidimetric standard.

Theory

52% sulfuric acid is in equilibrium with the average moisture in the air of a laboratory. Acid of this concentration is recommended for the reference standard solution. Primary standard sodium carbonate is slightly overneutralized with the reference standard sulfuric acid solution. The excess acid is titrated with standard sodium hydroxide solution. The neutralization reactions take place according to the equations:

$$H_2SO_4 + Na_2CO_3 \rightarrow Na_2SO_4 + CO_2 + H_2O$$
$$H_2SO_4 + 2NaOH \rightarrow Na_2SO_4 + 2H_2O$$

Special Apparatus

1. MCA no. 4 Normax burette, preferably with Teflon stopcock, 100-ml total capacity, with 75-ml bulb and stem graduated from 75 to 100 ml in 0.1-ml divisions. This burette should be jacketed with water.
2. Lunge weighing pipette or weighing bottles.

Reagents

1. C. P. or higher quality concentrated sulfuric acid.
2. Primary standard grade sodium carbonate.
3. Standard sodium hydroxide, N/4.904 solution, CO_2-free.
4. Phenolphthalein, methyl red or methyl purple indicator solution. The indicator chosen for the standardization must be used for subsequent titrations.

147

Procedure

The concentrated sulfuric acid is diluted with sufficient CO_2-free distilled water so that its specific gravity is about 1.420.

A catch weight of about 10 grams of acid is weighed and placed aside for further treatment. The amount of sulfuric acid in the sample is neutralized by 1.0808 times its weight of sodium carbonate (previously dried overnight at 105°C). As an excess of acid is necessary to expel all of the carbonic acid, the following formula is used:

1.0808 (grams 100% H_2SO_4 — 0.02) = weight of Na_2CO_3 required.

The required amount of sodium carbonate is weighed and transferred to a 600-ml Erlenmeyer flask and 100 ml of distilled water is added. The acid is carefully added to the flask and the solution is boiled for 15 minutes to expel carbon dioxide. (A small filtering funnel inserted in the neck of the flask prevents loss during the boiling of the acid and carbonate mixture.)

Excess of acid is titrated with the standard sodium hydroxide solution to the end-point of the chosen indicator. Sufficient samples should be run to provide a good average; however, a minimum of three samples generally agrees with good results.

Calculations

$$\frac{(A\,B) + (C)}{W} 100 = \% \ H_2SO_4$$

Where: A = ml NaOH.

B = Normality × meq.wt.H_2SO_4 = grams H_2SO_4 per ml NaOH

C = Grams Na_2CO_3 × Purity Factor × meq.wt.H_2SO_4/meq.wt.Na_2CO_3

W = Weight of sample in grams.

Example: A = 7.51
B = 0.20392 × 0.04904 = 0.01000
C = 5.5402 × 0.9999 × 0.04904/0.05300
W = 10.0126

$$\frac{(7.51 \times 0.01000) + (5.5402 \times 0.9999 \times 0.9252)}{10.0126} \times 100 = 51.94\% \ H_2SO_4$$

Reproducibility

Duplicate determinations should agree within 0.01% H_2SO_4.

References

W. W. Scott, *Scott's Standard Methods of Chemical Analysis*, 5th Ed., 2, 2191–2203, D. Van Nostrand Co., Inc. (1939).

Preparation and Standardization of Approximately N/4.904 Sodium Hydroxide

Scope

A solution of sodium hydroxide, approximately N/4.904, is prepared. This solution is standardized with the reference standard sulfuric acid.

Precautions

Concentrated sodium hydroxide is an extremely corrosive liquid. When using this material, exercise care to protect face and body from burns.

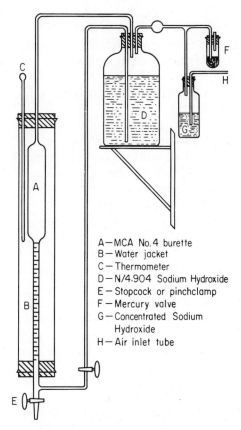

A — MCA No. 4 burette
B — Water jacket
C — Thermometer
D — N/4.904 Sodium Hydroxide
E — Stopcock or pinchclamp
F — Mercury valve
G — Concentrated Sodium
      Hydroxide
H — Air inlet tube

Fig. 53. Acidimetric titration apparatus.

Special Apparatus

1. MCA no. 4 Normax burette, 100-ml total capacity, with 75-ml bulb and stem graduated from 75 to 100 ml in 0.1-ml divisions.
   This burette should be jacketed with water.
2. Lunge weighing pipette.
3. See sketch for apparatus assembly (Fig. 53).

Reagents

1. Reference standard sulfuric acid.
2. Reagent grade sodium hydroxide, pellets.
3. Phenolphthalein, methyl red or methyl purple indicator solution. The indicator chosen for the standardization must be used for subsequent titrations. If phenolphthalein indicator is used, CO_2-free water must be used.

Procedure

To prepare 13 gallons of approximately N/4.904 sodium hydroxide solution, weigh 420 grams of reagent grade sodium hydroxide pellets on a trip balance. Dissolve pellets in distilled water made up to 650-ml volume. Store this solution in stoppered 1,000-ml graduated cylinders for two weeks or more to permit impurities to settle.

After allowing the solution to settle, decant the solution through a medium porosity sintered glass crucible with the aid of a vacuum. Use 60 ml of the filtrate for final adjustment and add remainder to 43 liters of distilled water. The 43 liters of solution, after thorough agitation, is ready for adjustment and standardization.

Using a Lunge weighing pipette or glass bulbs, weigh 1.7–1.9 grams of the reference standard sulfuric acid and slowly add to 50–150 ml of distilled water in a titrating vessel. (In general, it is a good practice to use the same quantity of water in subsequent analyses as in the standardization.) Add indicator solution and titrate with the N/4.904 sodium hydroxide solution to the end-point.

Sufficient standard samples should be titrated to provide a good average; a minimum of three samples should be run. Average normality is then calculated and temperature of the approximately N/4.904 sodium hydroxide solution at standardization is recorded. (For convenience in subsequent determinations, the solution may be adjusted to a titer of 0.01000 gram H_2SO_4 per ml NaOH.)

A temperature correction of 0.00032 ml per ml of titrating solution per 1°C (0.00015 ml per ml of titrating solution per 1°F) above or below the temperature at standardization must be made on all subsequent determinations with this standard sodium hydroxide solution. For temperatures above that at standardization, subtract this correction; for temperatures below, add this correction.

Calculations

$$\text{Normality of NaOH} = \frac{A\,B}{C\,D}$$

Where: A = Weight of sulfuric acid used in grams
         B = Strength of sulfuric acid expressed decimally
         C = ml NaOH used
         D = Molecular equivalent weight H_2SO_4

Example:
    A = 1.8056
    B = 0.5236
    C = 94.56
    D = 0.04904

$$\frac{(1.8056)\ (0.5236)}{(94.56)\ (0.04904)} = 0.20387 \text{ Normality or } N/4.9051$$

Reproducibility

Duplicate determinations should agree within 0.00004 Normality.

References

W. W. Scott, *Scott's Standard Methods of Chemical Analysis*, 5th Ed., 2, 2191–2203, D. Van Nostrand Co., Inc. (1939).

N. A. Lange, *Handbook of Chemistry*, 6th Ed., 254–255, Handbook Publishers, Inc. (1946).

Determination of Acidity

Scope

This method is applicable to all strengths of sludge, spent, virgin and commercial grades of sulfuric acid.

Theory

Acid samples are weighed in glass bulbs, the acid-filled bulb is crushed in distilled water, and the solution is titrated with standard sodium hydroxide to the methyl red end-point. The neutralization reaction takes place according to the equation:

$$H_2SO_4 + 2NaOH \rightarrow Na_2SO_4 + 2H_2O$$

Precautions

Particular care must be taken when crushing sample bulbs containing oleum. Uncontrolled dilution may cause loss of sample and even possible burns.

Special Apparatus

1. MCA no. 4 burette, preferably with Teflon stopcock, 100-ml total capacity, with 75-ml bulb and stem graduated from 75 to 100 ml in 0.1-ml divisions. This burette should be jacketed with water.
2. Porcelain, glass or other suitable titrating vessel and stirring rod or porcelain spatula with flattened head for crushing.
3. Small glass bulbs capable of containing 0.8 to 1.5 grams of sulfuric acid.
4. Lead bulb holders 1½ to 2 inches in diameter and ⅛-inch thick with a ⅛-inch hole in the center.

Reagents

1. Standard sodium hydroxide, N/4.904 solution, CO_2-free.
2. Methyl red indicator, 0.1% solution.

Procedure

Cut the stem of a sealed sampling bulb about 60 mm from the bulb with a sharp triangular file. Carefully weigh the sampling bulb to the nearest 0.1 mg and record. Holding the stem of the bulb, gently heat the glass bulb above the flame of a Bunsen burner by turning the stem between the fingers in order to control the heating operation.

The bulb while still warm is placed (with the stem through a dry lead bulb holder) into the well-shaken sample of acid. The amount of acid drawn into the bulb is regulated according to the strength of the acid being sampled so that the volume of sodium hydroxide will be 75 to 100 ml. When this quantity of acid has been taken, quickly seal the stem by heating the tip in the Bunsen burner flame. Rinse the stem with water to remove any acid that may be outside the stem. Carefully dry the bulb and stem with lint-free tissue paper. The filled sampling bulb is reweighed and the weight recorded. The sample weight is computed. The sampling bulb is placed in distilled water in the titrating vessel. The amount of water used should be the same as in the standardization of sodium hydroxide.

Very carefully, crush the stem of the sampling bulb. Finally, after rolling the unbroken bulb about while submerged in the water until the vigorous reaction of dilution has ceased, crush the bulb. (Care must be exercised to crush the sampling bulb and stem completely so that no entrapping pocket is left to hold either acid or caustic). Add 3 drops of the methyl red indicator solution to the diluted sample. Carefully titrate the prepared sample with the standard sodium hydroxide solution to the methyl red end-point. The volume of sodium hydroxide and the temperature of the water in the water-jacket about the burette are both recorded. A temperature correction of 0.00015 ml per ml of titrating solution per 1°F (0.00027 ml per ml of titrating solution per 1°C) above or below the temperature at standardization of the standard hydroxide solution must be made. For temperature above that at standardization, subtract this correction; for temperature below, add this correction.

Calculations

$$\frac{(A)\ (B)\ (100)}{W} = \%\ H_2SO_4$$

Where:

A = ml NaOH (Corrected to temperature of standardization)

B = (Normality) (Molecular equivalent weight H_2SO_4) = grams H_2SO_4 per ml NaOH

W = Weight of sample in grams

Example:

A = 87.21 ml (observed volume = 87.27 ml)
   (observed temperature = 79°F)
   (standardization temperature = 75°F)

(87.27) − (0.00015) (4) (87.27) = 87.22 ml

For convenience, the Temperature Correction graph (Fig. 54) may be used in lieu of the above calculations.

B = (0.20392) (0.04904) = 0.01000.
W = 0.8852

$$\frac{(87.22)\ (0.20392)\ (0.04904)\ (100)}{0.8852} = 98.53\%\ H_2SO_4$$

Reproducibility

Duplicate samples should agree within 0.05% H_2SO_4.

References

W. W. Scott, *Scott's Standard Methods of Chemical Analysis*, 5th Ed., 2, 2191–2203, D. Van Nostrand Co., Inc. (1939).

Temperature Correction

There are two effects which must be accounted for in making temperature corrections. These are: (1) the change in volume of titrating solution and (2) the change in volume of the burette with changes in temperature. These two effects are always in opposite directions. When the temperature of titration is higher than standardization temperature, the change in solution volume gives a higher burette reading and the change in burette volume gives a lower burette reading, and vice versa. Therefore, these effects must be combined by algebraic addition.

Values for density of sodium hydroxide solutions of 1, 2, 3 and 4% at temperatures of 20°C (68°F), 30°C (86°F) and 40°C (104°F) were obtained from *International Critical Tables* (1st Edition, Vol. III, page 79). By extrapolation, values are obtained for the density of 0.8% sodium hydroxide (0.2N) at these three temperatures. By interpolation, values are obtained for the density of 0.2N sodium hydroxide at 1°F intervals between 68° and 95°F. These values were converted to volumes, and an average value was calculated for the change in volume per °F over this temperature range. The value thus obtained was 0.000163 ml per °F. To this was added, algebraically, the value used by the U.S. Bureau of Standards as the coefficient of cubic expansion for glass. This value was 0.000025 ml per ml/°C or 0.000013 ml per ml/°F. Hence the net average value for volume change of the solution in the burette—the temperature correction—is 0.00015 ml per ml per °F (Figure 54).

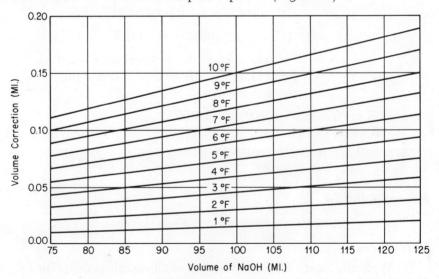

Fig. 54. Temperature correction for volume change of NaOH in a burette.

References

W. W. Scott, *Scott's Standard Methods of Chemical Analysis*, 5th Ed., 2, 2191–2203, 2229, D. Van Nostrand Co., Inc. (1939).

International Critical Tables, 1st Edition, Vol. III, p. 79, McGraw-Hill Publishing Co. (1926).

Kolthoff and Furman, *Volumetric Analysis*, Vol. II, p. 20, John Wiley and Sons (1929).

Treadwell and Hall, *Analytical Chemistry*, Vol. II, p. 453, John Wiley and Sons (1943).

Determination of Total Iron
in Virgin Sulfuric Acid

Scope

This method is applicable to the determination of ferric iron in all strengths of virgin sulfuric acid.

Theory

The thiocyanate method is based upon the formation of the ferric ion and thiocyanate ion complex, $Fe(CNS)_3 \cdot 9KCNS \cdot 4H_2O$, which produces a red color proportional to the amount of ferric iron present in the sample. This method is particularly useful for samples available in strongly acid solution, thus simplifying adjustment of acidity because optimum results are obtainable around pH 1 to 2.

Limitations

Silver, copper, cobalt and mercuric chloride interfere with this determination. Nitric acid gives a color with thiocyanates that may be mistaken for iron.

Special Apparatus

1. 100-ml Nessler Color Comparison Tubes.
2. Photoelectric Colorimeter or Spectrophotometer (optional).

Reagents

1. Reagent grade potassium thiocyanate, 10% solution.

2. Reagent grade concentrated sulfuric acid.

3. Reagent grade potassium permanganate, 0.1 N solution.

4. Standard ferric iron solution, 0.0001 grams Fe/ml.

Procedure

Pipette 10 grams of the acid sample into 10 ml of distilled water in a beaker, add a slight excess of $KMnO_4$, and heat the solution to dissolve any iron in suspension. Pour the cooled acid into a 100-ml Nessler tube with the rinsings of the beaker. Add 10 ml of 10% potassium thiocyanate solution and make up to 100 ml with distilled water.

Measurement of the iron content of the sample may be made by (1) visual comparison with a standard iron solution treated in the same manner as the sample, or (2) reading the light transmittance of the sample in a spectrophotometer at a wave-length of 480 millimicrons or in a colorimeter, such as the Klett-Summerson, using the appropriate light filter. In either case, the measurement should be made immediately, because the color of the thiocyanate complex fades rapidly on standing.

For visual comparison, add 10 grams of reagent grade concentrated sulfuric acid to 20 ml of distilled water and treat in the same manner as the sample. Add the standard iron solution drop by drop to the solution in the Nessler tube until the color matches that of the sample.

For instrumental measurement, a calibration curve may be made with a series of standard iron solutions covering the range between 0.005 and 0.0300 gram iron per 100 ml of solution. Light transmittance or scale reading is plotted against iron content. The iron content of samples may then be measured by determining light transmittance of the sample and reading from the calibration curve the corresponding quantity of iron. With either instrument, a standard solution should be run at regular intervals to insure the continuing validity of the calibration curve.

Calculations

$$\frac{(A)\ (B)\ (100)}{W} = \% \text{ Fe}$$

Where:

A = ml of standard iron solution
B = 0.0001 grams Fe/ml
W = Weight of the sample in grams

Example:

A = 1.2 ml
B = 0.0001 grams Fe/ml
W = 10 grams

$$\frac{(1.2)\ (0.0001)\ (100)}{10} = 0.0012\% \text{ Fe}$$

Reproducibility

Duplicate determinations should agree within 0.0002% Fe.

References

W. W. Scott, *Scott's Standard Methods of Chemical Analysis*, 5th Ed., 2, 2230, D. Van Nostrand Co., Inc. (1939).

F. S. Snell and C. T. Snell, *Colorimetric Methods of Analysis*, 3rd Ed., 2, 307–315, D. Van Nostrand Co., Inc. (1953).

Determination of Total Iron in Sludge or Spent Acid

Scope

This method is applicable to all strengths of sludge or spent sulfuric acid.

Theory

This method is based upon the oxidation of any carbon in the acid by ignition, the residue being taken up in reagent grade sulfuric acid. Iron is then determined by the thiocyanate method based upon the formation of the ferric ion and thiocyanate ion complex, $Fe(CNS)_3 \cdot 9KCNS \cdot 4H_2O$, which produces a red color proportional to the amount of ferric iron present in the sample.

Limitations

Silver, copper, cobalt and mercuric chloride interfere with this determination. Nitric acid gives a color with thiocyanates that may be mistaken for iron.

Special Apparatus

1. 100-ml Nessler Color Comparison Tubes.
2. Photoelectric Colorimeter (optional).

Reagents

1. Reagent grade potassium thiocyanate, 10% solution.
2. Reagent grade concentrated sulfuric acid.
3. Reagent grade potassium permanganate, 0.1 N solution.
4. Standard ferric chloride solution, 0.0001 grams Fe/ml.

Procedure

Evaporate 10 ml of the sample to dryness in a fused silica dish and carefully ignite over a Meker burner to oxidize all the carbon. Cool the sample and add enough sulfuric acid to dissolve the iron oxide (approximately 20 ml). Heat the sample solution, if necessary, to effect solution. The sample is cooled and diluted to 250 ml with distilled water in a 250-ml volumetric flask. Pipette a 25-ml aliquot portion into a 100-ml Nessler tube and add sufficient 0.1N potassium permanganate to maintain a pink color. Add 10 ml of the 10% potassium thiocyanate solution and make up to 100 ml with distilled water. Measurement of the iron content of the sample may be made by (1) visual comparison with a standard iron solution treated in the same manner as the sample, or (2) reading the light transmittance of the sample in a spectrophotometer at a wave-length of 480 millimicrons or in a colorimeter, such as the Klett-Summerson, using the appropriate light filter. In either case, the measurement should be made immediately, because the color of the thiocyanate complex fades rapidly on standing.

For visual comparison, add 10 grams of reagent grade concentrated sulfuric acid to 20 ml of distilled water and treat in the same manner as the sample. Add the standard iron solution drop by drop to the solution in the Nessler tube until the color matches that of the sample.

For instrumental measurement, a calibration curve may be made with a series of standard iron solutions covering the range between 0.005 and 0.0300 gram iron per 100 ml of solution. Light transmittance or scale reading is plotted against iron content. The iron content of samples may then be measured by determining light transmittance of the sample and reading from the calibration curve the corresponding quantity of iron. With either instrument, a standard solution should be run at regular intervals to insure the continuing validity of the calibration curve.

Calculations

$$\frac{(A)\ (B)\ (C)\ (100)}{(D)\ (E)} = \%\ Fe$$

Where:

A = ml of standard iron solution used
B = 0.0001 grams Fe/ml
C = Dilution factor
D = ml of sample used
E = Specific gravity of sample

Example:

A = 6.0 ml
B = 0.0001 grams Fe/ml
C = 10
D = 10 ml
E = 1.690

$$\frac{(6.0)\ (0.0001)\ (10)\ (100)}{(10)\ (1.690)} = 0.036\% \text{ Fe}$$

Reproducibility

Duplicate determinations should agree within 0.0002% Fe.

Reference

W. W. Scott, *Scott's Standard Methods of Chemical Analysis*, 5th Ed., 2, 2230, D. Van Nostrand Co., Inc. (1939).

Determination of Ferrous Iron
in Sulfuric Acid

Scope

This method has been used to determine ferrous iron in the presence of ferric iron in virgin sulfuric acid.

Theory

Ferrous iron reacts with ferricyanide to form a colloidal dispersion of ferrous ferricyanide with a deep blue color, which is compared with standards prepared in a similar manner.

Reagents

1. Sulfuric acid, reagent grade.
2. Potassium ferricyanide, $K_3Fe(CN)_6$, reagent grade: 0.5% solution in freshly boiled and cooled distilled water. This solution must be freshly prepared.
3. Standard ferrous iron solution: 0.0702 gm. of crystal ferrous ammonium sulfate, $FeSO_4 \cdot (NH_4)_2SO_4 \cdot 6H_2O$, and 10 ml of 1:5 sulfuric acid in 1 liter of solution, made to volume with freshly boiled and cooled distilled water. Each ml contains 0.01 mg of ferrous iron. This must be freshly made.

Procedure

Add 70 ml of water to each of a series of Nessler tubes. To each, add 10 ml of 1:5 sulfuric acid and suitable volumes of standard ferrous iron solution for a series of standards covering the expected range of ferrous iron concentration in the sample. Then add 15 ml of 0.5% potassium ferricyanide solution and make to volume with distilled water. The sample of acid to be tested is prepared in a Nessler tube in a similar manner. Sample weight may be determined either by direct weighing or by calculation from the volume pipetted into the Nessler tube. Acidity of the final mixture must be maintained at 2 ml concentrated sulfuric acid per 100 ml volume. Any difference between sample volume and the required 2 ml is made up by adding reagent grade sulfuric acid. Make to volume, mix and compare with the standards after 15 minutes.

Calculations

$$\frac{(A)\ (B)\ (1000)}{W} = \text{ppm ferrous iron}$$

Where:

$A =$ ml of standard iron solution
$B =$ mg of ferrous iron per ml of standard iron solution
$W =$ Sample weight in grams

Example:

$A = 0.8$
$B = 0.01$
$W = 2.0010$

$$\frac{(0.8)\ (0.01)\ (1000)}{2.0010} = 4.0\ \text{ppm ferrous iron}$$

Reproducibility

Duplicate determinations should agree within 0.5 ppm.

References

Snell and Snell, *Colorimetric Methods of Analysis*, 3rd., Ed., II, 332, D. Van Nostrand Co., Inc. (1949).

Determination of Ash in Sulfuric Acid

Scope

This method is used to determine the ash content of all grades of sulfuric acid.

Theory

In the test for ash, the volatile matter in the sulfuric acid is expelled by heating and the nonvolatile residue is weighed.

Precautions

Care must be exercised in heating the acid as spattering will occur should excess heat be applied. Always decompose acids under a good hood equipped with a safety shield.

Special Apparatus

1. Lunge weighing pipette.
2. 100-ml. platinum or fused silica dish.

Procedure

A platinum or fused silica dish is heated to red heat with a Meker burner for 30 minutes, cooled in a desiccator for 30 minutes, and weighed to constant weight.

A 10- to 20-gram sample of sulfuric acid is weighed in a Lunge weighing pipette or weighing bottle. The acid is then placed in the platinum or fused silica dish and the weighing pipette or weighing bottle is reweighed. The dish is slowly heated until the acid coagulates (if sludge acid) or until fumes are no longer evolved. The dish is then heated to a red heat with a Meker burner for 30 minutes or until all of the carbon, if any, has been decomposed. The dish is then cooled for 30 minutes in a desiccator and weighed. The increased weight of the dish is due to the ash, which is composed of substances not volatile at red heat and generally containing iron oxide. (Blasting is not recommended as the magnetic oxide, Fe_3O_4, will form).

Calculations

$$\frac{(A) (100)}{W} = \% \text{ Ash}$$

Where:

$A =$ Weight of ash in grams
$W =$ Weight of sample in grams

Example:

$A = 0.0160$ grams
$W = 20.0024$

$$\frac{0.0160 \times 100}{20.0024} = 0.08\% \text{ Ash}$$

Reproducibility

Duplicate determinations should agree within 0.005% ash for sludge or spent acids and within 0.0001% ash for virgin acid.

References

W. W. Scott, *Scott's Standard Methods of Chemical Analysis*, 5th Ed., 2, 2229, D. Van Nostrand Co., Inc. (1939).

Reagent Chemicals, American Chemical Society Specifications, 369, American Chemical Society (1950).

Determination of Arsenic
in Sulfuric Acid (Modified Gutzeit Method)

Scope

The following procedure furnishes a rapid and accurate method for determination of exceedingly small amounts of arsenic in virgin sulfuric acid, ranging from 0.001 milligrams to 0.5 milligrams As_2O_3.

Theory

The method depends upon the evolution of arsine by the action of hydrogen on arsenic compounds under the catalytic action of zinc, the reaction taking place either in alkaline or acid solutions. The evolved arsine reacts with mercuric chloride (or mercuric bromide) impregnated in a paper strip, forming a colored compound. From the length and intensity of the color stain the amount of arsenic is determined by comparison with standard stains.

Limitations

The amount of acid in the sample placed in the Gutzeit apparatus should be equivalent to 4.2 grams of sulfuric acid. Although the acidity of the sample should be kept close to the above amount, the results are not affected by slight variations.

Nitric acid, chlorine, bromine, iodine, hydrogen sulfide, sulfur dioxide and phosphine (PH_3) must be absent. Mercury, platinum, silver, palladium, nickel, cobalt and cupric sulfate are undesirable. Antimony should not exceed 0.1 mg.

Special Apparatus

1. 2-ml measuring pipette (Mohr type).
2. Small Gutzeit apparatus (Fig. 55)

Reagents

1. Standard arsenic solution, 0.001 mg As_2O_3/ml.
2. Reagent grade lead acetate, 1% solution.
3. Reagent grade mercuric chloride (or mercuric bromide), 5% solution in ethyl (or methyl) alcohol.
4. Reagent grade stannous chloride, 45% solution.
5. Reagent grade ferric oxide.
6. Reagent grade concentrated nitric acid.
7. Reagent grade concentrated sulfuric acid.
8. Reagent grade zinc, arsenic-free, granulated, 3–6 mesh.
9. Lead acetate paper.
10. Mercuric chloride (bromide) paper strips.

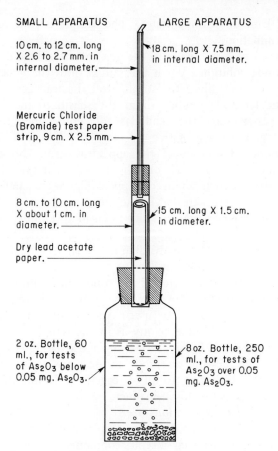

SMALL APPARATUS

10 cm. to 12 cm. long
X 2.6 to 2.7 mm. in
internal diameter.

Mercuric Chloride
(Bromide) test paper
strip, 9 cm. X 2.5 mm.

8 cm. to 10 cm. long
X about 1 cm. in
diameter.

Dry lead acetate
paper.

2 oz. Bottle, 60
ml., for tests
of As₂O₃ below
0.05 mg. As₂O₃.

LARGE APPARATUS

18 cm. long X 7.5 mm.
in internal diameter.

15 cm. long X 1.5 cm.
in diameter.

8 oz. Bottle, 250
ml., for tests of
As₂O₃ over 0.05
mg. As₂O₃.

Fig. 55. Gutzeit apparatus for arsenic determination.

Procedure

Because the small Gutzeit apparatus is limited to stains of As_2O_3 from 0.001 mg to 0.02 mg, the size of the sample of sulfuric acid must be varied in proportion to the arsenic content to insure stains that will fall between these limits. If the arsenic content is between 0.000001% and 0.000005% As_2O_3, then a sample of 165 ml (300 grams of 1.84 specific gravity) must be taken. For higher concentrations of arsenic, the size of the sample may be decreased proportionally. For a sample whose range of arsenic concentration is unknown, a series of samples must be run to bracket these limits.

For sulfuric acid with arsenic concentration between 0.000001% and 0.000005%, add 3 ml of concentrated nitric acid to 165 ml (300 grams) of the sample and evaporate to about 10 ml. Cool the sample, dilute with 20 ml of distilled water and evaporate to about 5 ml. Cool the sample and dilute with 10 ml of distilled water. The sample is now ready for the Gutzeit determination.

Place 0.1 gram of ferric oxide in the generator bottle and add 1 ml of stannous chloride solution. Wash the sample into the generator bottle, add the washings and dilute to 50 ml. Roll the lead acetate paper and insert into the large glass tube. Insert the sensitized mercuric chloride (bromide) paper strip into the small glass tube and connect the two tubes. Add 5 gm of granular arsenic-free zinc to the solution in the generator bottle and immediately connect the apparatus again. Shake the apparatus gently and allow to stand for 1 hour. The mercuric chloride (bromide) paper strip is then removed, dipped in molten paraffin and compared with standard stains treated in the same manner.

Because of the degeneration of stains upon long standing and the possible difference in the reagents, test papers and controls applied from one determination to the next, it is advisable to prepare standard stains in conjunction with each determination.

To prepare standard stains, treat 2 ml, 6 ml and 10 ml of the standard arsenic solution as directed above for the sulfuric acid sample. The same quantities of all reagents must be used. Add 10 ml of reagent grade sulfuric acid to provide the same acidity as in the sample. The stains thus produced will represent 0.002 mg, 0.006 mg and 0.01 mg As_2O_3.

To determine any possible arsenic in the reagents used, run a blank on these reagents by substituting 10 ml of reagent grade sulfuric acid for the sample and treating in the above manner.

Other procedural considerations are:
1. Nitric acid must be added to the sample to prevent possible volatilization of the unoxidized arsenic compounds upon heating. After adding nitric acid to the sulfuric acid, heat the sulfuric acid to dense fumes of sulfur trioxide to expel the nitric acid.
2. Interferences from sulfurous acid or hydrogen sulfide in the sulfuric acid are prevented by boiling the sulfuric acid.
3. The internal diameter of the small tube must not be large enough to permit curling of the paper strip.
4. Lead acetate paper must be used to remove any trace of hydrogen sulfide generated because this will react with the mercury in the test paper strip and interfere with the arsine stain.
5. Ferric oxide, reduced by stannous chloride, is used to prevent polarization between the zinc and the acid and thus aids in the evolution of arsine.
6. The temperature of the reaction in the generator bottle should be maintained between 75 and 80°F, not over 100°F. If necessary, a water bath should be used to maintain the proper temperature. High

temperatures cause frothing of the sample and may cause the sample to boil over, thus ruining the determination.

Calculations

$$\frac{(A)\ (B)\ (100)}{W} = \%\ As_2O_3$$

Where:

$A = $ ml of standard arsenic solution used
$B = 0.000001$ grams As_2O_3/ml
$W = $ Weight of sample in grams

Example:

$A = 6\ ml$
$B = 0.000001$ grams As_2O_3
$W = 300$ grams

$$\frac{(6.0)\ (0.000001)\ (100)}{300} = 0.000002\%\ As_2O_3$$

Reproducibility

Duplicate determinations should agree within $0.000001\%\ As_2O_3$.

References

W. W. Scott, *Scott's Standard Methods of Chemical Analysis*, 1, 101–108, D. Van Nostrand Co., Inc. (1939).

Reagent Chemicals, American Chemical Society Specifications, 369, American Chemical Society (1950).

Determination of Chlorides in Sulfuric Acid (Mohr Method)

Scope

This method is applicable to the determination of chlorides in sulfuric acid.

Theory

This procedure is based upon the volumetric determination of chlorides by titration with silver nitrate to the silver chromate end-point. The titration must be conducted in neutral solution. The following equations indicate the reactions involved:

$$2AgNO_3 + K_2CrO_4 \rightarrow Ag_2CrO_4 + 2KNO_3$$
$$Ag_2CrO_4 + 2Cl \rightarrow 2AgCl + CrO_4^=$$

Special Apparatus

1. Measuring pipette (Mohr type).

Reagents

1. Reagent grade sodium hydroxide, concentrated solution.
2. Reagent grade nitric acid, 1 N solution.
3. Reagent grade calcium carbonate, powder.
4. Reagent grade potassium chromate, 10% solution.
5. Phenolphthalein indicator, 1% solution.
6. Standard silver nitrate solution, 0.0001 grams Cl/ml.

Procedure

Cautiously add 25 grams of the sample to 100 ml of distilled water in a beaker. Add 1 ml of 1% phenolphthalein indicator and make alkaline with concentrated sodium hydroxide solution. Heat the solution to boiling and make slightly acid with 1 N nitric acid. Neutralize with calcium carbonate and add 1 ml of 10% potassium chromate solution. Titrate the solution with the standard silver nitrate to the silver chromate end-point.

Calculations

$$\frac{(A)\ (B)\ (100)}{W} = \%Cl$$

Where:

$A = $ ml of standard silver nitrate used
$B = 0.0001$ grams Cl/ml
$W = $ Weight of sample in grams

Example:

$A = 2.10$ ml
$B = 0.0001$ grams Cl/ml
$W = 25$ grams

$$\frac{(2.10)\ (0.0001)\ (100)}{25} = 0.0008\%\ Cl$$

Reproducibility

Duplicate determinations should agree within 0.0002% Cl.

References

W. W. Scott, *Scott's Standard Methods of Chemical Analysis*, 5th Ed., 1–2, 272–273, 2232, D. Van Nostrand Co., Inc. (1939).

Determination of Chlorides
in Sulfuric Acid (Turbidimetric Method)

Scope

This method is applicable to the determination of chlorides in virgin sulfuric acid.

Theory

In concentrations of less than 15 ppm, chlorides may be determined by comparison with standards of turbidity produced by the addition of silver nitrate.

Special Apparatus

1. 100-ml Nessler Color Comparison Tubes.
2. Photoelectric turbidimeter (optional).

Reagents

1. Reagent grade silver nitrate, 2% solution.
2. Reagent grade nitric acid, dilute (1:10).
3. Standard sodium chloride solution, 0.02 mg. Cl/ml.

Procedure

Add 2 grams of the sample to 50 ml of distilled water in a 100-ml Nessler tube. Add 1 ml of dilute nitric acid and 1 ml of 2% silver nitrate solution. Make up to 100 ml with distilled water and compare with the turbidity produced using the same procedure including known amounts of standard sodium chloride solution.

Calculations

$$\frac{(A)\ (B)\ (100)}{W} = \%\ Cl$$

Where:

A = ml of standard sodium chloride used
B = 0.00002 grams Cl/ml
W = Weight of sample in grams

Example:

A = 1.0 ml
B = 0.00002 grams Cl/ml
W = 2.0 grams

$$\frac{(1.0)\ (0.00002)\ (100)}{2.0} = 0.0010\%\ Cl.$$

Reproducibility

Duplicate determinations should agree within 0.0002% Cl.

References

U.S. Navy Department Specifications 51A2g, March 15, (1945).
Reagent Chemicals, American Chemical Society Specifications 369, American Chemical Society, (1950).

Determination of Nitrates
in Sulfuric Acid

Scope

This method is applicable to all strengths of sulfuric acid.

Theory

Nitrates are determined by the color developed with brucine in the presence of sulfuric acid. A suitable sample contains 0.01–0.20 mg. of nitrate nitrogen. The determination is made by the comparison with standards of the sulfur yellow color that follows the initial red color, rather than the original color, which cannot be relied upon.

Limitations

If nitrites are not to appear in the final results, 2 parts of sulfuric acid must be present for every part of water. To determine nitrites as well as nitrates, lessen the amount of sulfuric acid so that the ratio of water: sulfuric acid is 2:1. If the sample solution contains much organic matter or ferrous iron, it must be oxidized with a slight excess of 0.1% potassium permanganate. If this oxidation is carried out, nitrites will be oxidized to nitrates.

Precautions

Brucine sulfate is a highly poisonous alkaloid and must be handled with due caution.

Special Apparatus

1. 2-ml measuring pipette (Mohr type).

Reagents

1. U.S.P. brucine sulfate, 5% solution in concentrated sulfuric acid.
2. Reagent grade concentrated sulfuric acid, nitrate-free.
3. Standard potassium nitrate solution, 0.01 mg NO_3 per ml.

Procedure

To a 100-ml. Nessler tube add a sample of appropriate size. Make up to 15 ml. with nitrate-free concentrated sulfuric acid. Add 0.4 ml of the 5% brucine solution and mix. Carefully dilute to 30 ml with distilled water, mix and let stand for 3-5 minutes to let the color develop to full intensity. The heat of dilution is necessary for this color development, and it is important that the dilution be done in the same way for all samples and all standards. Dilute to volume with distilled water, mix, and compare with standards prepared using the same procedure. The standards should cover the range up to 0.1 mg. NO_3 per 100 ml. of final solution, which is equivalent to 10 ppm NO_3 for a 10-gram sample. If the nitrate content of the acid is more than 10 ppm, a sample smaller than 10 grams should be taken.

Calculations

$$\frac{(A)\ (B)\ (100)}{C\ D} = \%\ NO_3$$

Where:

A = ml standard potassium nitrate solution
B = grams NO_3 per ml of standard solution
C = ml of sample
D = Specific gravity of sample

Example:

$A = 5$ ml
$B = 0.00001$ grams NO_3 per ml
$C = 2.5$ ml
$D = 1.820$

$$\frac{(5)\ (0.00001)\ (100)}{(2.5)\ (1.820)} = 0.0011\ \%\ NO_3$$

Reproducibility

Duplicate determinations should agree within 0.0001% NO_3

References

F. D. Snell and C. T. Snell, *Colorimetric Methods of Analysis*, 3rd. Ed., 2, 798, D. Van Nostrand Co., Inc. (1953).

Determination of Ammonium Ion in Sulfuric Acid

Scope

This method is applicable to the determination of ammonium ion in sulfuric acid.

Theory

In reaction with ammonia, Nessler's reagent produces a yellow to reddish brown colloidal dispersion which is a very accurate indicator of the amount of ammonia present. This reaction is also used in the determination of ammonia in water, specific forms of organic nitrogen, and examination of many biological materials. The conventional method has been to compare the sample with artificial standards. Spectrophotometric reading at 410 millimicrons is suitable.

Special Apparatus

1. 100-ml Nessler Color Comparison Tubes.

Reagents

1. Reagent grade sodium hydroxide, 50% solution.
2. Nessler's reagent.
3. Gum arabic solution.
4. Standard ammonium chloride, 0.01 mg. NH_4/ml.

Procedure

Add a 2-ml sample of sulfuric acid to 50 ml of ammonia-free distilled water. Carefully neutralize the sample solution to litmus with 50% sodium hydroxide solution and boil for 5 minutes to coagulate the R_2O_3 precipitate. (Unless the neutralization is carried out carefully, ammonia may be lost in the subsequent boiling). Filter the solution into a 100-ml Nessler tube and dilute to 97 ml with ammonia-free distilled water. Mix the solution well and add, in succession, 1 ml of gum arabic solution and 2 ml of Nessler's reagent. Invert the Nessler tube only once or twice in order to effect thorough mixing. (Do not mix the solution by prolonged agitation because this affects the stability of the colored suspension). Allow the sample to stand 10 minutes. If a pronounced turbidity appears, repeat the procedure on another portion of the sample. Compare the sample with natural or artificial standards if it is satisfactory in intensity and clarity. If the intensity of the color is too great, repeat, using an appropriate dilution of the sample with ammonia-free distilled water. To compare the color developed in the sample with natural standards, make up a series of standards by diluting 0.4, 0.8, 1.4, 2.0, 2.8, 3.4 and 4.0 ml of the standard ammonium chloride solution to 97 ml with ammonia-free distilled water. Add 1 ml gum arabic solution and 2 ml of Nessler's reagent. Mix and compare after 10 minutes.

Calculations

$$\frac{(A)\ (B)\ (100)}{C\ D} = \%\ NH_4$$

Where: A = ml of standard ammonium chloride
             B = 0.00001 grams NH_4/ml
             C = ml of sample
             D = Specific gravity of sample

Example:

             A = 4.0 ml
             B = 0.00001 grams NH_4/ml
             C = 2.0 ml
             D = 1.829

$$\frac{(4.0)\ (0.00001)\ (100)}{(2.0)\ (1.829)} = 0.0011\%\ NH_4$$

Reproducibility

Duplicate determinations should agree within 0.0002% NH_4.

References

W. W. Scott, *Scott's Standard Methods of Chemical Analysis*, 5th Ed., 2, 2049, D. Van Nostrand Co., Inc., (1939).

Snell and Biffen, *Commercial Methods of Analysis*, 1st Ed., D. Van Nostrand Co., Inc.

F. D. Snell and C. T. Snell, *Colorimetric Methods of Analysis*, 3rd. Ed., 2, 808–819, D. Van Nostrand Co., Inc. (1949).

Determination of Ammonium Ion
in Sulfuric Acid (Alternate Method)

Scope

This method is applicable to the determination of ammonium ion in sulfuric acid.

Theory

In this procedure the sample of sulfuric acid is made alkaline with sodium hydroxide and the ammonia is distilled over. Nessler's reagent is added and the determination is made colorimetrically. In reaction with ammonia, Nessler's reagent produces a yellow to reddish brown colloidal dispersion which is a very accurate indicator of the amount of ammonia present. This reaction is also used in the determination of ammonia in water, specific forms of organic nitrogen, and examination of many biological materials. The conventional method has been to compare the sample with artificial or natural standards. Spectrophotometric reading at 410 millimicrons is suitable.

Special Apparatus

1. 50-ml Nessler Color Comparison Tubes.
2. 2-ml measuring pipette (Mohr type).

Reagents

1. Reagent grade sodium hydroxide, 10% solution.
2. Reagent grade hydrochloric acid, N/10 solution.
3. Nessler's reagent.
4. Standard ammonium chloride solution, 0.01 mg NH_4/ml.

Procedure

Carefully pipette 2.0 grams of the sample of sulfuric acid into 30 ml of cold distilled water in a 500-ml Kjehldahl flask. Cool in an ice bath and cautiously add 20 ml of freshly boiled 10% sodium hydroxide solution, keeping the temperature low. Cool, add 20 ml more of the 10% sodium hydroxide solution, and connect the flask through a spray trap (Kjehldahl connecting tube) to a condenser, the end of which dips beneath the surface of 10 ml of N/10 hydrochloric acid in a 250-ml Erlenmeyer flask. Apply heat to the sample solution in the Kjehldahl flask and distill over about 35 ml, add to the distillate 2 ml of the 10% sodium hydroxide solution and transfer to a 50-ml Nessler tube. Dilute the solution to 50 ml with distilled water and add 2 ml of Nessler's reagent. Mix thoroughly and compare with the color developed from standard ammonium chloride samples treated in the same manner. Convenient standards are produced from 1, 3, 6 and 10-ml portions of the standard ammonium chloride solution.

Calculation

$$\frac{(A)\ (B)\ (100)}{W} = \%\ NH_4$$

Where: A = ml standard ammonium chloride
B = 0.00001 grams NH_4/ml
W = Weight of sample in grams

Example:

$$A = 3.0 \, ml$$
$$B = 0.00001 \text{ grams } NH_4/ml$$
$$W = 2.0 \text{ grams}$$

$$\frac{(3.0)\,(0.00001)\,(100)}{2.0} = 0.0015\% \; NH_4$$

Reproducibility

Duplicate determinations should agree within 0.0002% NH_4.

References

W. W. Scott, *Scott's Standard Methods of Chemical Analysis*, 5th Ed., 2, 2049, D. Van Nostrand Co., Inc. (1939).

F. D. Snell and C. T. Snell, *Colorimetric Methods of Analysis*, 3rd. Ed., 2, 808–819, D. Van Nostrand Co., Inc. (1949).

Reagent Chemicals, American Chemical Society Specifications, 369. American Chemical Society, (1950).

Determination of Mercury in Virgin Sulfuric Acid

Scope

The basic technique of extraction with dithizone has been used for many years, with appropriate modifications, for determining traces of a number of metals in widely varying materials ranging from biologicals to metallic ores and alloys. This procedure is intended for the determination of mercury in sulfuric acid which contains no organic material that will interfere with measurement of the color developed in the test.

Theory

Divalent mercury reacts with dithizone in an acid medium to form the keto-complex which is soluble in carbon tetrachloride. This yellow-orange complex exhibits a maximum light absorption at 490 millimicrons. Measurement of light transmittance through a carbon tetrachloride solution at this wave length is used to determine the quantity of mercury present. The mixed-color method is used. The color of the solution is a combination of the yellow-orange of the dithizonate and the green of excess dithizone.

Limitations

Gold, silver, palladium and divalent platinum, if present, will interfere by forming colored complexes. Copper, however, is the only common metal which can interfere. The procedure given will eliminate interference from copper present in amounts not exceeding 0.5 mg.

Special Apparatus

1. Spectrophotometer with 50-mm cuvettes.
2. Separatory funnels, 250-ml and 125-ml, Squibb type, Pyrex. Soft glass is not satisfactory.
3. Support, funnel, wood six-place double shelf (Curtin Cat. #20277).
4. Boiling flasks, Pyrex 250-ml with short neck having outer 24/40 ⚮ joint.
5. Condensers, West type, Pyrex, with inner 24/40 ⚮ joint.
6. Gas-washing bottles, Pyrex, 250-ml (or 500-ml) with fritted glass tip on inlet line and 29/42 ⚮ joint on top.

Reagents

1. Dithizone (diphenylthiocarbazone) stock solution: 0.0120 gram dissolved in 500 ml of reagent grade carbon tetrachloride. This solution should be protected from light in a dark glass bottle and stored in a refrigerator.
2. Dithizone working solution: Dilute 9.0 ml of stock solution to 250 ml with reagent grade carbon tetrachloride. This solution should be protected from light in a dark glass bottle, and made up fresh daily.
3. Sulfuric acid, concentrated, reagent grade.
4. Nitric acid, concentrated, reagent grade.
5. Hydrochloric acid, concentrated, reagent grade.
6. Hydrochloric acid, 5N.
7. Carbon tetrachloride, reagent grade.
8. Mercuric chloride, reagent grade.
9. Hydroxylamine hydrochloride, 5% aqueous solution. This should be made up fresh daily.

Preparation of Calibration Curve

1. Dissolve 0.1354 gram of reagent grade mercuric chloride (which has been dried at 105°C for two hours) in water, add 50 ml of concentrated nitric acid, and dilute to 1 liter with distilled water. This makes a stock standard solution.

2. Dilute 10 ml of the stock solution to 1 liter to make a working standard containing 1 microgram of mercury per ml.

3. Into each of five 250-ml boiling flasks set in an ice bath, put about five ml of distilled water, and add carefully 10 grams of concentrated reagent grade sulfuric acid. Let cool and add to each flask 1 ml of concentrated nitric acid and 0.5 ml of concentrated hydrochloric acid.

4. Add to the flasks 0, 0.5, 1, 3 and 5 ml, respectively, of the working standard mercury solution.

5. Connect flasks to condensers and heat, refluxing for 5–10 minutes at such a rate that no fumes reach the top of the condensers. Remove the heat, cool and wash down the condensers into the flasks.

6. Transfer the solutions to gas-washing bottles and strip as much chlorine as possible by aspirating air through the solutions for 5–10 minutes.

7. Transfer the solutions to 250-ml separatory funnels and dilute to 200 ml with distilled water. Add to each funnel 2 ml of 5% hydroxylamine hydrochloride and mix.

8. Add to the first funnel 2 ml of stock dithizone solution and about 5 ml of carbon tetrachloride. Shake vigorously for about 15 seconds and let settle. Drain the carbon tetrachloride solution into a clean, dry separatory funnel, making sure that none of the water solution goes with it. Rinse the water solution with about 5 ml of carbon tetrachloride to collect all the dithizone and drain this into the funnel with the rest. The water solution may now be discarded.

9. Add to the dithizone solution 2 ml of 5N hydrochloric acid. Shake vigorously to mix thoroughly. Let solution settle. Drain and discard the dithizone solution, and rinse the water solution with carbon tetrachloride as before, and discard the carbon tetrachloride. Dilute the water solution to 100 ml with distilled water and mix.

10. With a volumetric pipette, add exactly 30 ml of the working dithizone solution and shake vigorously for 15 seconds. Let settle and drain the dithizone solution through a Whatman no. 41 filter paper into the 50-mm cuvette.

11. Place cuvette in the spectrophotometer and read the transmittance at 490 millimicrons with pure carbon tetrachloride as the reference solution set at 100% transmittance.

12. Repeat steps 8, 9, 10, 11 with each funnel in turn, recording the transmittance for each.

13. Plot the transmittance against mercury content on semi-log paper. This should give a straight line.

Analysis of Sample

1. Add an accurately weighed sample of sulfuric acid to about 5 ml of distilled water in a 250-ml boiling flask set in an ice bath. Let cool and add 1 ml of concentrated nitric acid and add 0.5 ml of concentrated hydrochloric acid. For acid containing less than 0.1 ppm Hg, use a 10-gram sample and dilute to 200 ml before extracting with dithizone. For acid containing higher concentrations of mercury, a smaller sample should be used, but the water solution should be about 1N in sulfuric acid for the first dithizone extraction. If a sample smaller than 5 gram is used, it is convenient to make up the difference with reagent grade sulfuric acid and dilute to 100 ml before extracting.

2. Follow steps 5 through 12 under Preparation of Calibration Curve above.

3. Carry a blank using all reagents and 10 grams of reagent grade sulfuric acid through the procedure with the samples.

Calculations

$$\frac{(A - B)\ (1000)}{W} = \text{ppm Hg}$$

Where:

> A = mg Hg in sample, read from calibration curve
> B = mg Hg in blank, read from calibration curve
> W = Sample weight in grams

Example:

> $A = 0.0030$
> $B = 0.0015$
> $W = 5.0460$

$$\frac{(0.0030\text{–}0.0015)\ (1000)}{5.0460} = 0.30 \text{ ppm}$$

Reproducibility

Duplicate determinations should agree to $\pm$ 0.030 ppm for a 5-gram sample or $\pm$ 0.015 ppm for a 10-gram sample.

References

E. B. Sandell, *Colorimetric Determination of Traces of Metals*, 2nd Edition, Chapters 4 and 28, Interscience Publishers, Inc., New York (1950).

Determination of Mercury
in Sludge or Spent Sulfuric Acid

Scope

This procedure is intended for the determination of mercury in sulfuric acid which contains carbon and/or organic compounds which will interfere with the colorimetric determination and must be removed.

Theory

Divalent mercury reacts with dithizone in an acid medium to form the keto-complex which is soluble in carbon tetrachloride. This yellow-orange complex exhibits a maximum light absorption at 490 millimicrons. Measurement of light transmittance through a carbon tetrachloride solution at this wave length is used to determine the quantity of mercury present. The mixed color method is used. The color of the solution is a combination of the yellow-orange of the dithizonate and the green of excess dithizone.

Limitations

Gold, silver, palladium and divalent platinum, if present, will interfere by forming colored complexes. Copper, however, is the only common metal which can interfere. The procedure given will eliminate interference from copper present in amounts not exceeding 0.5 mg.

Special Apparatus

1. Hot plate with regulator or Glas-Col heating mantle with Powerstat or equivalent regulating transformer.
2. Five two-neck boiling flasks, Pyrex, with outer 24/40 ℱ joints in both necks.
3. Addition thimble, Pyrex, with inner 24/40 ℱ joint.
4. Condenser, West type, Pyrex, with inner 24/40 ℱ joint.
5. Reflux trap, Pyrex.
6. Separatory funnels, 125-ml and 250-ml, Squibb type, Pyrex.
7. Spectrophotometer with 50-mm cuvettes.

Reagents

1. Dithizone (diphenylthiocarbazone) stock solution: 0.0120 gram dissolved in 500 ml of reagent grade carbon tetrachloride. This solution should be protected from light in a dark glass bottle and stored in a refrigerator.

2. Dithizone working solution: Dilute 9.0 ml of stock solution to 250 ml with reagent grade carbon tetrachloride. This solution should be protected from light in a dark glass bottle, and should be made up fresh daily.

3. Sulfuric acid, concentrated, reagent grade.

4. Nitric acid, concentrated, reagent grade.

5. Hydrochloric acid, 5N.

6. Potassium permanganate solution, approximately 0.1N.

7. Oxalic acid, reagent grade crystals.

8. Hydrogen peroxide solution, 30%, reagent grade.

9. Carbon tetrachloride, reagent grade.

10. Mercuric chloride, reagent grade.

11. Hydroxylamine hydrochloride, 5% aqueous solution. This solution should be made up fresh daily.

Preparation of Calibration Curve

1. Dissolve 0.1354 gram of reagent grade mercuric chloride (which has been dried at 105°C for two hours) in water, add 50 ml of concentrated nitric acid and dilute to 1 liter with mercury-free water. This makes a stock standard solution.

2. Dilute 10 ml of the stock standard to 1 liter to make a working standard containing 1 microgram of mercury per ml.

3. Into each of five 250-ml boiling flasks set in an ice bath, put about 5 ml of distilled water and add carefully 10 grams of concentrated reagent grade sulfuric acid. Let cool and add to each flask 1 ml of concentrated nitric acid and 0.5 ml of concentrated hydrochloric acid.

4. Add to the flasks 0, 0.5, 1, 3 and 5 ml, respectively, of the working standard mercury solution.

5. Connect the flasks to condensers and heat, refluxing for 5–10 minutes at such a rate that no fumes reach the top of the condensers. Remove the heat, cool and wash down the condensers into the flasks.

6. Transfer the solutions to gas washing bottles and strip as much chlorine as possible by aspirating air through the solutions for 5–10 minutes.

7. Transfer the solutions to 250-ml separatory funnels and dilute to 200 ml with distilled water. Add to each funnel 2 ml of 5% hydroxylamine hydrochloride and mix.

8. Add to the first funnel 2 ml of stock dithizone solution and about 5 ml of carbon tetrachloride. Shake vigorously for about 15 seconds and let settle. Drain the carbon tetrachloride solution into a clean, dry separatory funnel, making sure that none of the water solution goes with it. Rinse the water solution with about 5 ml of carbon tetrachloride to

collect all the dithizone and drain this into the funnel with the rest. The water solution may now be discarded.

9. Add to the dithizone solution 2 ml of 5N hydrochloric acid. Shake vigorously to mix thoroughly, and let settle. Drain and discard the dithizone solution, rinse the water solution with carbon tetrachloride as before, and discard the carbon tetrachloride. Dilute the water solution to 100 ml with distilled water and mix.

10. With a volumetric pipette, add exactly 30.0 ml of the working dithizone solution and shake vigorously for 15 seconds. Let settle and drain the dithizone solution through a Whatman no. 41 filter paper into the 50-mm cuvette.

11. Place cuvette in the spectrophotometer and read the transmittance at 490 millimicrons with pure carbon tetrachloride as the reference solution set at 100% transmittance.

12. Repeat steps 8, 9, 10, 11 with each funnel in turn, recording the transmittance for each.

13. Plot the transmittance against mercury content on semi-log paper. This should give a straight line.

Analysis of Sample

1. Transfer an accurately weighed sample of suitable size into the digestion flask (see Note 1 below).

2. Add 3 glass beads and assemble the digestion unit.

3. Place 5 ml of nitric acid in the addition thimble and heat the sample gradually to boiling.

4. Allow water to collect in the reflux trap and add the nitric acid gradually. Adjust the heat to prevent excessive foaming.

5. When the digestion nears completion, as evidenced by clearing of the boiling solution, open the reflux stopcock and return condensate at such a rate as to maintain a constant level in the trap.

6. Continue the digestion until a clear yellow-green solution is obtained.

7. Rinse the addition thimble with a few drops of distilled water and add 5 ml of hydrogen peroxide to the thimble. Add the peroxide drop by drop to the flask until brown fumes of nitrogen oxides cease to form.

8. Open the reflux stopcock and let all condensate drain into the flask. Leave the stopcock open and reflux for 15 minutes.

9. Remove from heat and cool to about 60°C. Add $KMnO_4$ solution drop by drop until a pink color is obtained which persists for five min-

utes. Add oxalic acid, two or three crystals at a time, until the pink color disappears (see note 2 below).

10. Let cool to room temperature and quantitatively transfer to a clean separatory funnel and adjust the solution by adding either water or reagent grade concentrated sulfuric acid until the acidity is 1N (see note 1 below).

11. Add 2 ml of stock dithizone solution and 5 ml of carbon tetrachloride, shake vigorously for 15 seconds to mix, and let settle. Drain the carbon tetrachloride solution into a clean, dry separatory funnel, add about 5 ml of carbon tetrachloride to the water solution and mix to collect all the remaining dithizone. Add this to the rest of the carbon tetrachloride in the second funnel. The water solution may now be discarded.

12. Add 2 ml of 5N hydrochloric acid to the dithizone solution. Shake vigorously to mix thoroughly and let settle. Drain and discard the dithizone solution, rinse the water solution with carbon tetrachloride, as before, and discard the carbon tetrachloride. Dilute the water solution to 100 ml with distilled water and mix.

13. With a volumetric pipette, add exactly 30 ml of the working dithizone solution and shake vigorously for 15 seconds. Let settle and drain the dithizone solution through a Whatman no. 41 filter paper into the 50-mm cuvette.

14. Place cuvette in the spectrophotometer and read the transmittance at 490 millimicrons with pure carbon tetrachloride as the reference solution set at 100% transmittance (see note 3 below).

15. Read from the calibration curve the milligrams of mercury in the sample.

16. Carry a blank using all reagents and 10 grams of reagent grade sulfuric acid through the procedure with the samples.

Notes

1. For acid containing less than 0.1 ppm Hg, use a 10-gram sample and dilute to 200 ml before extracting with dithizone. For acid containing a higher concentration of mercury, a smaller sample should be used, but the water solution should be about 1N in sulfuric acid for the first dithizone extraction. If a sample smaller than 5 grams is used, it is convenient to make up the difference with reagent grade sulfuric acid and dilute to 100 ml before extracting.

2. Dithizone is easily oxidized and the oxidation products are similar in visual appearance to the mercury dithizonate. If measured in a photom-

eter, the color of the oxidation products would be confused with the mercury color and a value for mercury would result which could be considerably in error. It is, therefore, very important that all oxidizing substances be eliminated before color development, and this makes necessary the elaborate combination of oxidizing agents and oxalic acid in the sample treatment.

3. Mercury dithizonate is light-sensitive, turning green if exposed to strong light. It is, therefore, advisable to obtain photometer readings as rapidly as possible once the final extraction is made.

Calculations

$$\frac{(A - B)\ (1000)}{W} = ppm\ Hg$$

Where:

$A =$ mg Hg in sample, read from calibration curve
$B =$ mg Hg in blank, read from calibration curve
$W =$ Sample weight in grams

Example:

$A = 0.0030$

$B = 0.0015$
$W = 5.0460$

$$\frac{(0.0030–0.0015)\ (1000)}{5.0460} = 0.30\ ppm$$

Reproducibility

Duplicate determinations should agree to $\pm$ 0.030 ppm for a 5-gram sample or $\pm$ 0.015 ppm for a 10-gram sample.

Reference

E. B. Sandell, *Colorimetric Determination of Traces of Metals*, 2nd Edition, Chapters 4 and 28, Interscience Publishers, Inc., New York (1950).

Determination of Lead in Sulfuric Acid

Scope

This procedure is applicable to the determination of trace amounts of lead in sulfuric acid.

Theory

The estimation of small amounts of lead by the intensity of the brown coloration produced by the sulfide in colloidal solution was proposed by Pelouze. The procedure was modified by others to overcome the color produced by impurities. By this procedure on a gram sample one part of lead per million may be detected and as high as 50 parts per million may be estimated.

Limitations

Nickel, arsenic, antimony, silver, zinc, tin, iron and aluminum, present in such amounts as commonly occur in the above materials, do not interfere.

Sulfuric acid discolored by organic matter should be mixed with 4 to 5 grams of potassium bisulfate, taken to fumes, and then diluted with water.

Precautions

Potassium cyanide is a violent poison. Poisoning may occur by ingestion, absorption through injured skin or inhalation of hydrogen cyanide liberated by the action of carbon dioxide or other acids. This material must be used in alkaline solutions to prevent the formation of hydrogen cyanide gas.

Special Apparatus

1. 100-ml Nessler Color Comparison Tubes

Reagents

1. Reagent grade potassium cyanide, 10% solution.
2. Reagent grade sodium sulfide, 10% solution.
3. Reagent grade sodium metabisulfite
4. Reagent grade concentrated hydrochloric acid
5. Reagent grade concentrated sulfuric acid
6. Reagent grade ammonium hydroxide
7. Alkaline tartrate solution: Dissolve 25 gm. of reagent grade sodium potassium tartrate in 50 ml. of distilled water. Add a little ammonia and 1 ml. of 10% sodium sulfide solution. Let stand for several hours, then filter off any precipitate which may have formed. Acidify the filtrate with IICl, boil until free of H_2S, and let cool. Again make ammoniacal and dilute to 100 ml. with distilled water.
8. Standard lead acetate solution 0.01 mg Pb/ml

Procedure

If the concentration of lead is between 10 and 50 ppm, a 1-gram sample is sufficient. If the concentration differs from the above limits, the size of the sample must be increased or decreased proportionally.

Add 1 gram of the sample to a small amount of distilled water in a 500-ml Erlenmeyer flask. To the sample solution, add 10 ml of the alkaline tartrate solution and 10 ml of hydrochloric acid, and heat to boiling. Small amounts of ferric iron are now reduced by adding 0.5 gram of sodium metabisulfite. Neutralize the solution to litmus with ammonium hydroxide and add 5 ml in excess. To repress any copper color that may be present and to reduce higher oxides, 3 ml of the 10% potassium cyanide solution is added. The mixture is heated until the solution becomes colorless. (If this does not happen, start over with a new sample.) Transfer the solution to a 100-ml Nessler tube and make up to 100 ml with distilled water. Add 4 drops of the 10% sodium sulfide solution and mix with a glass plunger to avoid vigorous agitation. (Remember that the tint depends to a large extent upon the size of the colloidal particles of lead. This in turn depends upon the nature of the salts in the solution and upon the manner in which the solution has been prepared. Vigorous agitation and salts of alkalis and alkaline earths tend to coagulate the colloidal sulfide.) The sample is immediately compared with standard samples prepared in the same manner.

To prepare standard samples to cover the range of 10 to 50 ppm lead, substitute 1 gram of reagent grade sulfuric acid for the sample and add to solutions containing 1, 3 and 5 ml of the standard lead solution. Treat in the same manner as the sample.

Calculations

$$\frac{(A)\ (B)\ (100)}{W} = \%\ Pb$$

Where:

A = ml of standard lead solution
B = 0.00001 grams Pb/ml
W = Weight of sample in grams

Example:

A = 3 ml
B = 0.00001 grams Pb/ml
W = 1.0 gram

$$\frac{(3)\ (0.00001)\ (100)}{1.0} = 0.0030\%\ Pb$$

Reproducibility

Duplicate determinations should agree within 0.0006% Pb.

Reference

W. W. Scott, *Scott's Standard Methods of Chemical Analysis*, 5th Ed., 1, 517–521, D. Van Nostrand Co., Inc. (1939).

Determination of Heavy Metals (as Pb) in Sulfuric Acid

Scope

This procedure is applicable to the determination of trace amounts of the heavy metals in sulfuric acid.

Theory

In the test for heavy metals, hydrogen sulfide is added to precipitate the heavy metal sulfides. The color thus imparted to the sample solution is compared to the color of a standard containing a known amount of lead, such as lead sulfide.

Special Apparatus

1. 2-ml measuring pipette (Mohr type).
2. 50-ml Nessler Color Comparison Tubes.

Reagents

1. Reagent grade sodium carbonate.
2. Reagent grade concentrated nitric acid.
3. Reagent grade acetic acid, 1N solution.
4. Phenolphthalein indicator, 1% solution.
5. Hydrogen sulfide water, saturated solution. (This solution must be freshly prepared.)
6. Standard lead nitrate solution, 0.01 mg Pb/ml.
7. Reagent grade sodium hydroxide, N/10 solution.

Procedure

Cautiously add 20 grams of the sample to 10 mg of sodium carbonate dissolved in a small amount of distilled water in a beaker. This size sample is suitable for the determination of 0.1 to 10 ppm of heavy metals in sulfuric acid. If the concentration varies above or below these limits, the size of the sample must be increased or decreased proportionally. Heat the solution over a low flame until nearly dry, then add 1 ml of concentrated nitric acid. Evaporate to dryness, add 20 ml of distilled water, and neutralize to phenolphthalein by adding N/10 sodium hydroxide drop by drop. Add 1 ml of 1N acetic acid and transfer the solution to a 50-ml Nessler tube, diluting to 40 ml with distilled water. Add 10 ml of hydrogen sulfide water and compare with standard sample prepared in the same manner.

To prepare the standard sample, substitute reagent grade sulfuric acid for the sample and treat in the above described manner. Add the standard lead solution, 1 ml at a time, to the solution in the Nessler tube until a balance in color has been attained.

Calculations

$$\frac{(A)\ (B)\ (100)}{W} = \%\ \text{Heavy Metals (as Pb)}$$

Where:
- A = ml of standard lead solution
- B = 0.00001 grams Pb/ml
- W = Weight of sample in grams

Example:
- A = 2 ml
- B = 0.00001 grams Pb/ml
- W = 20 grams

$$\frac{(2)\ (0.00001)\ (100)}{20} = 0.0001\%\ \text{Heavy Metals (such as Pb)}$$

Reproducibility

Duplicate determinations should agree within 0.00002%.

Reference

Reagent Chemicals, American Chemical Society Specifications, 369, American Chemical Society (1950).

Determination of Sulfur Dioxide in Sulfuric Acid

Scope

This method is applicable to the determination of sulfur dioxide in sulfuric acid in amounts larger than 25 ppm.

Theory

In the determination of sulfur dioxide, a known quantity of standard iodine is titrated with the sample of sulfuric acid to the starch indicator end-point.

Reagents

1. Standard iodine, N/10 solution.
2. Starch indicator solution.

Procedure

Add 1 ml of the standard N/10 iodine solution to 200 ml of distilled water in a beaker. Add 1 ml of starch solution and titrate with the sample of sulfuric acid until the blue color disappears at the end-point. (This titration should be conducted in an ice bath to suppress high temperatures caused by heat of dilution of sulfuric acid.)

Calculation

$$\frac{(A)\ (B)\ (100)}{(C)\ (D)} = \%\ SO_2$$

Where:

A = ml of standard iodine
B = (Normality) (molecular equivalent weight SO_2) =
  (0.1000) (0.03203)
C = ml of sulfuric acid
D = Specific gravity of sulfuric acid sample

Example:

A = 1.0 ml
B = (0.1000) (0.03203)
C = 12.4 ml
D = 1.835

$$\frac{(1.0)\ (0.1000)\ (0.03203)\ (100)}{(12.4)\ (1.835)} = 0.014\%\ SO_2$$

Reproducibility

Duplicate determinations should agree within 0.001% SO_2.

Reference

W. W. Scott, *Scott's Standard Methods of Chemical Analysis*, 5th Ed., 2, 2232, D. Van Nostrand Co., Inc. (1939).

Determination of Sulfur Dioxide in Sulfuric Acid (Alternate Method)

Scope

This method is used for determining small amounts of sulfur dioxide in sulfuric acid (up to 25 ppm).

Theory

The determination is based on the reaction between sulfur dioxide (or sulfurous acid) and potassium iodate-iodide solution. The equations for the reactions involved are:

$$KIO_3 + 5\,KI + 6\,HCl \rightarrow 6\,KCl + 3H_2O + 3\,I_2$$
$$3\,I_2 + 3\,H_2SO_3 + 3\,H_2O \rightarrow 3\,H_2SO_4 + 6\,HI$$

Limitations

Care must be exercised in setting the flow rate of stripping-air to avoid loss of sulfur dioxide. The precautions to be observed are described fully in the procedure below.

Special Apparatus

Required apparatus consists of a gas-washing bottle "A", which serves as a trap in the air line; a gas-washing bottle "B" (with fritted cylinder on the tip of the gas inlet line) which holds the sample; a titration vessel "C" which can be a 500-ml Erlenmeyer filtering flask; and a burette "D", which delivers, and measures, the KIO_3-KI solution. Air is blown through the sample to strip out the sulfur dioxide and carry it into the titration vessel, where it reacts with iodine liberated from the KIO_3. A fritted cylinder disperses the gas entering the titration vessel to insure intimate mixing, and a magnetic stirrer is used as a further aid in mixing. The burette tip is passed through a two-hole rubber stopper in the top of the flask, and the effluent air leaves through the sidearm of the flask. (See Fig. 56.)

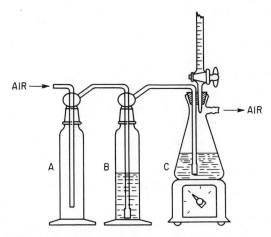

Fig. 56. Sulfur dioxide titration apparatus.

Reagents

1. Potassium iodate-iodide solution, 0.0156N (iodate reagent).
2. Starch solution, 1 gm./L.
3. Reagent grade hydrochloric acid.
4. Reagent grade sulfuric acid (SO_2-free).

Procedure

Weigh into bottle "B" an appropriate quantity of the acid to be analyzed. For sulfur dioxide content up to 5 ppm, use 500 grams; for 20–25 ppm, use 100 grams. If less than 500 grams of sample is used, add enough SO_2-free acid to make a total of about 500 grams. Into the titration vessel put 200–250 ml distilled water, 1–2 ml of starch solution, and 1–2 ml of concentrated HCl. Add enough iodate reagent to produce a faint blue color. This same color must be duplicated at the end-point of the titration. Start the stirrer and blow air through the sample and the titrating solution. The stripping-air should be started at a slow rate and increased as the sulfur dioxide is stripped from the sample. (A high initial flow rate of stripping-air and a relatively high sulfur dioxide content in the sample may result in overloading the titrating solution with sulfur dioxide, and some of the sulfur dioxide may escape without being titrated. A little experience will enable the analyst to determine the optimum stripping rate for each stage of the operation.) Add iodate reagent from the burette at such a rate as to maintain the blue starch-iodine color. Never let this color fade completely or some of the sulfur dioxide will pass through without being titrated. For quantities up to 5 ppm of sulfur dioxide, stripping is usually complete in about 15 minutes; for larger quantities, the time will be longer.

Calculations

$$\frac{(A) \ (B)}{W} = \text{ppm } SO_2$$

Where: A = ml of iodate reagent

B = (Normality of iodate reagent) x (meq. wt. of SO_2) x 10^6

W = Weight of sample in grams

Example:

A = 1.10 ml

B = 0.0156 x 0.03203 x 10^6 = 500

W = 550 grams

$$\frac{(1.10) \ (500)}{550} = 1.0 \text{ ppm } SO_2$$

Reproducibility

Duplicate determinations should agree within 0.2 ppm SO_2.

Determination of Carbon
in Sulfuric Acid

Scope

This method is suitable for the determination of the total carbon content of spent or sludge sulfuric acid (Fig. 57).

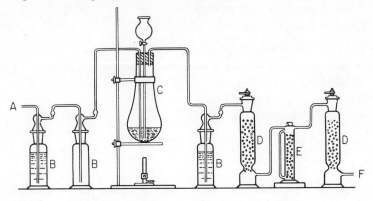

A–Air inlet.
B–Drechsel high-form gas-washing bottles.
C–Kjeldahl flask
D–Calcium Chloride absorption jars.
E–Nesbitt absorption bulb.
F–Outlet to vacuum.

Fig. 57. Carbon determination apparatus.

Theory

The wet combustion method is based upon the oxidation of carbon to carbon dioxide when the sulfuric acid to be tested is digested with a mixture of concentrated sulfuric acid and chromic acid. The carbon dioxide gas is absorbed in soda asbestos (Ascarite) or barium hydroxide solution. The increase in weight of the Ascarite is calculated as carbon dioxide. (If barium hydroxide is used, the excess is titrated with standard hydrochloric acid and the used portion is calculated as carbon dioxide.) This procedure is applicable to oxidation of free carbon, carbon combined in organic substances, and in certain instances to carbon combined with metals (where the substance may be decomposed by the action of the acid).

Special Apparatus

1. Drechsel high-form gas-washing bottles, 250-ml.
2. Kjeldahl flask, 500-ml.
3. Calcium chloride absorption jar.
4. Nesbitt absorption bulb, or
5. Milligan gas-washing bottles.

Reagents

1. Reagent grade chromium trioxide.
2. Reagent grade concentrated sulfuric acid.
3. Ascarite 8–20 mesh, or
4. Reagent grade barium hydroxide, 0.1 N solution.
5. Reagent grade potassium hydroxide, 30% solution.
6. Reagent grade calcium chloride.
7. Reagent grade hydrochloric acid, 0.1 N solution.
8. Phenolphthalein indicator, 1% solution.

Procedure

The first Drechsel bottle is filled with 30% potassium hydroxide solution to remove all carbon dioxide from the air drawn through the apparatus. The second Drechsel bottle is left empty and used as a safety trap. The third Drechsel bottle is filled with a saturated solution of chromium trioxide in concentrated sulfuric acid. This insures oxidation of all gases passing through the bottle. The calcium chloride jars are filled with calcium chloride to remove moisture from the air drawn through the apparatus. The Nesbitt absorption bulb is filled with Ascarite to absorb the carbon dioxide produced. (In case barium hydroxide is used as the carbon dioxide absorbent, 2 Milligan gas-washing bottles are substituted for the Nesbitt absorption bulb and are filled with exactly 50 ml of the 0.1N barium hydroxide solution with 1 ml of phenolphthalein indicator solution.)

Place 20 grams of chromium trioxide in the Kjeldahl flask. Aspirate air through the assembled apparatus slowly for at least 30 minutes. Disconnect the Nesbitt absorption bulb and weigh carefully for the initial weight. (If barium hydroxide is used, the Milligan bottles are connected at this time.) Connect the Nesbitt bulb again to the apparatus, close the stopper and draw a slow stream of air through the apparatus. All joints must be absolutely tight. The relative speed of bubbles passing through the potassium hydroxide bottle and the chromic acid bottle indicates whether the connections are tight or not. A weighed sample of the acid to be tested (1 to 3 grams) is washed into the Kjeldahl flask through a separatory funnel with reagent grade concentrated sulfuric acid, using 100 ml to wash out the separatory funnel. (Care must be taken when sample is washed into the flask to insure that no air is admitted.) Close the valve of the separatory funnel. Apply heat slowly with a Bunsen burner and boil gently (320°–360°F maximum) until chromium sulfate separates out and bumping commences. Turn off the burner and draw air through the system for an additional 5 minutes. Disconnect the Nesbitt bulb and weigh carefully. The increase in weight of the Nesbitt bulb is due to carbon dioxide. (If barium hydroxide is used, the excess is titrated with the 0.1N hydrochloric acid to the phenolphthalein end-point and the quantity of barium hydroxide consumed is calculated as carbon dioxide.)

A blank determination must be run on the reagents used. Substitute 100 ml of reagent grade concentrated sulfuric acid for the sample and acid-wash and follow the above described procedure.

Calculations

Using Ascarite as the absorbent:

$$\frac{(A - B)\ (C)\ (100)}{W} = \%\ \text{Carbon}$$

Where: A = Weight of carbon dioxide absorbed in grams
          B = Blank weight of carbon dioxide absorbed in grams
          C = Conversion factor of carbon dioxide to carbon ($12.01/44.01 = 0.2729$)
          W = Weight of sample in grams

Example:

$$A = 0.3694\ \text{grams}$$
$$B = 0.0033\ \text{grams}$$
$$C = 0.2729$$
$$W = 1.5745\ \text{grams}$$

$$\frac{(0.3694 - 0.0033)\ (0.2729)\ (100)}{1.5745} = 6.3\%\ \text{Carbon}$$

Using barium hydroxide as the absorbent:

$$\frac{(A - B - C)\ (D)\ (E)\ (100)}{W} = \%\ \text{Carbon}$$

Where: A = ml 0.1N barium hydroxide
                B = ml 0.1N hydrochloric acid
                C = ml blank determination
                D = Normality of barium hydroxide
                E = Molecular equivalent weight of carbon
                W = Weight of sample in grams

Example:

$$A = 100 \text{ ml}$$
$$B = 24.0 \text{ ml}$$
$$C = 1.2 \text{ ml}$$
$$D = 0.1000 \text{ normality}$$
$$E = 0.0060$$
$$W = 1.4212 \text{ grams}$$

$$\frac{(100 - 24.0 - 1.2)\,(0.1000)\,(0.0060)\,(100)}{1.4212} = 3.2\% \text{ Carbon}$$

Reproducibility

Duplicate determinations should agree within 0.1% carbon.

References

W. W. Scott, *Scott's Standard Methods of Chemical Analysis*, 5th Ed., 1, 226–228, D. Van Nostrand Co., Inc. (1939).

Chemical Plant Control Data, 6th Ed., 11–13, Chemical Construction Corporation, (1951).

N. A. Lange, *Handbook of Chemistry*, 6th Ed., 182–183, Handbook Publishers, Inc. (1946).

Determination of Free Water in Sulfuric Acid

Scope

This method is applicable to all grades of sludge and spent sulfuric acid.

Theory

This method is based upon the distillation of the sample with a water-immiscible volatile solvent. The water is collected as a distillate in a graduated tube.

Limitations

Alcohols interfere in this determination; consequently, the free water in sulfuric acid extracts of olefins may not be determined in this manner.

Precautions

Aniline has no appreciable local irritating action. It does have a dangerous systemic toxicity which may result from inhalation of vapors or from
absorption through the skin following contact with liquid material.
Aniline should be handled and used only in a hood.

Special Apparatus

1. Round-bottom flask, 500 ml., ℥ 24/40 joint.
2. Condenser, ℥ 24/40 joints.
3. ASTM graduated moisture trap with solvent return line, ℥ 24/40
   joints.

Reagents

1. Reagent grade toluene, anhydrous.
2. Reagent grade aniline, anhydrous.

Procedure

Weigh 15 to 20 grams of the acid sample into a clean, dry, round-bottom flask. Immerse the flask in an ice bath and add a mixture of 30 ml
of anhydrous aniline and 250 ml of anhydrous toluene. Mix well and
break up any lumps of aniline sulfate with a glass rod. Rinse any particles
adhering to the glass rod into the flask with anhydrous toluene. Warm
the flask up to room temperature and carefully dry the outside of the flask.
Connect the flask with a clean, dry water trap and reflux condenser. Heat
the flask with an electric hot plate or Glas-Col heating mantle and reflux
the contents for one hour at a rate of not more than two drops return
from drip tip per second. Record the volume of the condensed water at
room temperature.

Calculations

$$\frac{(A)\ (100)}{W} = \%\ \text{Free Water}$$

Where: A = ml of water condensate
            W = Weight of sample in grams

Example:

$A = 1.70\ \text{ml}$
$W = 18.60\ \text{grams}$
$$\frac{(1.70)\ (100)}{18.60} = 9.1\%\ \text{Free Water}$$

Reproducibility

Duplicate determinations should agree within 0.3% free water.

Reference

American Society for Testing Materials Standards, Part 5, 729, (1949).

Determination of Free Water
in Sulfuric Acid (Karl Fischer Method)

Scope

The Karl Fischer method for the determination of water is applicable to the determination of free water in sulfuric acid (Fig. 58).

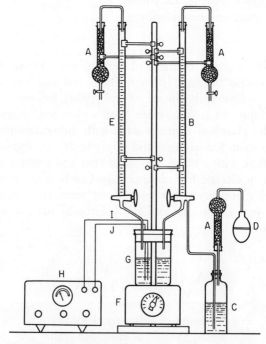

A—Drierite drying tube	F—Variable speed
B—50 ml. automatic burette	magnetic stirrer
C—Fischer reservoir bottle	G—Titration vessel
D—Rubber aspirator bulb	H—Beckman pH meter
E—50 ml. offset burette	I—Platinum electrode
	J—Platinum electrode

Fig. 58. Karl Fischer titration assembly.

Theory

The Karl Fischer reagent is a solution of iodine, sulfur dioxide and pyridine in methanol. Each of these components enters into the basic two-step reaction for water as illustrated below:

$$I_2 + SO_2 + 3C_6H_5N + H_2O \rightarrow 2\,C_6H_5NHI + C_6H_5NOSO_2$$
$$C_6H_5NOSO_2 + CH_3OH \rightarrow C_6H_5NHSO_4CH_3$$

Normally, sulfur dioxide, pyridine and methanol are present in excess; therefore, the strength of any preparation is dependent upon the iodine concentration. Pre-treatment of the sample with anhydrous ammonium chloride prevents decomposition of the Fischer reagent.

Usually, excess Fischer reagent is added to the sample after pre-treatment and the excess back-titrated with standard water in methanol. Detection of the end-point may be made visually, where there is no color interference from the sample, or electrometrically by using the dead stop end-point. The Fischer reagent method is highly specific for water and operates independently of the acidity of the sample.

Special Apparatus

1. Variable-speed magnetic stirrer with Teflon-covered stirring bar.
2. 50-ml burette, automatic.
3. 50-ml burette, offset.
4. Beckman pH meter or other suitable vacuum tube millivoltmeter.
5. Two platinum electrodes.
6. Karl Fischer type of titration cell.
7. Lunge weighing pipette.

Reagents

1. Reagent grade ammonium chloride, anhydrous.
2. Drierite, calcium sulfate, anhydrous, 8 mesh.
3. Reagent grade methyl alcohol, anhydrous.
4. Standard water-methanol solution, 5 ml H_2O/liter of methanol.
5. Standard Karl Fischer reagent. The Karl Fischer reagent must be standardized freshly before use because it is subject to parasitic side reactions which effect a gradual reduction in strength.

Procedure

Take a sufficient sample of the sulfuric acid to provide 0.04 — 0.1 grams of water. Quickly weigh the acid sample to the nearest milligram from a

Lunge weighing pipette into a clean, dry titrating flask. Stopper the flask. Add an excess of anhydrous ammonium chloride to the sample in the flask. (This should be done as quickly as possible and with sufficient care to prevent picking up moisture from the air.) Mix the ammonium chloride and acid with a dry flattened stirring rod and crush any soft lumps which form. Pipette 20 ml of anhydrous methanol into the flask, using anhydrous methanol to rinse the stirring rod. The ammonium chloride-sulfate mixture will not go into solution, but will remain as a finely divided solid which does not interfere with the titration if it is not allowed to cake at the bottom of the flask. Add 2 or 3 ml excess Fischer reagent. Place the flask upon the titration assembly and titrate the excess Fischer reagent with the standard water-in-methanol solution. Make a blank determination using 5 grams of ammonium chloride and 20 ml of anhydrous methanol.

If the sample is colored enough to interfere with visual determination of the end-point of the titration, the end-point may be determined potentiometrically. Past results indicate that the instrument used to detect the end-point of the water titration must be very sensitive and give a positive reaction for a change of only a few millivolts because the entire change is only 20 millivolts and time lag makes it imperative that the first part of the change be picked up by the detector. It has been demonstrated that current must not be drawn from the electrodes because of the probability of polarization. A vacuum tube millivoltmeter is strongly indicated. It need not indicate the extent of voltage change so long as it indicates the incidence of such change. The Beckman pH meter is thus suitable. It is used by attaching the electrode leads directly to the input terminals. Adjust the meter needle at the midpoint of the scale (for convenience only) when the electrodes are in the iodine solution before titration is started. Start the stirrer in the flask and run the standard water-in-methanol solution rapidly into the flask until the color changes from brown to orange. Fasten the key or adjust the selector switch to the correct range and continue the addition of the standard water-in-methanol drop by drop. Near the end-point, 10 seconds should be allowed between drops since the Karl Fischer reaction is inherently slow. When the titration is within about 1 ml of the end-point, the needle will show a very slight deflection to one side, then it will swing deliberately across the midpoint and off the scale. The titrating solution is cut off when this second deflection has just started and, if the end-point is true, the needle will continue across the scale. If the deflection is due to a temporary local concentration of titrating solution at the electrodes, the needle will return to its original position and more drops of solution must be added.

Calculations

$$\frac{(A - B - CD) \ (F) \ (100)}{W} = \% \ H_2O$$

Where: A = ml of Karl Fischer reagent
B = ml blank determination
C = ml of standard water-in-methanol used
D = ml of Karl Fischer reagent equivalent to 1 ml of standard water-in-methanol
F = Grams of H_2O equivalent to 1 ml of Karl Fischer reagent
W = Weight of sample in grams

Example:

A = 22.60 ml
B = 6.21 ml
C = 1.50 ml
D = 1.3021 ml Karl Fischer reagent/ml standard water-in-methanol
F = 0.00384 grams H_2O/ml Karl Fischer reagent
W = 1.2722 grams

$$\frac{(22.60 - 6.21 - 1.95) \ (0.00384) \ (100)}{1.2722} = 4.36\% \ H_2O$$

Reproducibility

Duplicate determinations should agree within 0.1% H_2O.

References

Almy, Griffin, and Wilcox, *Ind. Eng. Chem.*, Anal. Ed., *12*, 392, (1940).

Dicaprio, *Analytical Chemistry*, *19*, 1010, (1947).

Fischer, K., *Angew. Chem.*, *48*, 394, (1935).

W. H. Goff, W. S. Palmer, and R. F. Huhndorff, *Ind. Eng. Chem.*, Anal. Ed., *20*, 344, (1948).

C. D. McKinney, Jr., and R. T. Hall, *Ind. Eng. Chem.*, Anal. Ed., *15*, 460, (1943).

Mitchell, Kangas, and Seaman, *Analytical Chemistry*, 22, 484, (1950).

G. Wernimont and F. J. Hopkinson, *Ind. Eng. Chem.*, Anal. Ed. *15*, 272, (1943).

Determination of Foaming Characteristics
of Sulfuric Acid

Scope

This method may be used on all production grades of sulfuric acid.

Theory

This is an empirical test measuring concentration of emulsifying constituents present in sulfuric acid. By forming an emulsion of sulfuric acid and iso-octane and noting the time required for the emulsion to break, it may be determined whether the acid is likely to cause foaming problems in refinery alkylation process units.

Special Apparatus

1. Stoddard solvent and sulfonation bottle.
2. Stop-watch.

Reagent

1. Pure grade iso-octane.

Procedure

Pour the sample into the graduated sulfonation bottle to the 45-ml (the lower) mark. Add 10 ml of pure grade iso-octane to the measured sample. Stopper the bottle and shake vigorously for 15 seconds and allow to stand. A total of 95% of the emulsion formed should break within 6 minutes. Duplicate determinations should be made.

Reproducibility

Duplicate determinations should agree within one minute.

Determination of Color
in Sulfuric Acid

Scope

This method is used by the American Public Health Association for determining color in water. The color of the standards is similar to the yellow color which sometimes appears in clear sulfuric acid; therefore, a comparison can be made.

Theory

A series of solutions containing measured amounts of potassium chloroplatinate, K_2PtCl_6, and cobaltous chloride hydrate, $CoCl_2 \cdot 6H_2O$, in dilute hydrochloric acid, are used as standards for measuring the amount of color in sulfuric acid. The numbers assigned to the various standards correspond to the ppm of platinum present in the standards.

Limitations

This test is applicable only to the yellow color of the acid. Other colors which may occur in rare instances are not measurable by these standards, and suspended matter of any kind will interfere with the accurate determination of the color.

Special Apparatus

1. Nessler Color Comparison tubes, 100-ml, tall form, with ground glass caps. These are used for permanent storage of standards.
2. Nessler Color Comparison tubes, 100-ml, tall form.
3. Support for Nessler tube.

Reagents

1. Stock solution of color standard: Dissolve 1.245 gram potassium chloroplatinate and 1 gram cobaltous chloride in 200 ml of distilled water and 100 ml of concentrated reagent grade hydrochloric acid; dilute to 1 liter with distilled water. This stock solution contains 0.500 gram of platinum and 0.250 gram of cobalt, and has a color of 500 units.

2. Working color standards: Dilute the stock solution with distilled water in Nessler tubes as follows:

To make color "10", dilute 2 ml stock solution to 100 ml
To make color "20", dilute 4 ml stock solution to 100 ml
To make color "30", dilute 6 ml stock solution to 100 ml etc.

The color is quite stable and these standards can be stored indefinitely in Nessler tubes with ground glass caps.

Procedure

The sample is compared with an equal volume of color standards in Nessler tubes, and is reported to have the color value of the standard which matches it.

Reproducibility

Duplicate determinations should agree within 5 units of color.

References

Standard Methods for the Examination of Water, Sewage, and Industrial Waters, 10th Ed., A.P.H.A. New York, N.Y.

Preparation of Indicators

Alphazurine

Dissolve 0.45 gram methyl red sodium salt (Eastman Organic No. 1462) and 0.55 gram alphazurine (National Aniline No. 205) in 1 liter of distilled water.

Bromcresol Green

This indicator solution may be purchased from a laboratory supply company, ready for use.

Methyl Orange, 0.1% Solution

Dissolve 1 gram of methyl orange powder in distilled water and dilute to 1 liter.

Methyl Purple Solution

This indicator is purchased in solution, ready for use.

Methyl Red, 0.1% Solution

A. Dissolve 0.1 gram of methyl red powder in 60 ml of ethyl or isopropyl alcohol and dilute to 100 ml with distilled water.

B. Dissolve 0.1 gram of methyl red sodium salt in distilled water and dilute to 100 ml.

Phenolphthalein, 1% Solution

Dissolve 1 gram of phenolphthalein powder in 50 ml of ethyl or isopropyl alcohol and dilute to 100 ml with distilled water.

Potassium Chromate, 10%

Dissolve 100 grams of potassium chromate, K_2CrO_4, in a small amount of distilled water and add a drop or two of silver nitrate solution. Filter out any precipitate that forms and dilute the filtrate to 1000 ml.

Starch Solution

Triturate 2.5 grams of soluble starch with a little cold water to make a thin paste; add this paste slowly, with constant stirring, to 1 liter of boiling distilled water.

THQ

This is a powdered mixture which is purchased from laboratory supply houses ready for use.

Tropaolin

Dissolve 0.0018 gm. of tropaolin 00 (Orange IV) in 100 ml. of distilled water. This substance is slow to dissolve and will take hours of stirring.

Preparation and Standardization of Standard Iron Solution (Iron Wire)

Scope

This solution serves as a standard for comparison with samples being analyzed for iron content by the colorimetric comparison of the ferric-thiocyanate complex.

Reagents

1. Primary standard grade iron wire.

2. Reagent grade concentrated hydrochloric acid.

3. Reagent grade concentrated nitric acid.

Procedure

Dissolve 1.0000 gram of primary standard grade iron wire in 50 ml of concentrated hydrochloric acid and 10 ml of concentrated nitric acid and dilute to 1 liter in a volumetric flask, mixing thoroughly. This may be retained as a stock solution, (0.001 grams Fe/ml). Dilute 100 ml of the stock solution to 1 liter in a volumetric flask, mixing thoroughly. This will provide a standard iron solution equivalent to 0.0001 grams Fe per ml.

References

W. W. Scott, *Scott's Standard Methods of Chemical Analysis*, 5th Ed., I, 486, D. Van Nostrand Co., Inc. (1939).

Snell & Snell, *Colorimetric Methods of Analysis*, 3rd. Ed., II, 306–310, D. Van Nostrand Co., Inc. (1949).

Preparation and Standardization of Standard Iron Solution (Ferrous Ammonium Sulfate)

Scope

This solution serves as a standard for comparison with samples being analyzed for iron content by the colorimetric comparison of the ferric-thiocyanate complex.

Reagents

1. Reagent grade ferrous ammonium sulfate.
2. Reagent grade sulfuric acid, dilute, 1:1 solution.
3. Reagent grade potassium permanganate, 0.1% solution.
4. Reagent grade ammonium hydroxide.

Procedure

Dissolve 7.022 grams of reagent grade ferrous ammonium sulfate, $FeSO_4 \cdot (NH_4)_2SO_4 \cdot 6H_2O$, in 100 ml of distilled water and add 10 ml of dilute (1:1) sulfuric acid. Warm and add 0.1% potassium permanganate dropwise until a faint pink color remains in the solution. Cool and dilute to 1000 ml. This solution contains 0.001 gram of iron per ml. A 100-ml aliquot of this solution may be diluted to 1 liter to give a solution containing 0.0001 grams of Fe per ml.

References

W. W. Scott, *Scott's Standard Methods of Chemical Analysis*, 5th Ed., I, 486, D. Van Nostrand Co., Inc. (1939).

F. D. Snell and C. T. Snell, *Colorimetric Methods of Analysis*, 3rd Ed., II, 306, 310, D. Van Nostrand Co., Inc. (1949).

Preparation and Standardization of
N/10 Potassium Permanganate Solution

Scope

This is a standard oxidizing agent of rather wide use because of its oxidizing power. It is used to oxidize ferrous iron to ferric iron in the tests for iron in hydrochloric and sulfuric acids. It may also be used for the titration of many oxidizable substances, such as arsenic (As^{+++}) and lead (Pb^+); also for nitrites, oxalates, and others.

Reagents

1. Reagent grade potassium permanganate.
2. Reagent grade sodium oxalate.
3. Reagent grade sulfuric acid, dilute, 20:1 solution.

Procedure

Dissolve in distilled water 3.25 grams of potassium permanganate for each liter of N/10 solution desired, and dilute to final volume with distilled water. Let stand for at least 12 hours and then filter through asbestos to remove manganese dioxide and any other sediment which may have formed. The solution should be kept in a bottle of dark–colored glass, or in one which has been painted with an opaque paint, to shield the solution from the action of light.

The National Bureau of Standards recommends standardization against sodium oxalate by the following procedure:

Weigh accurately about 0.3 grams of reagent grade sodium oxalate which has been dried at 105°C. for 1 hour. Transfer to a 600-ml beaker and add 250 ml of dilute sulfuric acid which has been boiled for 10–15 minutes and cooled to room temperature. Stir until the oxalate is dissolved, then add 39–40 ml of potassium permanganate at a rate of 25–35 ml per minute while stirring slowly. Let the solution stand until the pink color disappears, then heat to 55–60°C. and complete the titration by adding the potassium permanganate until a faint pink color persists for 30 seconds. Add the last 0.5–1.0 ml dropwise, with particular care to allow each drop to become decolorized before adding the next one.

Determine the excess of permanganate required to impart a pink color to the solution. This can be done by matching the color obtained by adding potassium permanganate to the same volume of the diluted sulfuric acid at 55–60°C. This correction usually amounts to 0.03–0.05 ml.

Calculations

$$\frac{W}{(M)\ (P)} = \text{Normality of potassium permanganate.}$$

Where: W = Weight in grams of sodium oxalate
          M = Meq. wt. of sodium oxalate
          P = ml of potassium permanganate

Example:

          W = 0.3052 grams
          M = 0.067
          P = 45.50 ml

$$\frac{(0.3052)}{(0.067)\ (45.50)} = 0.1001 \text{ Normality of potassium permanganate}$$

References

W. W. Scott, Scott's Standard Methods of Chemical Analysis, 5th Ed., I, 1209–1210, D. Van Nostrand Co., Inc. (1939).

Hillebrand, Lundell, Bright, and Hoffman, Applied Inorganic Analysis, 2nd Ed., 185–187, John Wiley and Sons, Inc. (1953).

Preparation of Standard N/10
Potassium Dichromate Solution

Theory

This is a primary standard which may be made up by weighing out the exact amount needed for the volume of reagent desired. This is a very stable solution and should retain its strength indefinitely unless exposed to the atmosphere enough to allow evaporation of water from the solution, or contamination by vapors (SO_2, etc.). It is used for standardizing reducing agents, such as sodium thiosulfate, by direct titration; or standardizing other oxidizing agents (iodine, potassium permanganate) indirectly by titration with reducing agents which have been standardized against the potassium dichromate. It may also be used for quantitative titration of certain oxidizable materials such as ferrous iron.

Reagents

1. Primary standard grade potassium dichromate.

Procedure

Dissolve exactly 4.9035 grams of potassium dichromate, previously dried at 110°C. for 2 hours, in freshly boiled and cooled distilled water. Dilute to exactly 1000 ml in a 1000-ml volumetric flask.

Reference

W. W. Scott, *Scott's Standard Methods of Chemical Analysis*, 5th Ed., I, 1208, D. Van Nostrand Co., Inc. (1939).

Preparation and Standardization of
N/10 Iodine Solution

Scope

This solution is used for the determination of the sulfur dioxide content of mineral acids, and is also used to determine the sulfur dioxide content of process gas streams.

Reagents

1. Reagent grade iodine.

2. Reagent grade potassium iodide.

3. Standard N/10 sodium thiosulfate solution.

4. Starch indicator solution.

Procedure

Weigh 12.7 grams of reagent grade iodine for each liter of N/10 solution desired. Dissolve 20 grams of potassium iodide per liter of solution desired in as little distilled water as possible; then add the iodine. Stir until the iodine is completely dissolved, then dilute to final volume with distilled water.

Standardize this solution by titration with standard N/10 sodium thiosulfate solution as follows:

Measure 50 ml of iodine solution with a volumetric pipette into a 250-ml iodine flask containing 100 ml of distilled water and titrate with sodium thiosulfate solution to a faint yellow color. Add 1 ml of starch solution and continue the titration until the deep blue color just disappears. (NOTE: The iodine should be kept in a dark glass bottle, or one which has been painted with an opaque paint, to protect the solution from the action of light. If the solution is thus protected and kept from contact with cork or rubber, and dust is not allowed to enter the bottle, the strength should remain constant for two months or longer. If conditions of use vary from these, experience will indicate the intervals at which the solution should be restandardized.)

Calculations

$$\frac{(V)\ (N)}{M} = \text{Normality of iodine}$$

Where: V = ml of standard sodium thiosulfate
             N = Normality of standard sodium thiosulfate
             M = ml of iodine

Example:

$V = 49.88$ ml
$N = 0.1004$
$M = 50.00$ ml

$$\frac{(49.88)\,(0.1004)}{50.00} = 0.1002\ N$$

References

W. W. Scott, *Scott's Standard Methods of Chemical Analysis*, 5th Ed., I, 1207, D. Van Nostrand Co., Inc. (1939).

Hillebrand, Lundell, Bright, and Hoffman, *Applied Inorganic Analysis*, 2nd Ed., 193–195, John Wiley and Sons, Inc. (1953).

Preparation and Standardization of N/10
Sodium Thiosulfate Solution

Scope

This is a reducing agent generally used in iodometric titrations.

Reagents

1. Reagent grade sodium thiosulfate, $Na_2S_2O_3 \cdot 5H_2O$.

2. Standard potassium dichromate, N/10 solution.

3. Reagent grade potassium iodide.

4. Reagent grade hydrochloric acid, dilute, 1:1 solution.

5. Starch indicator solution.

Procedure

Weigh 25 grams of reagent grade sodium thiosulfate for each liter of solution desired. Dissolve in freshly boiled hot distilled water. Cool to room temperature and dilute to volume with freshly boiled distilled water in a volumetric flask. The solution should be allowed to stand for a week or two and then filtered or decanted to remove precipitated sulfur before standardization and use. Also, the solution should be standardized at intervals of 2 or 3 weeks, since it tends to deteriorate slowly on standing.

This solution may be standardized with any of several oxidizing agents, but it is preferable to use a primary standard such as potassium dichromate or potassium iodate. For either of these standards measure an appropriate volume of N/10 solution into distilled water in an iodine flask containing 2 to 3 grams potassium iodide and 10 ml dilute hydrochloric acid per 200 ml of solution. (NOTE: The acid solution should be freed of dissolved air by previous boiling or by stripping with carbon dioxide.) For the standardization of sodium thiosulfate with potassium dichromate, the solution being titrated should have a volume of at least 150 to 200 ml in order to secure as much contrast as possible between the blue of the starch-iodine complex and the green of the trivalent chromium resulting from reduction of potassium dichromate. Store in a dark place for 5 to 10 minutes to allow complete liberation of iodine, then titrate with sodium thiosulfate to a yellow-brown. Add starch indicator solution and proceed with the titration until a deep blue solution is obtained. From this point add sodium thiosulfate solution dropwise, mixing well after each drop, until the deep blue fades to a light green. This is the end point.

Calculations

$$\frac{(V)(N)}{M} = \text{Normality of Na}_2\text{S}_2\text{O}_3$$

Where: $V = $ ml of potassium dichromate
$N = $ Normality of potassium dichromate
$M = $ ml of sodium thiosulfate

Example:

$V = 150.00$ ml
$N = 0.1000$
$M = 149.10$ ml

$$\frac{(150.00)(0.1000)}{149.10} = 0.1006 \text{ N}$$

References

W. W. Scott, *Scott's Standard Methods of Chemical Analysis*, 5th Ed., I, 452–453, D. Van Nostrand Co., Inc. (1939).

Hillebrand, Lundell, Bright, and Hoffman, *Applied Inorganic Analysis*, 2nd Ed., 196–198, John Wiley & Sons, Inc. (1953).

Preparation and Standardization of N/10 Hydrochloric Acid

Scope

This is a useful general reagent for alkalimetry, especially for titrations where the presence of sulfates is undesirable for any reason.

Reagents

1. Reagent grade concentrated hydrochloric acid.
2. Standard N/10 sodium hydroxide.
3. Phenolphthalein indicator solution.

Procedure

Pipette 9 ml of reagent grade concentrated hydrochloric acid into a 1000-ml volumetric flask and dilute to volume with distilled water.

This solution may be standardized by titration with standard sodium hydroxide. Measure 50 ml of hydrochloric acid solution into a beaker with burette or volumetric pipette and titrate with standard N/10 sodium hydroxide using phenolphthalein indicator.

Calculations

$$\frac{(V)(N)}{M} = \text{Normality of hydrochloric acid}$$

Where: V = ml of standard sodium hydroxide
N = Normality of standard sodium hydroxide
M = ml of hydrochloric acid

Example:

V = 49.95 ml
N = 0.1001
M = 50.00 ml

$$\frac{(49.95)(0.1001)}{50.00} = 0.1000 \text{ N}$$

Reference

Hillebrand, Lundell, Bright, and Hoffman, *Applied Inorganic Analysis,* 2nd Ed., 174–176, John Wiley and Sons, Inc. (1953).

Preparation and Standardization of N/10 Barium Hydroxide Solution

Scope

This solution is used for the quantitative absorption of carbon dioxide in the determination of carbon in sulfuric acid.

Reagents

1. Reagent grade barium hydroxide.
2. Standard N/10 hydrochloric acid.
3. Phenolphthalein indicator solution.

Procedure

Dissolve about 20 grams of $Ba(OH)_2 \cdot 8H_2O$ (reagent grade barium hydroxide), in distilled water and dilute to 1000 ml. Let stand for 2 days, until the barium carbonate residue has completely settled, and carefully siphon out the clear supernatant liquid into a bottle which has been flushed out with carbon dioxide-free air for 2 hours.

Standardize by titration with standard hydrochloric acid as follows:

Measure 40–45 ml of N/10 hydrochloric acid into a beaker from a burette. Pipette 50 ml of the barium hydroxide solution into the acid, holding the tip of the pipette near the surface of the liquid so that there is as little exposure of the barium hydroxide to the atmosphere as possible. Add 1 ml. of phenolphthalein indicator solution and complete the titration with the hydrochloric acid from the burette, to the disappearance of the pink color.

The barium hydroxide solution is standardized against hydrochloric acid because its intended use involves titration with standard hydrochloric acid. The solution should be standardized immediately before use because of its susceptibility to contamination by atmospheric carbon dioxide. Also, if the solution is to be used for another purpose, it should be standardized against a standard sample of the material to be analyzed. For example, before using it to analyze a sulfate sample, it should be standardized against standard sulfuric acid.

Calculations

$$\frac{(V)(N)}{M} = \text{Normality of barium hydroxide}$$

Where: $V = $ ml of standard hydrochloric acid
$N = $ Normality of standard hydrochloric acid
$M = $ ml of barium hydroxide

Example:

$V = 49.90 \, \text{ml}$
$N = 0.1001$
$M = 50.00 \, \text{ml}$

$$\frac{(49.90)(0.1001)}{50.00} = 0.0999 \, \text{N}$$

References

Treadwell and Hall, *Analytical Chemistry*, 9th Ed., II, 491, John Wiley and Sons, Inc. (1942).

Preparation of Standard Sodium Chloride Solution

Scope

This solution is used as a primary standard for standardizing silver nitrate solutions. The silver nitrate solutions so standardized are used to titrate chlorides in water analyses, and are made up so that 1 ml silver nitrate solution is equivalent to (will precipitate) 1 mg of chloride. The sodium chloride solution is made up to contain 1 mg of chloride per ml so that the two solutions are equivalent, volume for volume.

Reagents

1. Primary standard grade sodium chloride.

Procedure

Dissolve 1.6489 grams of dry sodium chloride in distilled water and dilute to 1000 ml. This solution contains 1 mg Cl per ml. (NOTE: This solution is very stable and will keep indefinitely.)

References

W. W. Scott, *Scott's Standard Methods of Chemical Analysis*, 5th Ed., II, 2094, D. Van Nostrand Co., Inc. (1939).

Preparation of Standard Nitrate Solution

Scope

This solution is used as a standard source of nitrate nitrogen in the determination of nitrates in sulfuric acid.

Reagents

1. Reagent grade potassium nitrate.

Procedure

Dissolve 0.1631 grams of dried reagent grade potassium nitrate in distilled water and dilute to 1000 ml. This will provide a stock solution containing 0.1 mg of nitrate per ml. To prepare the standard solution for use, dilute 10 ml of the stock solution to 100 ml with distilled water. This solution contains 0.01 mg nitrate per ml.

References

F. D. Snell and C. T. Snell, *Colorimetric Methods of Analysis*, 3rd. Ed., II, 792, D. Van Nostrand Co., Inc. (1949).

Preparation and Standardization of Standard Lead Solution for Determination of Lead

Scope

This solution is used as a standard in the determination of lead in mineral acids.

Reagents

1. Reagent grade lead acetate.
2. Reagent grade concentrated nitric acid.

Procedure

Dry a portion of lead acetate at 110°C. to constant weight to remove the water of crystallization. Dissolve 0.1569 grams of the anhydrous salt in 100 ml of distilled water to which 1 ml of concentrated nitric acid has been added, and dilute to 1 liter in a volumetric flask. This will provide a stock solution containing 0.10 mg Pb per ml. (NOTE: The solution should be prepared and stored in containers free from lead. Its strength should be checked every few months to learn if the lead content has changed by reaction with the container.)

To prepare the standard lead solution (0.01 mg Pb per ml), dilute 10 ml of the lead stock solution to 100 ml with distilled water in a volumetric flask. This solution must be freshly prepared.

References

W. W. Scott, *Scott's Standard Methods of Chemical Analysis*, 5th Ed., I, 518, D. Van Nostrand Co., Inc. (1939).

Snell & Snell, *Colorimetric Methods of Analysis*, 3rd Ed., II, 34–35, D. Van Nostrand Co., Inc. (1949).

Preparation and Standardization of Standard Lead Solution for Determination of Heavy Metals

Scope

This solution is used as a standard in the determination of heavy metals (as Pb) in mineral acids.

Reagents

1. Reagent grade lead nitrate.
2. Reagent grade concentrated nitric acid.

Procedure

Dissolve 0.1600 grams of reagent grade lead nitrate in 100 ml of distilled water to which 1 ml of concentrated nitric acid has been added, and dilute to 1 liter in a volumetric flask. This will provide a stock solution containing 0.10 mg Pb per ml (NOTE: The solution should be prepared and stored in containers free from lead. Its strength should be checked every few months to learn if the lead content has changed by reaction with the container.)

To prepare the standard lead solution (0.01 mg Pb per ml) dilute 10 ml of the stock lead solution to 100 ml with distilled water in a volumetric flask. This solution must be freshly prepared.

References

W. W. Scott, *Scott's Standard Methods of Chemical Analysis*, 5th Ed., I, 518, D. Van Nostrand Co., Inc. (1939).

Snell and Snell, *Colorimetric Methods of Analysis*, 3rd. Ed., II, 34–35, D. Van Nostrand Co., Inc. (1949).

Preparation of Reagents for Arsenic Determination

Scope

These reagents are used in the determination of arsenic in mineral acids by the Gutzeit method.

Procedure

1. Standard Arsenic Solution:
   Dissolve 1.0000 gm of primary, standard–grade, resublimed arsenious oxide, As_2O_3, in 25 ml of arsenic-free 20% sodium hydroxide. Neutralize with dilute sulfuric acid. Dilute to 1000 ml with distilled water to which has been added 10 ml of concentrated sulfuric acid. Dilute 10 ml of this solution to 1000 ml with distilled water to which has been added 10 ml of concentrated sulfuric acid. Finally, dilute 100 ml of the latter solution to 1000 ml with distilled water containing 10 ml of concentrated sulfuric acid. This final solution contains 0.001 mg/ml of arsenious oxide, As_2O_3.

2. Reagent grade lead acetate, 1% solution:
   Dissolve 1 gm of lead acetate in 99 ml of distilled water and add enough glacial acetic acid to clear the solution.

3. Lead acetate paper:
   Cut strips of filter paper of the proper size and saturate them with the 1% lead acetate solution. Spread on sheets of paper to dry.

4. Reagent grade mercuric chloride (or mercuric bromide), 5% solution:
   Dissolve 5 gm of mercuric chloride (or bromide) in 100 ml of ethyl (or methyl) alcohol.

5. Mercuric chloride (or bromide) paper strips:
   Sheets of pre-cut paper strips are commercially available. The Han-ford-Pratt Company manufactures Improved Form Arsenic Strips (unsensitized) for the determination of arsenic by the A.O.A.C. method. These strips are produced in sheets of 32 strips (2.5 mm by 9 cm) and have been devised to insure maximum uniformity and convenience in handling. To sensitize these strips, place a sheet (loosely folded longitudinally) in a 100-ml graduated cylinder filled with the mercuric chloride (bromide) solution and let stand for 1 hour. Remove the sheet from the solution and, holding it by the ends, wave rapidly in the air until almost dry. (Do not suspend for drying). Place between clean sheets of paper under pressure (as in a book) for straightening. Finally, cut the sheet in two across the center guide marks. Free ends are now all from the same area on the sheet and are uniformly impregnated, so use these ends for the deposition of the stain. Because the stain varies with the age of impregnation, it is essential to prepare the sensitized strips immediately before using. Do not use later than two hours after preparation.

6. Reagent grade stannous chloride, 45% solution:
   Dissolve 40 gm of stannous chloride in 50 ml of distilled water containing 2.5 ml of concentrated arsenic-free hydrochloric acid.

7. Reagent grade ferric oxide:
   Dissolve 84 gm of $Fe(NH_4)(SO_4)_2 \cdot 12H_2O$ (ferric ammonium sulfate), in distilled water which contains 10 ml of "mixed acid," and make up to 1000 ml. Ten ml of this solution is equivalent to 0.5 gram Fe_2O_3.
   The "mixed acid" is made as follows: One volume of arsenic-free concentrated H_2SO_4 is diluted with four volumes of distilled water, and to this are added 10 gm of NaCl per 100 ml of solution.

References

W. W. Scott, *Scott's Standard Methods of Chemical Analysis*, 5th Ed., I, 102–104, D. Van Nostrand Co., Inc. (1939).

Preparation of Standard Ammonium Chloride Solution

Scope

This solution is a standard source of nitrogen in the form of ammonia. It is used as a standard in the determination of ammonia in sulfuric and hydrochloric acids.

Reagents

1. Reagent grade ammonium chloride.

Procedure

Dissolve 3.820 grams of reagent grade ammonium chloride in 1000 ml of ammonia-free distilled water and dilute 10 ml of this solution to 1000 ml with ammonia-free distilled water. The final solution contains 0.01 mg/ml of nitrogen, or 0.012 mg/ml of ammonia.

References

W. W. Scott, *Scott's Standard Methods of Chemical Analysis*, 5th Ed., II, 2049, D. Van Nostrand Co., Inc. (1939).

Snell & Snell, *Colorimetric Methods of Analysis*, 3rd. Ed., II, 814, D. Van Nostrand Co., Inc. (1949).

Preparation of Nessler's Reagent Solution

Scope

This solution is used in the determination of ammonia in mineral acids, and ammonia in water. It may also be used to determine certain forms of organic nitrogen.

Reagents

1. Reagent grade potassium iodide.
2. Reagent grade mercuric chloride, saturated solution.
3. Reagent grade potassium hydroxide, 50% solution.

Procedure

Dissolve 50 grams of reagent grade potassium iodide in about 35 ml of cold ammonia-free distilled water. Add a saturated solution of reagent grade mercuric chloride until a slight permanent precipitate forms, then add 400 ml of a clear 50% solution of potassium hydroxide. Dilute to 1000 ml, let stand until clear, and decant the clear solution. Store in a stoppered bottle out of the light.

The solution as prepared above is very stable, if protected from contamination, and can be used indefinitely. This reagent should give a color with 0.001 mg of ammonia in 50 ml of water within 5 minutes after addition, and should not give a precipitate with a reasonable amount of ammonia within 2 hours.

References

W. W. Scott, *Scott's Standard Methods of Chemical Analysis*, 5th Ed., II, 2049, D. Van Nostrand Co. (1939).

Hillebrand, Lundell, Bright, and Hoffman, *Applied Inorganic Analysis*, 2nd Ed., 790, John Wiley & Sons, Inc. (1953).

F. D. Snell and C. T. Snell, *Colorimetric Methods of Analysis*, 3rd Ed. II, 815, D. Van Nostrand Co., Inc. (1949).

Snell and Biffen, *Commercial Methods of Analysis*, 1st Ed., 720, Mc-Graw-Hill Book Co., Inc. (1944).

Preparation of Gum Arabic Solution

Scope

This is a protective colloid used with Nessler's reagent in the determination of ammonia in sulfuric acid. Its function is to prevent precipitation of the colored suspension formed when Nessler's reagent reacts with ammonia.

Reagents

1. Powdered gum arabic.

2. Permutit powder.

Procedure

With vigorous stirring, add 10 grams of powdered gum arabic to 190 ml of distilled water. Continue stirring until dispersion is complete. Transfer the mixture to a flask and add 4 grams of Permutit powder. Shake at intervals for 10 minutes and allow to settle. Decant 10 ml of the cloudy supernatant liquid, dilute to 50 ml, and add 5 ml of Nessler's reagent. If more than a very faint color develops repeat the treatments with Permutit powder until further additions have no more effect in reducing the ammonia concentration. Remove the remaining reducing impurities by treating the solution with one-tenth its volume of Nessler's reagent, allow to stand and decant when ready to use.

References

F. D. Snell and C. T. Snell, *Colorimetric Methods of Analysis*, 3rd. Ed., II, 816, D. Van Nostrand Co., Inc. (1949).

Preparation and Standardization of
Standard Silver Nitrate Solution

Scope

This solution is used for titration of chlorides by the Mohr method. It can be used to determine chlorides in plant water supplies and boiler waters, and for acid or alkaline solutions containing small amounts of chloride if these are made neutral before titration.

Reagents

1. Reagent grade silver nitrate.
2. Reagent grade potassium chromate, 10% solution.
3. Standard chloride solution, 0.001 gm Cl per ml.

Procedure

Dissolve 4.9 gm of reagent grade silver nitrate in distilled water and make up to 1000 ml. This solution will titrate approximately 1 mg Cl per ml of solution.

Standardize against the standard chloride solution (0.001 gm Cl/ml) and calculate the dilution necessary to make the silver nitrate solution exactly equivalent to 1 mg Cl per ml. For example, if 10.00 ml of silver nitrate solution titrates 10.42 ml of standard chloride solution, then dilute 100 ml of silver nitrate solution to 104.2 ml. It will then be exactly equivalent to 0.001 gm Cl per ml.

References

Betz Handbook of Industrial Water Conditioning, 5th Ed., 225, Betz Laboratories (1957).

FLOW SHEETS

OF PROCESSES

USING SULFURIC ACID

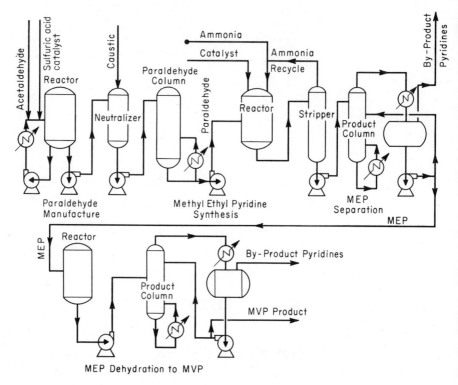

Methyl Vinyl Pyridine: Sulfuric acid assists the trimerization of acetaldehyde to paraldehyde. (*Hydrocarbon Processing and Petroleum Refiner, December 1955, Copyright Gulf Publishing Company.*)

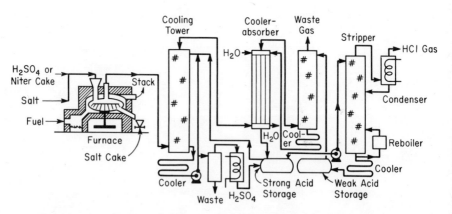

Hydrochloric Acid: Salt and sulfuric acid are mixed and heated in a rotary furnace. (*Faith, Keyes and Clark, "Industrial Chemicals", Copyright John Wiley & Sons.*)

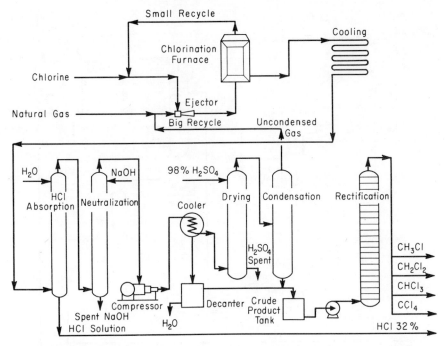

Chloromethanes: Sulfuric acid removes water vapor from the gaseous product steam. (*Hydrocarbon Processing and Petroleum Refiner, Nov. 1961, Copyright Gulf Publishing Company.*)

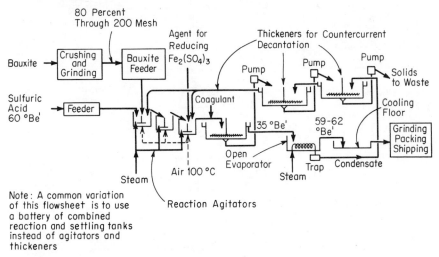

Aluminum Sulfate: Sulfuric acid reacts with bauxite to form aluminum sulfate in the Dorr process. (*Faith, Keyes and Clarke, "Industrial Chemicals", Copyright John Wiley & Sons.*)

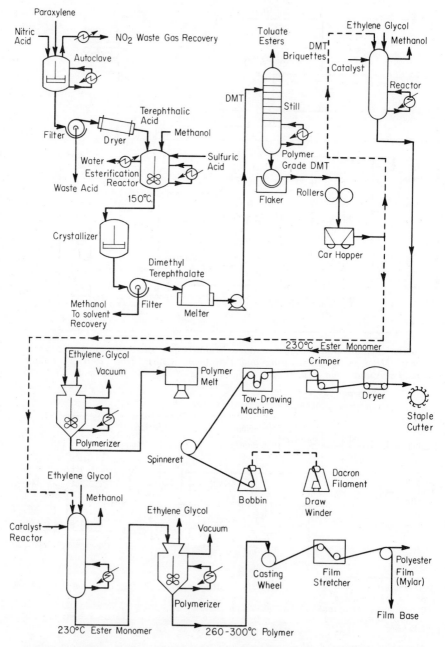

Dacron: Sulfuric acid catalyzes the esterification of terephthalic acid and methanol. (*Chemical Engineering, March 1963, Copyright McGraw-Hill, Inc.*)

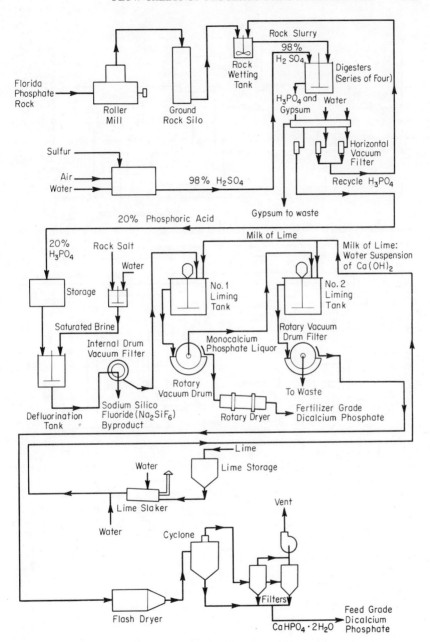

Dicalcium Phosphate: Sulfuric acid digests ground phosphate rock to produce phosphoric acid and gypsum. (*Chemical Engineering, Nov. 1955, Copyright McGraw-Hill, Inc.*)

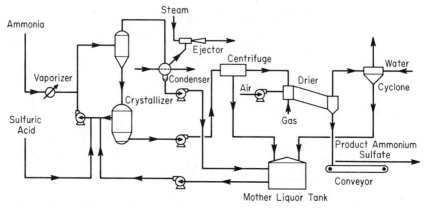

Ammonium Sulfate: Sulfuric acid reacts with ammonia vapor in the Fluor process. (*Hydrocarbon Processing and Petroleum Refiner, Nov. 1959, Copyright Gulf Publishing Company.*)

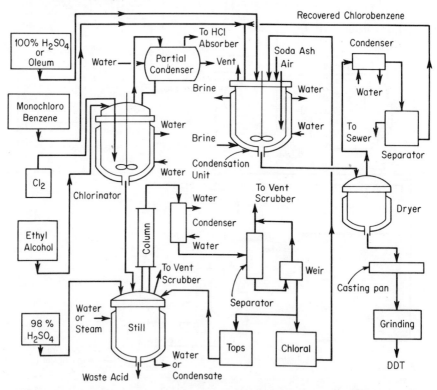

DDT: Strong sulfuric acid decomposes the intermediate product, chloral-alcoholate. Oleum promotes condensation of the chloral and chlorobenzene to form DDT. (*R. Norris Shreve, "Chemical Process Industries", Copyright 1956 McGraw-Hill Book Company.*)

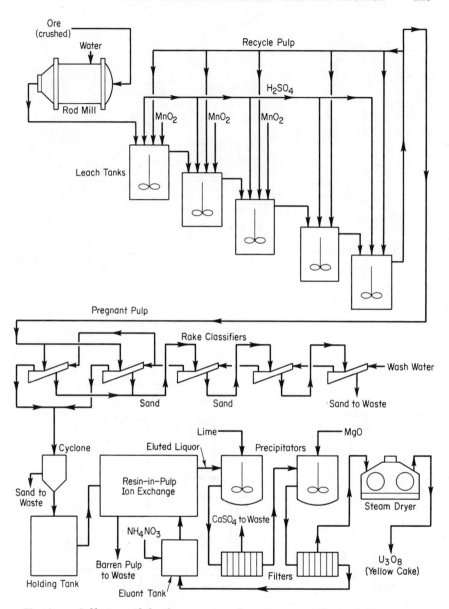

Uranium: Sulfuric acid leaches uranium from its ore. (*Chemical Engineering, May 1957, Copyright McGraw-Hill, Inc.*)

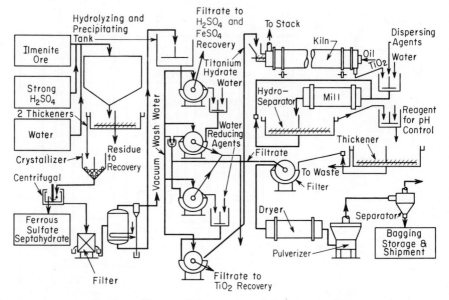

Titanium Dioxide: Hot sulfuric acid digests ground ilmenite ore. (*R. Norris Shreve,* "*Chemical Process Industries,*" *Copyright 1956 McGraw-Hill Book Company.*)

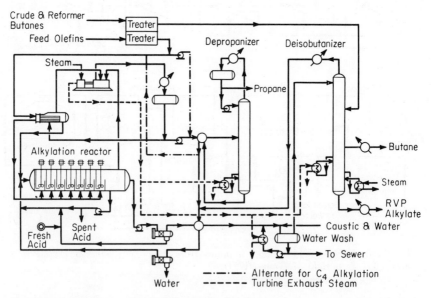

Petroleum Alkylate: Sulfuric acid reacts with hydrocarbons in M. W. Kellogg's cascade alkylation process. (*Hydrocarbon Processing and Petroleum Refiner, Sept. 1962, Copyright Gulf Publishing Company.*)

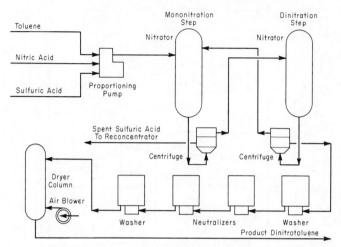

Dinitrotoluene: Sulfuric acid catalyzes the nitration of toluene. (*Hydrocarbon Processing and Petroleum Refiner, Nov. 1962, Copyright Gulf Publishing Company.*)

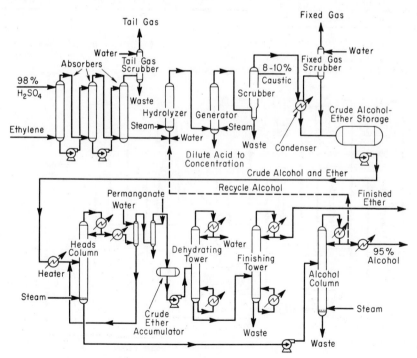

Ethyl Alcohol and Ethyl Ether: Sulfuric acid reacts with ethylene in a plate column to produce a mixture of hydrolyzable sulfates. (*Hydrocarbon Processing and Petroleum Refiner, Nov. 1959, Copyright Gulf Publishing Company.*)

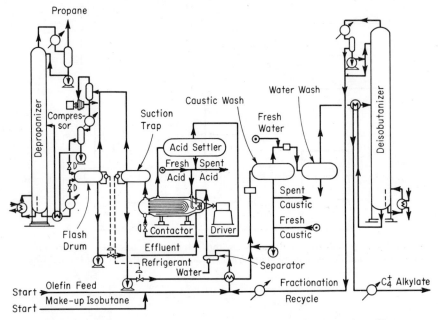

Petroleum Alkylate: Sulfuric acid reacts with hydrocarbons in the effluent refrigeration alkylation process. (*Hydrocarbon Processing and Petroleum Refiner, Sept. 1962, Copyright Gulf Publishing Company.*)

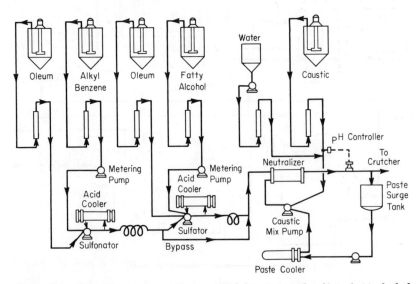

Detergents: Oleum is used to sulfonate alkyl benzene and sulfate fatty alcohols to form the basic ingredients for many detergents. (*Industrial and Engineering Chemistry, Vol. 51, No. 1. Copyright 1959 American Chemical Society.*)

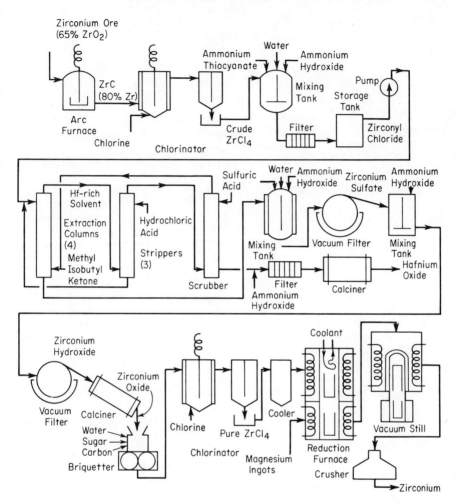

Zirconium: Sulfuric acid precipitates zirconium (as the sulfate) from zirconyl chloride solution and strips hafnium from the solvent extract. (*Chemical Engineering, Jan. 1958, Copyright McGraw-Hill, Inc.*)

TECHNICAL DATA

TABLE XX. PRICE EQUIVALENTS

100%	Equivalent Price As			
Price	60° Baumé	66° Baumé	98%	104.5%
10.00	7.77	9.32	9.80	10.45
10.01	7.77	9.33	9.81	10.46
10.02	7.78	9.34	9.82	10.47
10.03	7.79	9.35	9.83	10.48
10.04	7.80	9.36	9.84	10.49
10.05	7.81	9.37	9.85	10.50
10.06	7.81	9.37	9.86	10.51
10.07	7.82	9.38	9.87	10.52
10.08	7.83	9.39	9.88	10.53
10.09	7.84	9.40	9.89	10.54
10.10	7.84	9.41	9.90	10.55
10.11	7.85	9.42	9.91	10.56
10.12	7.86	9.43	9.92	10.58
10.13	7.87	9.44	9.93	10.59
10.14	7.88	9.45	9.94	10.60
10.15	7.88	9.46	9.95	10.61
10.16	7.89	9.47	9.96	10.62
10.17	7.90	9.48	9.97	10.63
10.18	7.91	9.49	9.98	10.64
10.19	7.91	9.50	9.99	10.65
10.20	7.92	9.51	10.00	10.66
10.21	7.93	9.51	10.01	10.67
10.22	7.94	9.52	10.02	10.68
10.23	7.95	9.53	10.03	10.69
10.24	7.95	9.54	10.04	10.70
10.25	7.96	9.55	10.05	10.71
10.26	7.97	9.56	10.05	10.72
10.27	7.98	9.57	10.06	10.73
10.28	7.98	9.58	10.07	10.74
10.29	7.99	9.59	10.08	10.75
10.30	8.00	9.60	10.09	10.76
10.31	8.01	9.61	10.10	10.77
10.32	8.02	9.62	10.11	10.78
10.33	8.02	9.63	10.12	10.79
10.34	8.03	9.64	10.13	10.81
10.35	8.04	9.65	10.14	10.82
10.36	8.05	9.65	10.15	10.83
10.37	8.05	9.66	10.16	10.84
10.38	8.06	9.67	10.17	10.85
10.39	8.07	9.68	10.18	10.86
10.40	8.08	9.69	10.19	10.87
10.41	8.09	9.70	10.20	10.88
10.42	8.09	9.71	10.21	10.89
10.43	8.10	9.72	10.22	10.90
10.44	8.11	9.73	10.23	10.91
10.45	8.12	9.74	10.24	10.92
10.46	8.12	9.75	10.25	10.93
10.47	8.13	9.76	10.26	10.94
10.48	8.14	9.77	10.27	10.95
10.49	8.15	9.78	10.28	10.96

100% Price	Equivalent Price As			
	60° Baumé	66° Baumé	98%	104.5%
10.50	8.16	9.78	10.29	10.97
10.51	8.16	9.79	10.30	10.98
10.52	8.17	9.80	10.31	10.99
10.53	8.18	9.81	10.32	11.00
10.54	8.19	9.82	10.33	11.01
10.55	8.19	9.83	10.34	11.02
10.56	8.20	9.84	10.35	11.04
10.57	8.21	9.85	10.36	11.05
10.58	8.22	9.86	10.37	11.06
10.59	8.23	9.87	10.38	11.07
10.60	8.23	9.88	10.39	11.08
10.61	8.24	9.89	10.40	11.09
10.62	8.25	9.90	10.41	11.10
10.63	8.26	9.91	10.42	11.11
10.64	8.26	9.92	10.43	11.12
10.65	8.27	9.92	10.44	11.13
10.66	8.28	9.93	10.45	11.14
10.67	8.29	9.94	10.46	11.15
10.68	8.30	9.95	10.47	11.16
10.69	8.30	9.96	10.48	11.17
10.70	8.31	9.97	10.49	11.18
10.71	8.32	9.98	10.50	11.19
10.72	8.33	9.99	10.51	11.20
10.73	8.33	10.00	10.52	11.21
10.74	8.34	10.01	10.53	11.22
10.75	8.35	10.02	10.54	11.23
10.76	8.36	10.03	10.54	11.24
10.77	8.37	10.04	10.55	11.25
10.78	8.37	10.05	10.56	11.27
10.79	8.38	10.06	10.57	11.28
10.80	8.39	10.06	10.58	11.29
10.81	8.40	10.07	10.59	11.30
10.82	8.40	10.08	10.60	11.31
10.83	8.41	10.09	10.61	11.32
10.84	8.42	10.10	10.62	11.33
10.85	8.43	10.11	10.63	11.34
10.86	8.43	10.12	10.64	11.35
10.87	8.44	10.13	10.65	11.36
10.88	8.45	10.14	10.66	11.37
10.89	8.46	10.15	10.67	11.38
10.90	8.47	10.16	10.68	11.39
10.91	8.47	10.17	10.69	11.40
10.92	8.48	10.18	10.70	11.41
10.93	8.49	10.19	10.71	11.42
10.94	8.50	10.19	10.72	11.43
10.95	8.50	10.20	10.73	11.44
10.96	8.51	10.21	10.74	11.45
10.97	8.52	10.22	10.75	11.46
10.98	8.53	10.23	10.76	11.47
10.99	8.54	10.24	10.77	11.48

(cont'd)

TABLE XX. PRICE EQUIVALENTS (cont'd)

100% Price	Equivalent Price As			
	60° Baumé	66° Baume	98%	104.5%
11.00	8.54	10.25	10.78	11.50
11.01	8.55	10.26	10.79	11.51
11.02	8.56	10.27	10.80	11.52
11.03	8.57	10.28	10.81	11.53
11.04	8.57	10.29	10.82	11.54
11.05	8.58	10.30	10.83	11.55
11.06	8.59	10.31	10.84	11.56
11.07	8.60	10.32	10.85	11.57
11.08	8.61	10.33	10.86	11.58
11.09	8.61	10.33	10.87	11.59
11.10	8.62	10.34	10.88	11.60
11.11	8.63	10.35	10.89	11.61
11.12	8.64	10.36	10.90	11.62
11.13	8.64	10.37	10.91	11.63
11.14	8.65	10.38	10.92	11.64
11.15	8.66	10.39	10.93	11.65
11.16	8.67	10.40	10.94	11.66
11.17	8.68	10.41	10.95	11.67
11.18	8.68	10.42	10.96	11.68
11.19	8.69	10.43	10.97	11.69
11.20	8.70	10.44	10.98	11.70
11.21	8.71	10.45	10.99	11.71
11.22	8.71	10.46	11.00	11.72
11.23	8.72	10.47	11.01	11.74
11.24	8.73	10.47	11.02	11.75
11.25	8.74	10.48	11.03	11.76
11.26	8.75	10.49	11.03	11.77
11.27	8.75	10.50	11.04	11.78
11.28	8.76	10.51	11.05	11.79
11.29	8.77	10.52	11.06	11.80
11.30	8.78	10.53	11.07	11.81
11.31	8.78	10.54	11.08	11.82
11.32	8.79	10.55	11.09	11.83
11.33	8.80	10.56	11.10	11.84
11.34	8.81	10.57	11.11	11.85
11.35	8.82	10.58	11.12	11.86
11.36	8.82	10.59	11.13	11.87
11.37	8.83	10.60	11.14	11.88
11.38	8.84	10.61	11.15	11.89
11.39	8.85	10.61	11.16	11.90
11.40	8.85	10.62	11.17	11.91
11.41	8.86	10.63	11.18	11.92
11.42	8.87	10.64	11.19	11.93
11.43	8.88	10.65	11.20	11.94
11.44	8.89	10.66	11.21	11.95
11.45	8.89	10.67	11.22	11.97
11.46	8.90	10.68	11.23	11.98
11.47	8.91	10.69	11.24	11.99
11.48	8.92	10.70	11.25	12.00
11.49	8.92	10.71	11.26	12.01

100%	Equivalent Price As			
Price	60° Baumé	66° Baumé	98%	104.5%
11.50	8.93	10.72	11.27	12.02
11.51	8.94	10.73	11.28	12.03
11.52	8.95	10.74	11.29	12.04
11.53	8.96	10.74	11.30	12.05
11.54	8.96	10.75	11.31	12.06
11.55	8.97	10.76	11.32	12.07
11.56	8.98	10.77	11.33	12.08
11.57	8.99	10.78	11.34	12.09
11.58	8.99	10.79	11.35	12.10
11.59	9.00	10.80	11.36	12.11
11.60	9.01	10.81	11.37	12.12
11.61	9.02	10.82	11.38	12.13
11.62	9.03	10.83	11.39	12.14
11.63	9.03	10.84	11.40	12.15
11.64	9.04	10.85	11.41	12.16
11.65	9.05	10.86	11.42	12.17
11.66	9.06	10.87	11.43	12.18
11.67	9.06	10.88	11.44	12.20
11.68	9.07	10.88	11.45	12.21
11.69	9.08	10.89	11.46	12.22
11.70	9.09	10.90	11.47	12.23
11.71	9.10	10.91	11.48	12.24
11.72	9.10	10.92	11.49	12.25
11.73	9.11	10.93	11.50	12.26
11.74	9.12	10.94	11.51	12.27
11.75	9.13	10.95	11.52	12.28
11.76	9.13	10.96	11.52	12.29
11.77	9.14	10.97	11.53	12.30
11.78	9.15	10.98	11.54	12.31
11.79	9.16	10.99	11.55	12.32
11.80	9.17	11.00	11.56	12.33
11.81	9.17	11.01	11.57	12.34
11.82	9.18	11.02	11.58	12.35
11.83	9.19	11.02	11.59	12.36
11.84	9.20	11.03	11.60	12.37
11.85	9.20	11.04	11.61	12.38
11.86	9.21	11.05	11.62	12.39
11.87	9.22	11.06	11.63	12.40
11.88	9.23	11.07	11.64	12.41
11.89	9.23	11.08	11.65	12.43
11.90	9.24	11.09	11.66	12.44
11.91	9.25	11.10	11.67	12.45
11.92	9.26	11.11	11.68	12.46
11.93	9.27	11.12	11.69	12.47
11.94	9.27	11.13	11.70	12.48
11.95	9.28	11.14	11.71	12.49
11.96	9.29	11.15	11.72	12.50
11.97	9.30	11.15	11.73	12.51
11.98	9.30	11.16	11.74	12.52
11.99	9.31	11.17	11.75	12.53

(cont'd)

TABLE XX. PRICE EQUIVALENTS (cont'd)

100% Price	Equivalent Price As			
	60° Baumé	66° Baumé	98%	104.5%
12.00	9.32	11.18	11.76	12.54
12.01	9.33	11.19	11.77	12.55
12.02	9.34	11.20	11.78	12.56
12.03	9.34	11.21	11.79	12.57
12.04	9.35	11.22	11.80	12.58
12.05	9.36	11.23	11.81	12.59
12.06	9.37	11.24	11.82	12.60
12.07	9.37	11.25	11.83	12.61
12.08	9.38	11.26	11.84	12.62
12.09	9.39	11.27	11.85	12.63
12.10	9.40	11.28	11.86	12.64
12.11	9.41	11.29	11.87	12.65
12.12	9.41	11.29	11.88	12.67
12.13	9.42	11.30	11.89	12.68
12.14	9.43	11.31	11.90	12.69
12.15	9.44	11.32	11.91	12.70
12.16	9.44	11.33	11.92	12.71
12.17	9.45	11.34	11.93	12.72
12.18	9.46	11.35	11.94	12.73
12.19	9.47	11.36	11.95	12.74
12.20	9.48	11.37	11.96	12.75
12.21	9.48	11.38	11.97	12.76
12.22	9.49	11.39	11.98	12.77
12.23	9.50	11.40	11.99	12.78
12.24	9.51	11.41	12.00	12.79
12.25	9.51	11.42	12.01	12.80
12.26	9.52	11.43	12.01	12.81
12.27	9.53	11.43	12.02	12.82
12.28	9.54	11.44	12.03	12.83
12.29	9.55	11.45	12.04	12.84
12.30	9.55	11.46	12.05	12.85
12.31	9.56	11.47	12.06	12.86
12.32	9.57	11.48	12.07	12.87
12.33	9.58	11.49	12.08	12.88
12.34	9.58	11.50	12.09	12.90
12.35	9.59	11.51	12.10	12.91
12.36	9.60	11.52	12.11	12.92
12.37	9.61	11.53	12.12	12.93
12.38	9.62	11.54	12.13	12.94
12.39	9.62	11.55	12.14	12.95
12.40	9.63	11.56	12.15	12.96
12.41	9.64	11.56	12.16	12.97
12.42	9.65	11.57	12.17	12.98
12.43	9.65	11.58	12.18	12.99
12.44	9.66	11.59	12.19	13.00
12.45	9.67	11.60	12.20	13.01
12.46	9.68	11.61	12.21	13.02
12.47	9.69	11.62	12.22	13.03
12.48	9.69	11.63	12.23	13.04
12.49	9.70	11.64	12.24	13.05

100% Price	Equivalent Price As			
	60° Baumé	66° Baumé	98%	104.5%
12.50	9.71	11.65	12.25	13.06
12.51	9.72	11.66	12.26	13.07
12.52	9.72	11.67	12.27	13.08
12.53	9.73	11.68	12.28	13.09
12.54	9.74	11.69	12.29	13.10
12.55	9.75	11.70	12.30	13.11
12.56	9.76	11.70	12.31	13.13
12.57	9.76	11.71	12.32	13.14
12.58	9.77	11.72	12.33	13.15
12.59	9.78	11.73	12.34	13.16
12.60	9.79	11.74	12.35	13.17
12.61	9.79	11.75	12.36	13.18
12.62	9.80	11.76	12.37	13.19
12.63	9.81	11.77	12.38	13.20
12.64	9.82	11.78	12.39	13.21
12.65	9.83	11.79	12.40	13.22
12.66	9.83	11.80	12.41	13.23
12.67	9.84	11.81	12.42	13.24
12.68	9.85	11.82	12.43	13.25
12.69	9.86	11.83	12.44	13.26
12.70	9.86	11.84	12.45	13.27
12.71	9.87	11.84	12.46	13.28
12.72	9.88	11.85	12.47	13.29
12.73	9.89	11.86	12.48	13.30
12.74	9.90	11.87	12.49	13.31
12.75	9.90	11.88	12.50	13.32
12.76	9.91	11.89	12.50	13.33
12.77	9.92	11.90	12.51	13.34
12.78	9.93	11.91	12.52	13.36
12.79	9.93	11.92	12.53	13.37
12.80	9.94	11.93	12.54	13.38
12.81	9.95	11.94	12.55	13.39
12.82	9.96	11.95	12.56	13.40
12.83	9.97	11.96	12.57	13.41
12.84	9.97	11.97	12.58	13.42
12.85	9.98	11.97	12.59	13.43
12.86	9.99	11.98	12.60	13.44
12.87	10.00	11.99	12.61	13.45
12.88	10.00	12.00	12.62	13.46
12.89	10.01	12.01	12.63	13.47
12.90	10.02	12.02	12.64	13.48
12.91	10.03	12.03	12.65	13.49
12.92	10.03	12.04	12.66	13.50
12.93	10.04	12.05	12.67	13.51
12.94	10.05	12.06	12.68	13.52
12.95	10.06	12.07	12.69	13.53
12.96	10.07	12.08	12.70	13.54
12.97	10.07	12.09	12.71	13.55
12.98	10.08	12.10	12.72	13.56
12.99	10.09	12.11	12.73	13.57

(cont'd)

TABLE XX. PRICE EQUIVALENTS (cont'd)

100% Price	Equivalent Price As			
	60° Baumé	66° Baumé	98%	104.5%
13.00	10.10	12.11	12.74	13.59
13.01	10.10	12.12	12.75	13.60
13.02	10.11	12.13	12.76	13.61
13.03	10.12	12.14	12.77	13.62
13.04	10.13	12.15	12.78	13.63
13.05	10.14	12.16	12.79	13.64
13.06	10.14	12.17	12.80	13.65
13.07	10.15	12.18	12.81	13.66
13.08	10.16	12.19	12.82	13.67
13.09	10.17	12.20	12.83	13.68
13.10	10.17	12.21	12.84	13.69
13.11	10.18	12.22	12.85	13.70
13.12	10.19	12.23	12.86	13.71
13.13	10.20	12.24	12.87	13.72
13.14	10.21	12.25	12.88	13.73
13.15	10.21	12.25	12.89	13.74
13.16	10.22	12.26	12.90	13.75
13.17	10.23	12.27	12.91	13.76
13.18	10.24	12.28	12.92	13.77
13.19	10.24	12.29	12.93	13.78
13.20	10.25	12.30	12.94	13.79
13.21	10.26	12.31	12.95	13.80
13.22	10.27	12.32	12.96	13.81
13.23	10.28	12.33	12.97	13.83
13.24	10.28	12.34	12.98	13.84
13.25	10.29	12.35	12.99	13.85
13.26	10.30	12.36	12.99	13.86
13.27	10.31	12.37	13.00	13.87
13.28	10.31	12.38	13.01	13.88
13.29	10.32	12.38	13.02	13.89
13.30	10.33	12.39	13.03	13.90
13.31	10.34	12.40	13.04	13.91
13.32	10.35	12.41	13.05	13.92
13.33	10.35	12.42	13.06	13.93
13.34	10.36	12.43	13.07	13.94
13.35	10.37	12.44	13.08	13.95
13.36	10.38	12.45	13.09	13.96
13.37	10.38	12.46	13.10	13.97
13.38	10.39	12.47	13.11	13.98
13.39	10.40	12.48	13.12	13.99
13.40	10.41	12.49	13.13	14.00
13.41	10.42	12.50	13.14	14.01
13.42	10.42	12.51	13.15	14.02
13.43	10.43	12.52	13.16	14.03
13.44	10.44	12.52	13.17	14.04
13.45	10.45	12.53	13.18	14.06
13.46	10.45	12.54	13.19	14.07
13.47	10.46	12.55	13.20	14.08
13.48	10.47	12.56	13.21	14.09
13.49	10.48	12.57	13.22	14.10

100% Percent	Equivalent Price As			
	60° Baumé	66° Baumé	98%	104.5%
13.50	10.49	12.58	13.23	14.11
13.51	10.49	12.59	13.24	14.12
13.52	10.50	12.60	13.25	14.13
13.53	10.51	12.61	13.26	14.14
13.54	10.52	12.62	13.27	14.15
13.55	10.52	12.63	13.28	14.16
13.56	10.53	12.64	13.29	14.17
13.57	10.54	12.65	13.30	14.18
13.58	10.55	12.66	13.31	14.19
13.59	10.56	12.66	13.32	14.20
13.60	10.56	12.67	13.33	14.21
13.61	10.57	12.68	13.34	14.22
13.62	10.58	12.69	13.35	14.23
13.63	10.59	12.70	13.36	14.24
13.64	10.59	12.71	13.37	14.25
13.65	10.60	12.72	13.38	14.26
13.66	10.61	12.73	13.39	14.27
13.67	10.62	12.74	13.40	14.29
13.68	10.63	12.75	13.41	14.30
13.69	10.63	12.76	13.42	14.31
13.70	10.64	12.77	13.43	14.32
13.71	10.65	12.78	13.44	14.33
13.72	10.66	12.79	13.45	14.34
13.73	10.66	12.79	13.46	14.35
13.74	10.67	12.80	13.47	14.36
13.75	10.68	12.81	13.48	14.37
13.76	10.69	12.82	13.48	14.38
13.77	10.70	12.83	13.49	14.39
13.78	10.70	12.84	13.50	14.40
13.79	10.71	12.85	13.51	14.41
13.80	10.72	12.86	13.52	14.42
13.81	10.73	12.87	13.53	14.43
13.82	10.73	12.88	13.54	14.44
13.83	10.74	12.89	13.55	14.45
13.84	10.75	12.90	13.56	14.46
13.85	10.76	12.91	13.57	14.47
13.86	10.77	12.92	13.58	14.48
13.87	10.77	12.93	13.59	14.49
13.88	10.78	12.93	13.60	14.50
13.89	10.79	12.94	13.61	14.52
13.90	10.80	12.95	13.62	14.53
13.91	10.80	12.96	13.63	14.54
13.92	10.81	12.97	13.64	14.55
13.93	10.82	12.98	13.65	14.56
13.94	10.83	12.99	13.66	14.57
13.95	10.84	13.00	13.67	14.58
13.96	10.84	13.01	13.68	14.59
13.97	10.85	13.02	13.69	14.60
13.98	10.86	13.03	13.70	14.61
13.99	10.87	13.04	13.71	14.62

(cont'd)

TABLE XX. PRICE EQUIVALENTS (cont'd)

100% Price	\multicolumn{4}{c}{Equivalent Price As}			
	60° Baumé	66° Baumé	98%	104.5%
14.00	10.87	13.05	13.72	14.63
14.01	10.88	13.06	13.73	14.64
14.02	10.89	13.07	13.74	14.65
14.03	10.90	13.07	13.75	14.66
14.04	10.90	13.08	13.76	14.67
14.05	10.91	13.09	13.77	14.68
14.06	10.92	13.10	13.78	14.69
14.07	10.93	13.11	13.79	14.70
14.08	10.94	13.12	13.80	14.71
14.09	10.94	13.13	13.81	14.72
14.10	10.95	13.14	13.82	14.73
14.11	10.96	13.15	13.83	14.74
14.12	10.97	13.16	13.84	14.76
14.13	10.97	13.17	13.85	14.77
14.14	10.98	13.18	13.86	14.78
14.15	10.99	13.19	13.87	14.79
14.16	11.00	13.20	13.88	14.80
14.17	11.01	13.21	13.89	14.81
14.18	11.01	13.21	13.90	14.82
14.19	11.02	13.22	13.91	14.83
14.20	11.03	13.23	13.92	14.84
14.21	11.04	13.24	13.93	14.85
14.22	11.04	13.25	13.94	14.86
14.23	11.05	13.26	13.95	14.87
14.24	11.06	13.27	13.96	14.88
14.25	11.07	13.28	13.97	14.89
14.26	11.08	13.29	13.97	14.90
14.27	11.08	13.30	13.98	14.91
14.28	11.09	13.31	13.99	14.92
14.29	11.10	13.32	14.00	14.93
14.30	11.11	13.33	14.01	14.94
14.31	11.11	13.34	14.02	14.95
14.32	11.12	13.34	14.03	14.96
14.33	11.13	13.35	14.04	14.97
14.34	11.14	13.36	14.05	14.99
14.35	11.15	13.37	14.06	15.00
14.36	11.15	13.38	14.07	15.01
14.37	11.16	13.39	14.08	15.02
14.38	11.17	13.40	14.09	15.03
14.39	11.18	13.41	14.10	15.04
14.40	11.18	13.42	14.11	15.05
14.41	11.19	13.43	14.12	15.06
14.42	11.20	13.44	14.13	15.07
14.43	11.21	13.45	14.14	15.08
14.44	11.22	13.46	14.15	15.09
14.45	11.22	13.47	14.16	15.10
14.46	11.23	13.48	14.17	15.11
14.47	11.24	13.48	14.18	15.12
14.48	11.25	13.49	14.19	15.13
14.49	11.25	13.50	14.20	15.14

100% Price	Equivalent Price As			
	66° Baumé	66° Baumé	98%	104.5%
14.50	11.26	13.51	14.21	15.15
14.51	11.27	13.52	14.22	15.16
14.52	11.28	13.53	14.23	15.17
14.53	11.29	13.54	14.24	15.18
14.54	11.29	13.55	14.25	15.19
14.55	11.30	13.56	14.26	15.20
14.56	11.31	13.57	14.27	15.21
14.57	11.32	13.58	14.28	15.22
14.58	11.32	13.59	14.29	15.24
14.59	11.33	13.60	14.30	15.25
14.60	11.34	13.61	14.31	15.26
14.61	11.35	13.62	14.32	15.27
14.62	11.36	13.62	14.33	15.28
14.63	11.36	13.63	14.34	15.29
14.64	11.37	13.64	14.35	15.30
14.65	11.38	13.65	14.36	15.31
14.66	11.39	13.66	14.37	15.32
14.67	11.39	13.67	14.38	15.33
14.68	11.40	13.68	14.39	15.34
14.69	11.41	13.69	14.40	15.35
14.70	11.42	13.70	14.41	15.36
14.71	11.43	13.71	14.42	15.37
14.72	11.43	13.72	14.43	15.38
14.73	11.44	13.73	14.44	15.39
14.74	11.45	13.74	14.45	15.40
14.75	11.46	13.75	14.46	15.41
14.76	11.46	13.75	14.46	15.42
14.77	11.47	13.76	14.47	15.43
14.78	11.48	13.77	14.48	15.45
14.79	11.49	13.78	14.49	15.46
14.80	11.50	13.79	14.50	15.47
14.81	11.50	13.80	14.51	15.48
14.82	11.51	13.81	14.52	15.49
14.83	11.52	13.82	14.53	15.50
14.84	11.53	13.83	14.54	15.51
14.85	11.53	13.84	14.55	15.52
14.86	11.54	13.85	14.56	15.53
14.87	11.55	13.86	14.57	15.54
14.88	11.56	13.87	14.58	15.55
14.89	11.57	13.88	14.59	15.56
14.90	11.57	13.89	14.60	15.57
14.91	11.58	13.89	14.61	15.58
14.92	11.59	13.90	14.62	15.59
14.93	11.60	13.91	14.63	15.60
14.94	11.60	13.92	14.64	15.61
14.95	11.61	13.93	14.65	15.62
14.96	11.62	13.94	14.66	15.63
14.97	11.63	13.95	14.67	15.64
14.98	11.63	13.96	14.68	15.65
14.99	11.64	13.97	14.69	15.66

(cont'd)

TABLE XX. PRICE EQUIVALENTS (cont'd)

100% Price	Equivalent Price As			
	60° Baumé	60° Baumé	98%	104.5%
15.00	11.65	13.98	14.70	15.68
15.01	11.66	13.99	14.71	15.69
15.02	11.67	14.00	14.72	15.70
15.03	11.67	14.01	14.73	15.71
15.04	11.68	14.02	14.74	15.72
15.05	11.69	14.03	14.75	15.73
15.06	11.70	14.03	14.76	15.74
15.07	11.70	14.04	14.77	15.75
15.08	11.71	14.05	14.78	15.76
15.09	11.72	14.06	14.79	15.77
15.10	11.73	14.07	14.80	15.78
15.11	11.74	14.08	14.81	15.79
15.12	11.74	14.09	14.82	15.80
15.13	11.75	14.10	14.83	15.81
15.14	11.76	14.11	14.84	15.82
15.15	11.77	14.12	14.85	15.83
15.16	11.77	14.13	14.86	15.84
15.17	11.78	14.14	14.87	15.85
15.18	11.79	14.15	14.88	15.86
15.19	11.80	14.16	14.89	15.87
15.20	11.81	14.16	14.90	15.88
15.21	11.81	14.17	14.91	15.89
15.22	11.82	14.18	14.92	15.90
15.23	11.83	14.19	14.93	15.92
15.24	11.84	14.20	14.94	15.93
15.25	11.84	14.21	14.95	15.94
15.26	11.85	14.22	14.95	15.95
15.27	11.86	14.23	14.96	15.96
15.28	11.87	14.24	14.97	15.97
15.29	11.88	14.25	14.98	15.98
15.30	11.88	14.26	14.99	15.99
15.31	11.89	14.27	15.00	16.00
15.32	11.90	14.28	15.01	16.01
15.33	11.91	14.29	15.02	16.02
15.34	11.91	14.30	15.03	16.03
15.35	11.92	14.30	15.04	16.04
15.36	11.93	14.31	15.05	16.05
15.37	11.94	14.32	15.06	16.06
15.38	11.95	14.33	15.07	16.07
15.39	11.95	14.34	15.08	16.08
15.40	11.96	14.35	15.09	16.09
15.41	11.97	14.36	15.10	16.10
15.42	11.98	14.37	15.11	16.11
15.43	11.98	14.38	15.12	16.12
15.44	11.99	14.39	15.13	16.13
15.45	12.00	14.40	15.14	16.15
15.46	12.01	14.41	15.15	16.16
15.47	12.02	14.42	15.16	16.17
15.48	12.02	14.43	15.17	16.18
15.49	12.03	14.44	15.18	16.19

100% Price	Equivalent Price As			
	60° Baumé	66° Baumé	98%	104.5%
15.50	12.04	14.44	15.19	16.20
15.51	12.05	14.45	15.20	16.21
15.52	12.05	14.46	15.21	16.22
15.53	12.06	14.47	15.22	16.23
15.54	12.07	14.48	15.23	16.24
15.55	12.08	14.49	15.24	16.25
15.56	12.09	14.50	15.25	16.26
15.57	12.09	14.51	15.26	16.27
15.58	12.10	14.52	15.27	16.28
15.59	12.11	14.53	15.28	16.29
15.60	12.12	14.54	15.29	16.30
15.61	12.12	14.55	15.30	16.31
15.62	12.13	14.56	15.31	16.32
15.63	12.14	14.57	15.32	16.33
15.64	12.15	14.57	15.33	16.34
15.65	12.16	14.58	15.34	16.35
15.66	12.16	14.59	15.35	16.36
15.67	12.17	14.60	15.36	16.38
15.68	12.18	14.61	15.37	16.39
15.69	12.19	14.62	15.38	16.40
15.70	12.19	14.63	15.39	16.41
15.71	12.20	14.64	15.40	16.42
15.72	12.21	14.65	15.41	16.43
15.73	12.22	14.66	15.42	16.44
15.74	12.23	14.67	15.43	16.45
15.75	12.23	14.68	15.44	16.46
15.76	12.24	14.69	15.44	16.47
15.77	12.25	14.70	15.45	16.48
15.78	12.26	14.71	15.46	16.49
15.79	12.26	14.71	15.47	16.50
15.80	12.27	14.72	15.48	16.51
15.81	12.28	14.73	15.49	16.52
15.82	12.29	14.74	15.50	16.53
15.83	12.30	14.75	15.51	16.54
15.84	12.30	14.76	15.52	16.55
15.85	12.31	14.77	15.53	16.56
15.86	12.32	14.78	15.54	16.57
15.87	12.33	14.79	15.55	16.58
15.88	12.33	14.80	15.56	16.59
15.89	12.34	14.81	15.57	16.61
15.90	12.35	14.82	15.58	16.62
15.91	12.36	14.83	15.59	16.63
15.92	12.37	14.84	15.60	16.64
15.93	12.37	14.85	15.61	16.65
15.94	12.38	14.85	15.62	16.66
15.95	12.39	14.86	15.63	16.67
15.96	12.40	14.87	15.64	16.68
15.97	12.40	14.88	15.65	16.69
15.98	12.41	14.89	15.66	16.70
15.99	12.42	14.90	15.67	16.71

(cont'd)

TABLE XX. PRICE EQUIVALENTS (cont'd)

100% Price	Equivalent Price As			
	60° Baumé	66° Baumé	98%	104.5%
16.00	12.43	14.91	15.68	16.72
16.01	12.43	14.92	15.69	16.73
16.02	12.44	14.93	15.70	16.74
16.03	12.45	14.94	15.71	16.75
16.04	12.46	14.95	15.72	16.76
16.05	12.47	14.96	15.73	16.77
16.06	12.47	14.97	15.74	16.78
16.07	12.48	14.98	15.75	16.79
16.08	12.49	14.98	15.76	16.80
16.09	12.50	14.99	15.77	16.81
16.10	12.50	15.00	15.78	16.82
16.11	12.51	15.01	15.79	16.83
16.12	12.52	15.02	15.80	16.85
16.13	12.53	15.03	15.81	16.86
16.14	12.54	15.04	15.82	16.87
16.15	12.54	15.05	15.83	16.88
16.16	12.55	15.06	15.84	16.89
16.17	12.56	15.07	15.85	16.90
16.18	12.57	15.08	15.86	16.91
16.19	12.57	15.09	15.87	16.92
16.20	12.58	15.10	15.88	16.93
16.21	12.59	15.11	15.89	16.94
16.22	12.60	15.12	15.90	16.95
16.23	12.61	15.12	15.91	16.96
16.24	12.61	15.13	15.92	16.97
16.25	12.62	15.14	15.93	16.98
16.26	12.63	15.15	15.93	16.99
16.27	12.64	15.16	15.94	17.00
16.28	12.64	15.17	15.95	17.01
16.29	12.65	15.18	15.96	17.02
16.30	12.66	15.19	15.97	17.03
16.31	12.67	15.20	15.98	17.04
16.32	12.68	15.21	15.99	17.05
16.33	12.68	15.22	16.00	17.06
16.34	12.69	15.23	16.01	17.08
16.35	12.70	15.24	16.02	17.09
16.36	12.71	15.25	16.03	17.10
16.37	12.71	15.26	16.04	17.11
16.38	12.72	15.26	16.05	17.12
16.39	12.73	15.27	16.06	17.13
16.40	12.74	15.28	16.07	17.14
16.41	12.75	15.29	16.08	17.15
16.42	12.75	15.30	16.09	17.16
16.43	12.76	15.31	16.10	17.17
16.44	12.77	15.32	16.11	17.18
16.45	12.78	15.33	16.12	17.19
16.46	12.78	15.34	16.13	17.20
16.47	12.79	15.35	16.14	17.21
16.48	12.80	15.36	16.15	17.22
16.49	12.81	15.37	16.16	17.23

100% Price	Equivalent Price As			
	60° Baumé	66° Baumé	98%	104.5%
16.50	12.82	15.38	16.17	17.24
16.51	12.82	15.39	16.18	17.25
16.52	12.83	15.39	16.19	17.26
16.53	12.84	15.40	16.20	17.27
16.54	12.85	15.41	16.21	17.28
16.55	12.85	15.42	16.22	17.29
16.56	12.86	15.43	16.23	17.31
16.57	12.87	15.44	16.24	17.32
16.58	12.88	15.45	16.25	17.33
16.59	12.89	15.46	16.26	17.34
16.60	12.89	15.47	16.27	17.35
16.61	12.90	15.48	16.28	17.36
16.62	12.91	15.49	16.29	17.37
16.63	12.92	15.50	16.30	17.38
16.64	12.92	15.51	16.31	17.39
16.65	12.93	15.52	16.32	17.40
16.66	12.94	15.53	16.33	17.41
16.67	12.95	15.53	16.34	17.42
16.68	12.96	15.54	16.35	17.43
16.69	12.96	15.55	16.36	17.44
16.70	12.97	15.56	16.37	17.45
16.71	12.98	15.57	16.38	17.46
16.72	12.99	15.58	16.39	17.47
16.73	12.99	15.59	16.40	17.48
16.74	13.00	15.60	16.41	17.49
16.75	13.01	15.61	16.42	17.50
16.76	13.02	15.62	16.42	17.51
16.77	13.03	15.63	16.43	17.52
16.78	13.03	15.64	16.44	17.54
16.79	13.04	15.65	16.45	17.55
16.80	13.05	15.66	16.46	17.56
16.81	13.06	15.67	16.47	17.57
16.82	13.06	15.67	16.48	17.58
16.83	13.07	15.68	16.49	17.59
16.84	13.08	15.69	16.50	17.60
16.85	13.09	15.70	16.51	17.61
16.86	13.10	15.71	16.52	17.62
16.87	13.10	15.72	16.53	17.63
16.88	13.11	15.73	16.54	17.64
16.89	13.12	15.74	16.55	17.65
16.90	13.13	15.75	16.56	17.66
16.91	13.13	15.76	16.57	17.67
16.92	13.14	15.77	16.58	17.68
16.93	13.15	15.78	16.59	17.69
16.94	13.16	15.79	16.60	17.70
16.95	13.17	15.80	16.61	17.71
16.96	13.17	15.81	16.62	17.72
16.97	13.18	15.81	16.63	17.73
16.98	13.19	15.82	16.64	17.74
16.99	13.20	15.83	16.65	17.75

(cont'd)

TABLE XX. PRICE EQUIVALENTS (cont'd)

100% Price	Equivalent Price As			
	60° Baumé	66° Baumé	98%	104.5%
17.00	13.20	15.84	16.66	17.77
17.01	13.21	15.85	16.67	17.78
17.02	13.22	15.86	16.68	17.79
17.03	13.23	15.87	16.69	17.80
17.04	13.23	15.88	16.70	17.81
17.05	13.24	15.89	16.71	17.82
17.06	13.25	15.90	16.72	17.83
17.07	13.26	15.91	16.73	17.84
17.08	13.27	15.92	16.74	17.85
17.09	13.27	15.93	16.75	17.86
17.10	13.28	15.94	16.76	17.87
17.11	13.29	15.94	16.77	17.88
17.12	13.30	15.95	16.78	17.89
17.13	13.30	15.96	16.79	17.90
17.14	13.31	15.97	16.80	17.91
17.15	13.32	15.98	16.81	17.92
17.16	13.33	15.99	16.82	17.93
17.17	13.34	16.00	16.83	17.94
17.18	13.34	16.01	16.84	17.95
17.19	13.35	16.02	16.85	17.96
17.20	13.36	16.03	16.86	17.97
17.21	13.37	16.04	16.87	17.98
17.22	13.37	16.05	16.88	17.99
17.23	13.38	16.06	16.89	18.01
17.24	13.39	16.07	16.90	18.02
17.25	13.40	16.08	16.91	18.03
17.26	13.41	16.08	16.91	18.04
17.27	13.41	16.09	16.92	18.05
17.28	13.42	16.10	16.93	18.06
17.29	13.43	16.11	16.94	18.07
17.30	13.44	16.12	16.95	18.08
17.31	13.44	16.13	16.96	18.09
17.32	13.45	16.14	16.97	18.10
17.33	13.46	16.15	16.98	18.11
17.34	13.47	16.16	16.99	18.12
17.35	13.48	16.17	17.00	18.13
17.36	13.48	16.18	17.01	18.14
17.37	13.49	16.19	17.02	18.15
17.38	13.50	16.20	17.03	18.16
17.39	13.51	16.21	17.04	18.17
17.40	13.51	16.22	17.05	18.18
17.41	13.52	16.22	17.06	18.19
17.42	13.53	16.23	17.07	18.20
17.43	13.54	16.24	17.08	18.21
17.44	13.55	16.25	17.09	18.22
17.45	13.55	16.26	17.10	18.24
17.46	13.56	16.27	17.11	18.25
17.47	13.57	16.28	17.12	18.26
17.48	13.58	16.29	17.13	18.27
17.49	13.58	16.30	17.14	18.28

100%	Equivalent Price As			
Price	60° Baumé	66° Baumé	98%	104.5%
17.50	13.59	16.31	17.15	18.29
17.51	13.60	16.32	17.16	18.30
17.52	13.61	16.33	17.17	18.31
17.53	13.62	16.34	17.18	18.32
17.54	13.62	16.35	17.19	18.33
17.55	13.63	16.35	17.20	18.34
17.56	13.64	16.36	17.21	18.35
17.57	13.65	16.37	17.22	18.36
17.58	13.65	16.38	17.23	18.37
17.59	13.66	16.39	17.24	18.38
17.60	13.67	16.40	17.25	18.39
17.61	13.68	16.41	17.26	18.40
17.62	13.69	16.42	17.27	18.41
17.63	13.69	16.43	17.28	18.42
17.64	13.70	16.44	17.29	18.43
17.65	13.71	16.45	17.30	18.44
17.66	13.72	16.46	17.31	18.45
17.67	13.72	16.47	17.32	18.47
17.68	13.73	16.48	17.33	18.48
17.69	13.74	16.49	17.34	18.49
17.70	13.75	16.49	17.35	18.50
17.71	13.76	16.50	17.36	18.51
17.72	13.76	16.51	17.37	18.52
17.73	13.77	16.52	17.38	18.53
17.74	13.78	16.53	17.39	18.54
17.75	13.79	16.54	17.40	18.55
17.76	13.79	16.55	17.40	18.56
17.77	13.80	16.56	17.41	18.57
17.78	13.81	16.57	17.42	18.58
17.79	13.82	16.58	17.43	18.59
17.80	13.83	16.59	17.44	18.60
17.81	13.83	16.60	17.45	18.61
17.82	13.84	16.61	17.46	18.62
17.83	13.85	16.62	17.47	18.63
17.84	13.86	16.63	17.48	18.64
17.85	13.86	16.63	17.49	18.65
17.86	13.87	16.64	17.50	18.66
17.87	13.88	16.65	17.51	18.67
17.88	13.89	16.66	17.52	18.68
17.89	13.90	16.67	17.53	18.70
17.90	13.90	16.68	17.54	18.71
17.91	13.91	16.69	17.55	18.72
17.92	13.92	16.70	17.56	18.73
17.93	13.93	16.71	17.57	18.74
17.94	13.93	16.72	17.58	18.75
17.95	13.94	16.73	17.59	18.76
17.96	13.95	16.74	17.60	18.77
17.97	13.96	16.75	17.61	18.78
17.98	13.97	16.76	17.62	18.79
17.99	13.97	16.76	17.63	18.80

(cont'd)

TABLE XX. PRICE EQUIVALENTS (cont'd)

100% Price	Equivalent Price As			
	60° Baumé	66° Baumé	98%	104.5%
18.00	13.98	16.77	17.64	18.81
18.01	13.99	16.78	17.65	18.82
18.02	14.00	16.79	17.66	18.83
18.03	14.00	16.80	17.67	18.84
18.04	14.01	16.81	17.68	18.85
18.05	14.02	16.82	17.69	18.86
18.06	14.03	16.83	17.70	18.87
18.07	14.03	16.84	17.71	18.88
18.08	14.04	16.85	17.72	18.89
18.09	14.05	16.86	17.73	18.90
18.10	14.06	16.87	17.74	18.91
18.11	14.07	16.88	17.75	18.92
18.12	14.07	16.89	17.76	18.94
18.13	14.08	16.90	17.77	18.95
18.14	14.09	16.90	17.78	18.96
18.15	14.10	16.91	17.79	18.97
18.16	14.10	16.92	17.80	18.98
18.17	14.11	16.93	17.81	18.99
18.18	14.12	16.94	17.82	19.00
18.19	14.13	16.95	17.83	19.01
18.20	14.14	16.96	17.84	19.02
18.21	14.14	16.97	17.85	19.03
18.22	14.15	16.98	17.86	19.04
18.23	14.16	16.99	17.87	19.05
18.24	14.17	17.00	17.88	19.06
18.25	14.17	17.01	17.89	19.07
18.26	14.18	17.02	17.89	19.08
18.27	14.19	17.03	17.90	19.09
18.28	14.20	17.04	17.91	19.10
18.29	14.21	17.04	17.92	19.11
18.30	14.21	17.05	17.93	19.12
18.31	14.22	17.06	17.94	19.13
18.32	14.23	17.07	17.95	19.14
18.33	14.24	17.08	17.96	19.15
18.34	14.24	17.09	17.97	19.17
18.35	14.25	17.10	17.98	19.18
18.36	14.26	17.11	17.99	19.19
18.37	14.27	17.12	18.00	19.20
18.38	14.28	17.13	18.01	19.21
18.39	14.28	17.14	18.02	19.22
18.40	14.29	17.15	18.03	19.23
18.41	14.30	17.16	18.04	19.24
18.42	14.31	17.17	18.05	19.25
18.43	14.31	17.17	18.06	19.26
18.44	14.32	17.18	18.07	19.27
18.45	14.33	17.19	18.08	19.28
18.46	14.34	17.20	18.09	19.29
18.47	14.35	17.21	18.10	19.30
18.48	14.35	17.22	18.11	19.31
18.49	14.36	17.23	18.12	19.32

100%	Equivalent Price As			
Price	60° Baumé	66° Baumé	98%	104.5%
18.50	14.37	17.24	18.13	19.33
18.51	14.38	17.25	18.14	19.34
18.52	14.38	17.26	18.15	19.35
18.53	14.39	17.27	18.16	19.36
18.54	14.40	17.28	18.17	19.37
18.55	14.41	17.29	18.18	19.38
18.56	14.42	17.30	18.19	19.40
18.57	14.42	17.31	18.20	19.41
18.58	14.43	17.32	18.21	19.42
18.59	14.44	17.32	18.22	19.43
18.60	14.45	17.33	18.23	19.44
18.61	14.45	17.34	18.24	19.45
18.62	14.46	17.35	18.25	19.46
18.63	14.47	17.36	18.26	19.47
18.64	14.48	17.37	18.27	19.48
18.65	14.49	17.38	18.28	19.49
18.66	14.49	17.39	18.29	19.50
18.67	14.50	17.40	18.30	19.51
18.68	14.51	17.41	18.31	19.52
18.69	14.52	17.42	18.32	19.53
18.70	14.52	17.43	18.33	19.54
18.71	14.53	17.44	18.34	19.55
18.72	14.54	17.45	18.35	19.56
18.73	14.55	17.45	18.36	19.57
18.74	14.56	17.46	18.37	19.58
18.75	14.56	17.47	18.38	19.59
18.76	14.57	17.48	18.38	19.60
18.77	14.58	17.49	18.39	19.61
18.78	14.59	17.50	18.40	19.63
18.79	14.59	17.51	18.41	19.64
18.80	14.60	17.52	18.42	19.65
18.81	14.61	17.53	18.43	19.66
18.82	14.62	17.54	18.44	19.67
18.83	14.63	17.55	18.45	19.68
18.84	14.63	17.56	18.46	19.69
18.85	14.64	17.57	18.47	19.70
18.86	14.65	17.58	18.48	19.71
18.87	14.66	17.58	18.49	19.72
18.88	14.66	17.59	18.50	19.73
18.89	14.67	17.60	18.51	19.74
18.90	14.68	17.61	18.52	19.75
18.91	14.69	17.62	18.53	19.76
18.92	14.70	17.63	18.54	19.77
18.93	14.70	17.64	18.55	19.78
18.94	14.71	17.65	18.56	19.79
18.95	14.72	17.66	18.57	19.80
18.96	14.73	17.67	18.58	19.81
18.97	14.73	17.68	18.59	19.82
18.98	14.74	17.69	18.60	19.83
18.99	14.75	17.70	18.61	19.84

(cont'd)

TABLE XX. PRICE EQUIVALENTS (cont'd)

100% Price	Equivalent Price As			
	60° Baumé	66° Baumé	98%	104.5%
19.00	14.76	17.71	18.62	19.86
19.01	14.77	17.72	18.63	19.87
19.02	14.77	17.72	18.64	19.88
19.03	14.78	17.73	18.65	19.89
19.04	14.79	17.74	18.66	19.90
19.05	14.80	17.75	18.67	19.91
19.06	14.80	17.76	18.68	19.92
19.07	14.81	17.77	18.69	19.93
19.08	14.82	17.78	18.70	19.94
19.09	14.83	17.79	18.71	19.95
19.10	14.83	17.80	18.72	19.96
19.11	14.84	17.81	18.73	19.97
19.12	14.85	17.82	18.74	19.98
19.13	14.86	17.83	18.75	19.99
19.14	14.87	17.84	18.76	20.00
19.15	14.87	17.85	18.77	20.01
19.16	14.88	17.86	18.78	20.02
19.17	14.89	17.86	18.79	20.03
19.18	14.90	17.87	18.80	20.0∠
19.19	14.90	17.88	18.81	20.05
19.20	14.91	17.89	18.82	20.06
19.21	14.92	17.90	18.83	20.07
19.22	14.93	17.91	18.84	20.08
19.23	14.94	17.92	18.85	20.10
19.24	14.94	17.93	18.86	20.11
19.25	14.95	17.94	18.87	20.12
19.26	14.96	17.95	18.87	20.13
19.27	14.97	17.96	18.88	20.14
19.28	14.97	17.97	18.89	20.15
19.29	14.98	17.98	18.90	20.16
19.30	14.99	17.99	18.91	20.17
19.31	15.00	17.99	18.92	20.18
19.32	15.01	18.00	18.93	20.19
19.33	15.01	18.01	18.94	20.20
19.34	15.02	18.02	18.95	20.21
19.35	15.03	18.03	18.96	20.22
19.36	15.04	18.04	18.97	20.23
19.37	15.04	18.05	18.98	20.24
19.38	15.05	18.06	18.99	20.25
19.39	15.06	18.07	19.00	20.26
19.40	15.07	18.08	19.01	20.27
19.41	15.08	18.09	19.02	20.28
19.42	15.08	18.10	19.03	20.29
19.43	15.09	18.11	19.04	20.30
19.44	15.10	18.12	19.05	20.31
19.45	15.11	18.13	19.06	20.33
19.46	15.11	18.13	19.07	20.34
19.47	15.12	18.14	19.08	20.35
19.48	15.13	18.15	19.09	20.36
19.49	15.14	18.16	19.10	20.37

100%	Equivalent Price As			
Price	60° Baumé	66° Baumé	98%	104.5%
19.50	15.15	18.17	19.11	20.38
19.51	15.15	18.18	19.12	20.39
19.52	15.16	18.19	19.13	20.40
19.53	15.17	18.20	19.14	20.41
19.54	15.18	18.21	19.15	20.42
19.55	15.18	18.22	19.16	20.43
19.56	15.19	18.23	19.17	20.44
19.57	15.20	18.24	19.18	20.45
19.58	15.21	18.25	19.19	20.46
19.59	15.22	18.26	19.20	20.47
19.60	15.22	18.27	19.21	20.48
19.61	15.23	18.27	19.22	20.49
19.62	15.24	18.28	19.23	20.50
19.63	15.25	18.29	19.24	20.51
19.64	15.26	18.30	19.25	20.52
19.65	15.26	18.31	19.26	20.53
19.66	15.27	18.32	19.27	20.54
19.67	15.28	18.33	19.28	20.56
19.68	15.29	18.34	19.29	20.57
19.69	15.29	18.35	19.30	20.58
19.70	15.30	18.36	19.31	20.59
19.71	15.31	18.37	19.32	20.60
19.72	15.32	18.38	19.33	20.61
19.73	15.32	18.39	19.34	20.62
19.74	15.33	18.40	19.35	20.63
19.75	15.34	18.41	19.36	20.64
19.76	15.35	18.41	19.36	20.65
19.77	15.36	18.42	19.37	20.66
19.78	15.36	18.43	19.38	20.67
19.79	15.37	18.44	19.39	20.68
19.80	15.38	18.45	19.40	20.69
19.81	15.39	18.46	19.41	20.70
19.82	15.39	18.47	19.42	20.71
19.83	15.40	18.48	19.43	20.72
19.84	15.41	18.49	19.44	20.73
19.85	15.42	18.50	19.45	20.74
19.86	15.43	18.51	19.46	20.75
19.87	15.43	18.52	19.47	20.76
19.88	15.44	18.53	19.48	20.77
19.89	15.45	18.54	19.49	20.79
19.90	15.46	18.54	19.50	20.80
19.91	15.46	18.55	19.51	20.81
19.92	15.47	18.56	19.52	20.82
19.93	15.48	18.57	19.53	20.83
19.94	15.49	18.58	19.54	20.84
19.95	15.50	18.59	19.55	20.85
19.96	15.50	18.60	19.56	20.86
19.97	15.51	18.61	19.57	20.87
19.98	15.52	18.62	19.58	20.88
19.99	15.53	18.63	19.59	20.89

(cont'd)

TABLE XX. PRICE EQUIVALENTS (cont'd)

100%	Equivalent Price As			
Price	60° Baumé	66° Baumé	98%	104.5%
20.00	15.53	18.64	19.60	20.90
20.01	15.54	18.65	19.61	20.91
20.02	15.55	18.66	19.62	20.92
20.03	15.56	18.67	19.63	20.93
20.04	15.57	18.68	19.64	20.94
20.05	15.57	18.68	19.65	20.95
20.06	15.58	18.69	19.66	20.96
20.07	15.59	18.70	19.67	20.97
20.08	15.60	18.71	19.68	20.98
20.09	15.60	18.72	19.69	20.99
20.10	15.61	18.73	19.70	21.00
20.11	15.62	18.74	19.71	21.01
20.12	15.63	18.75	19.72	21.03
20.13	15.63	18.76	19.73	21.04
20.14	15.64	18.77	19.74	21.05
20.15	15.65	18.78	19.75	21.06
20.16	15.66	18.79	19.76	21.07
20.17	15.67	18.80	19.77	21.08
20.18	15.67	18.81	19.78	21.09
20.19	15.68	18.82	19.79	21.10
20.20	15.69	18.82	19.80	21.11
20.21	15.70	18.83	19.81	21.12
20.22	15.70	18.84	19.82	21.13
20.23	15.71	18.85	19.83	21.14
20.24	15.72	18.86	19.84	21.15
20.25	15.73	18.87	19.85	21.16
20.26	15.74	18.88	19.85	21.17
20.27	15.74	18.89	19.86	21.18
20.28	15.75	18.90	19.87	21.19
20.29	15.76	18.91	19.88	21.20
20.30	15.77	18.92	19.89	21.21
20.31	15.77	18.93	19.90	21.22
20.32	15.78	18.94	19.91	21.23
20.33	15.79	18.95	19.92	21.24
20.34	15.80	18.95	19.93	21.26
20.35	15.81	18.96	19.94	21.27
20.36	15.81	18.97	19.95	21.28
20.37	15.82	18.98	19.96	21.29
20.38	15.83	18.99	19.97	21.30
20.39	15.84	19.00	19.98	21.31
20.40	15.84	19.01	19.99	21.32
20.41	15.85	19.02	20.00	21.33
20.42	15.86	19.03	20.01	21.34
20.43	15.87	19.04	20.02	21.35
20.44	15.88	19.05	20.03	21.36
20.45	15.88	19.06	20.04	21.37
20.46	15.89	19.07	20.05	21.38
20.47	15.90	19.08	20.06	21.39
20.48	15.91	19.09	20.07	21.40
20.49	15.91	19.09	20.08	21.41

100% Price	Equivalent Price As			
	60° Baumé	66° Baumé	98%	104.5%
20.50	15.92	19.10	20.09	21.42
20.51	15.93	19.11	20.10	21.43
20.52	15.94	19.12	20.11	21.44
20.53	15.95	19.13	20.12	21.45
20.54	15.95	19.14	20.13	21.46
20.55	15.96	19.15	20.14	21.47
20.56	15.97	19.16	20.15	21.49
20.57	15.98	19.17	20.16	21.50
20.58	15.98	19.18	20.17	21.51
20.59	15.99	19.19	20.18	21.52
20.60	16.00	19.20	20.19	21.53
20.61	16.01	19.21	20.20	21.54
20.62	16.02	19.22	20.21	21.55
20.63	16.02	19.23	20.22	21.56
20.64	16.03	19.23	20.23	21.57
20.65	16.04	19.24	20.24	21.58
20.66	16.05	19.25	20.25	21.59
20.67	16.05	19.26	20.26	21.60
20.68	16.06	19.27	20.27	21.61
20.69	16.07	19.28	20.28	21.62
20.70	16.08	19.29	20.29	21.63
20.71	16.09	19.30	20.30	21.64
20.72	16.09	19.31	20.31	21.65
20.73	16.10	19.32	20.32	21.66
20.74	16.11	19.33	20.33	21.67
20.75	16.12	19.34	20.34	21.68
20.76	16.12	19.35	20.34	21.69
20.77	16.13	19.36	20.35	21.70
20.78	16.14	19.36	20.36	21.72
20.79	16.15	19.37	20.37	21.73
20.80	16.16	19.38	20.38	21.74
20.81	16.16	19.39	20.39	21.75
20.82	16.17	19.40	20.40	21.76
20.83	16.18	19.41	20.41	21.77
20.84	16.19	19.42	20.42	21.78
20.85	16.19	19.43	20.43	21.79
20.86	16.20	19.44	20.44	21.80
20.87	16.21	19.45	20.45	21.81
20.88	16.22	19.46	20.46	21.82
20.89	16.23	19.47	20.47	21.83
20.90	16.23	19.48	20.48	21.84
20.91	16.24	19.49	20.49	21.85
20.92	16.25	19.50	20.50	21.86
20.93	16.26	19.50	20.51	21.87
20.94	16.26	19.51	20.52	21.88
20.95	16.27	19.52	20.53	21.89
20.96	16.28	19.53	20.54	21.90
20.97	16.29	19.54	20.55	21.91
20.98	16.30	19.55	20.56	21.92
20.99	16.30	19.56	20.57	21.93

(cont'd)

TABLE XX. PRICE EQUIVALENTS (cont'd)

100% Price	Equivalent Price As			
	60° Baumé	66° Baumé	98%	104.5%
	16.31	19.57	20.58	21.95
21.00	16.32	19.58	20.59	21.96
21.02	16.33	19.59	20.60	21.97
21.03	16.33	19.60	20.61	21.98
21.04	16.34	19.61	20.62	21.99
21.05	16.35	19.62	20.63	22.00
21.06	16.36	19.63	20.64	22.01
21.07	16.37	19.64	20.65	22.02
21.08	16.37	19.64	20.66	22.03
21.09	16.38	19.65	20.67	22.04
21.10	16.39	19.66	20.68	22.05
21.11	16.40	19.67	20.69	22.06
21.12	16.40	19.68	20.70	22.07
21.13	16.41	19.69	20.71	22.08
21.14	16.42	19.70	20.72	22.09
21.15	16.43	19.71	20.73	22.10
21.16	16.43	19.72	20.74	22.11
21.17	16.44	19.73	20.75	22.12
21.18	16.45	19.74	20.76	22.13
21.19	16.46	19.75	20.77	22.14
21.20	16.47	19.76	20.78	22.15
21.21	16.47	19.77	20.79	22.16
21.22	16.48	19.77	20.80	22.17
21.23	16.49	19.78	20.81	22.19
21.24	16.50	19.79	20.82	22.20
21.25	16.50	19.80	20.83	22.21
21.26	16.51	19.81	20.83	22.22
21.27	16.52	19.82	20.84	22.23
21.28	16.53	19.83	20.85	22.24
21.29	16.54	19.84	20.86	22.25
21.30	16.54	19.85	20.87	22.26
21.31	16.55	19.86	20.88	22.27
21.32	16.56	19.87	20.89	22.28
21.33	16.57	19.88	20.90	22.29
21.34	16.57	19.89	20.91	22.30
21.35	16.58	19.90	20.92	22.31
21.36	16.59	19.91	20.93	22.32
21.37	16.60	19.91	20.94	22.33
21.38	16.61	19.92	20.95	22.34
21.39	16.61	19.93	20.96	22.35
21.40	16.62	19.94	20.97	22.36
21.41	16.63	19.95	20.98	22.37
21.42	16.64	19.96	20.99	22.38
21.43	16.64	19.97	21.00	22.39
21.44	16.65	19.98	21.01	22.40
21.45	16.66	19.99	21.02	22.42
21.46	16.67	20.00	21.03	22.43
21.47	16.68	20.01	21.04	22.44
21.48	16.69	20.02	21.05	22.45
21.49	16.69	20.03	21.06	22.46

100% Price	Equivalent Price As			
	60° Baumé	66° Baumé	98%	104.5%
21.50	16.70	20.04	21.07	22.47
21.51	16.71	20.05	21.08	22.48
21.52	16.71	20.05	21.09	22.49
21.53	16.72	20.06	21.10	22.50
21.54	16.73	20.07	21.11	22.51
21.55	16.74	20.08	21.12	22.52
21.56	16.75	20.09	21.13	22.53
21.57	16.75	20.10	21.14	22.54
21.58	16.76	20.11	21.15	22.55
21.59	16.77	20.12	21.16	22.56
21.60	16.78	20.13	21.17	22.57
21.61	16.78	20.14	21.18	22.58
21.62	16.79	20.15	21.19	22.59
21.63	16.80	20.16	21.20	22.60
21.64	16.81	20.17	21.21	22.61
21.65	16.82	20.18	21.22	22.62
21.66	16.82	20.18	21.23	22.63
21.67	16.83	20.19	21.24	22.65
21.68	16.84	20.20	21.25	22.66
21.69	16.85	20.21	21.26	22.67
21.70	16.85	20.22	21.27	22.68
21.71	16.86	20.23	21.28	22.69
21.72	16.87	20.24	21.29	22.70
21.73	16.88	20.25	21.30	22.71
21.74	16.89	20.26	21.31	22.72
21.75	16.89	20.27	21.32	22.73
21.76	16.90	20.28	21.32	22.74
21.77	16.91	20.29	21.33	22.75
21.78	16.92	20.30	21.34	22.76
21.79	16.92	20.31	21.35	22.77
21.80	16.93	20.32	21.36	22.78
21.81	16.94	20.32	21.37	22.79
21.82	16.95	20.33	21.38	22.80
21.83	16.96	20.34	21.39	22.81
21.84	16.96	20.35	21.40	22.82
21.85	16.97	20.36	21.41	22.83
21.86	16.98	20.37	21.42	22.84
21.87	16.99	20.38	21.43	22.85
21.88	16.99	20.39	21.44	22.86
21.89	17.00	20.40	21.45	22.88
21.90	17.01	20.41	21.46	22.89
21.91	17.02	20.42	21.47	22.90
21.92	17.03	20.43	21.48	22.91
21.93	17.03	20.44	21.49	22.92
21.94	17.04	20.45	21.50	22.93
21.95	17.05	20.46	21.51	22.94
21.96	17.06	20.46	21.52	22.95
21.97	17.06	20.47	21.53	22.96
21.98	17.07	20.48	21.54	22.97
21.99	17.08	20.49	21.55	22.98

(cont'd)

TABLE XX. PRICE EQUIVALENTS (cont'd)

100% Price	Equivalent Price As			
	60° Baumé	66° Baumé	98%	104.5%
22.00	17.09	20.50	21.56	22.99
22.01	17.10	20.51	21.57	23.00
22.02	17.10	20.52	21.58	23.01
22.03	17.11	20.53	21.59	23.02
22.04	17.12	20.54	21.60	23.03
22.05	17.13	20.55	21.61	23.04
22.06	17.13	20.56	21.62	23.05
22.07	17.14	20.57	21.63	23.06
22.08	17.15	20.58	21.64	23.07
22.09	17.16	20.59	21.65	23.08
22.10	17.17	20.59	21.66	23.09
22.11	17.17	20.60	21.67	23.10
22.12	17.18	20.61	21.68	23.12
22.13	17.19	20.62	21.69	23.13
22.14	17.20	20.63	21.70	23.14
22.15	17.20	20.64	21.71	23.15
22.16	17.21	20.65	21.72	23.16
22.17	17.22	20.66	21.73	23.17
22.18	17.23	20.67	21.74	23.18
22.19	17.23	20.68	21.75	23.19
22.20	17.24	20.69	21.76	23.20
22.21	17.25	20.70	21.77	23.21
22.22	17.26	20.71	21.78	23.22
22.23	17.27	20.72	21.79	23.23
22.24	17.27	20.73	21.80	23.24
22.25	17.28	20.73	21.81	23.25
22.26	17.29	20.74	21.81	23.26
22.27	17.30	20.75	21.82	23.27
22.28	17.30	20.76	21.83	23.28
22.29	17.31	20.77	21.84	23.29
22.30	17.32	20.78	21.85	23.30
22.31	17.33	20.79	21.86	23.31
22.32	17.34	20.80	21.87	23.32
22.33	17.34	20.81	21.88	23.33
22.34	17.35	20.82	21.89	23.35
22.35	17.36	20.83	21.90	23.36
22.36	17.37	20.84	21.91	23.37
22.37	17.37	20.85	21.92	23.38
22.38	17.38	20.86	21.93	23.39
22.39	17.39	20.87	21.94	23.40
22.40	17.40	20.87	21.95	23.41
22.41	17.41	20.88	21.96	23.42
22.42	17.41	20.89	21.97	23.43
22.43	17.42	20.90	21.98	23.44
22.44	17.43	20.91	21.99	23.45
22.45	17.44	20.92	22.00	23.46
22.46	17.44	20.93	22.01	23.47
22.47	17.45	20.94	22.02	23.48
22.48	17.46	20.95	22.03	23.49
22.49	17.47	20.96	22.04	23.50

100%	Equivalent Price As			
Price	60° Baumé	66° Baumé	98%	104.5%
22.50	17.48	20.97	22.05	23.51
22.51	17.48	20.98	22.06	23.52
22.52	17.49	20.99	22.07	23.53
22.53	17.50	21.00	22.08	23.54
22.54	17.51	21.01	22.09	23.55
22.55	17.51	21.01	22.10	23.56
22.56	17.52	21.02	22.11	23.58
22.57	17.53	21.03	22.12	23.59
22.58	17.54	21.04	22.13	23.60
22.59	17.55	21.05	22.14	23.61
22.60	17.55	21.06	22.15	23.62
22.61	17.56	21.07	22.16	23.63
22.62	17.57	21.08	22.17	23.64
22.63	17.58	21.09	22.18	23.65
22.64	17.58	21.10	22.19	23.66
22.65	17.59	21.11	22.20	23.67
22.66	17.60	21.12	22.21	23.68
22.67	17.61	21.13	22.22	23.69
22.68	17.62	21.14	22.23	23.70
22.69	17.62	21.14	22.24	23.71
22.70	17.63	21.15	22.25	23.72
22.71	17.64	21.16	22.26	23.73
22.72	17.65	21.17	22.27	23.74
22.73	17.65	21.18	22.28	23.75
22.74	17.66	21.19	22.29	23.76
22.75	17.67	21.20	22.30	23.77
22.76	17.68	21.21	22.30	23.78
22.77	17.69	21.22	22.31	23.79
22.78	17.69	21.23	22.32	23.81
22.79	17.70	21.24	22.33	23.82
22.80	17.71	21.25	22.34	23.83
22.81	17.72	21.26	22.35	23.84
22.82	17.72	21.27	22.36	23.85
22.83	17.73	21.28	22.37	23.86
22.84	17.74	21.28	22.38	23.87
22.85	17.75	21.29	22.39	23.88
22.86	17.76	21.30	22.40	23.89
22.87	17.76	21.31	22.41	23.90
22.88	17.77	21.32	22.42	23.91
22.89	17.78	21.33	22.43	23.92
22.90	17.79	21.34	22.44	23.93
22.91	17.79	21.35	22.45	23.94
22.92	17.80	21.36	22.46	23.95
22.93	17.81	21.37	22.47	23.96
22.94	17.82	21.38	22.48	23.97
22.95	17.83	21.39	22.49	23.98
22.96	17.83	21.40	22.50	23.99
22.97	17.84	21.41	22.51	24.00
22.98	17.85	21.42	22.52	24.01
22.99	17.86	21.42	22.53	24.02

(cont'd)

TABLE XX. PRICE EQUIVALENTS (cont'd)

100% Price	Equivalent Price As			
	60° Baumé	66° Baumé	98%	104.5%
23.00	17.86	21.43	22.54	24.04
23.01	17.87	21.44	22.55	24.05
23.02	17.88	21.45	22.56	24.06
23.03	17.89	21.46	22.57	24.07
23.04	17.90	21.47	22.58	24.08
23.05	17.90	21.48	22.59	24.09
23.06	17.91	21.49	22.60	24.10
23.07	17.92	21.50	22.61	24.11
23.08	17.93	21.51	22.62	24.12
23.09	17.93	21.52	22.63	24.13
23.10	17.94	21.53	22.64	24.14
23.11	17.95	21.54	22.65	24.15
23.12	17.96	21.55	22.66	24.16
23.13	17.97	21.55	22.67	24.17
23.14	17.97	21.56	22.68	24.18
23.15	17.98	21.57	22.69	24.19
23.16	17.99	21.58	22.70	24.20
23.17	18.00	21.59	22.71	24.21
23.18	18.00	21.60	22.72	24.22
23.19	18.01	21.61	22.73	24.23
23.20	18.02	21.62	22.74	24.24
23.21	18.03	21.63	22.75	24.25
23.22	18.03	21.64	22.76	24.26
23.23	18.04	21.65	22.77	24.28
23.24	18.05	21.66	22.78	24.29
23.25	18.06	21.67	22.79	24.30
23.26	18.07	21.68	22.79	24.31
23.27	18.07	21.69	22.80	24.32
23.28	18.08	21.69	22.81	24.33
23.29	18.09	21.70	22.82	24.34
23.30	18.10	21.71	22.83	24.35
23.31	18.10	21.72	22.84	24.36
23.32	18.11	21.73	22.85	24.37
23.33	18.12	21.74	22.86	24.38
23.34	18.13	21.75	22.87	24.39
23.35	18.14	21.76	22.88	24.40
23.36	18.14	21.77	22.89	24.41
23.37	18.15	21.78	22.90	24.42
23.38	18.16	21.79	22.91	24.43
23.39	18.17	21.80	22.92	24.44
23.40	18.17	21.81	22.93	24.45
23.41	18.18	21.82	22.94	24.46
23.42	18.19	21.83	22.95	24.47
23.43	18.20	21.83	22.96	24.48
23.44	18.21	21.84	22.97	24.49
23.45	18.21	21.85	22.98	24.50
23.46	18.22	21.86	22.99	24.51
23.47	18.23	21.87	23.00	24.52
23.48	18.24	21.88	23.01	24.54
23.49	18.24	21.89	23.02	24.55

100%	Equivalent Price As			
Price	60° Baumé	66° Baumé	98%	104.5%
23.50	18.25	21.90	23.03	24.56
23.51	18.26	21.91	23.04	24.57
23.52	18.27	21.92	23.05	24.58
23.53	18.28	21.93	23.06	24.59
23.54	18.28	21.94	23.07	24.60
23.55	18.29	21.95	23.08	24.61
23.56	18.30	21.96	23.09	24.62
23.57	18.31	21.96	23.10	24.63
23.58	18.31	21.97	23.11	24.64
23.59	18.32	21.98	23.12	24.65
23.60	18.33	21.99	23.13	24.66
23.61	18.34	22.00	23.14	24.67
23.62	18.35	22.01	23.15	24.68
23.63	18.35	22.02	23.16	24.69
23.64	18.36	22.03	23.17	24.70
23.65	18.37	22.04	23.18	24.71
23.66	18.38	22.05	23.19	24.72
23.67	18.38	22.06	23.20	24.74
23.68	18.39	22.07	23.21	24.75
23.69	18.40	22.08	23.22	24.76
23.70	18.41	22.09	23.23	24.77
23.71	18.42	22.10	23.24	24.78
23.72	18.42	22.10	23.25	24.79
23.73	18.43	22.11	23.26	24.80
23.74	18.44	22.12	23.27	24.81
23.75	18.45	22.13	23.28	24.82
23.76	18.45	22.14	23.29	24.83
23.77	18.46	22.15	23.29	24.84
23.78	18.47	22.16	23.30	24.85
23.79	18.48	22.17	23.31	24.86
23.80	18.49	22.18	23.32	24.87
23.81	18.49	22.19	23.33	24.88
23.82	18.50	22.20	23.34	24.89
23.83	18.51	22.21	23.35	24.90
23.84	18.52	22.22	23.36	24.91
23.85	18.52	22.23	23.37	24.92
23.86	18.53	22.24	23.38	24.93
23.87	18.54	22.24	23.39	24.94
23.88	18.55	22.25	23.40	24.95
23.89	18.56	22.26	23.41	24.97
23.90	18.56	22.27	23.42	24.98
23.91	18.57	22.28	23.43	24.99
23.92	18.58	22.29	23.44	25.00
23.93	18.59	22.30	23.45	25.01
23.94	18.59	22.31	23.46	25.02
23.95	18.60	22.32	23.47	25.03
23.96	18.61	22.33	23.48	25.04
23.97	18.62	22.34	23.49	25.05
23.98	18.63	22.35	23.50	25.06
23.99	18.63	22.36	23.51	25.07

(cont'd)

TABLE XX. PRICE EQUIVALENTS (cont'd)

100% Price	Equivalent Price As			
	60° Baumé	66° Baumé	98%	104.5%
24.00	18.64	22.37	23.52	25.08
24.01	18.65	22.37	23.53	25.09
24.02	18.66	22.38	23.54	25.10
24.03	18.66	22.39	23.55	25.11
24.04	18.67	22.40	23.56	25.12
24.05	18.68	22.41	23.57	25.13
24.06	18.69	22.42	23.58	25.14
24.07	18.70	22.43	23.59	25.15
24.08	18.70	22.44	23.60	25.16
24.09	18.71	22.45	23.61	25.17
24.10	18.72	22.46	23.62	25.18
24.11	18.73	22.47	23.63	25.19
24.12	18.73	22.48	23.64	25.21
24.13	18.74	22.49	23.65	25.22
24.14	18.75	22.50	23.66	25.23
24.15	18.76	22.51	23.67	25.24
24.16	18.77	22.51	23.68	25.25
24.17	18.77	22.52	23.69	25.26
24.18	18.78	22.53	23.70	25.27
24.19	18.79	22.54	23.71	25.28
24.20	18.80	22.55	23.72	25.29
24.21	18.80	22.56	23.73	25.30
24.22	18.81	22.57	23.74	25.31
24.23	18.82	22.58	23.75	25.32
24.24	18.83	22.59	23.76	25.33
24.25	18.83	22.60	23.77	25.34
24.26	18.84	22.61	23.77	25.35
24.27	18.85	22.62	23.78	25.36
24.28	18.86	22.63	23.79	25.37
24.29	18.87	22.64	23.80	25.38
24.30	18.87	22.65	23.81	25.39
24.31	18.88	22.65	23.82	25.40
24.32	18.89	22.66	23.83	25.41
24.33	18.90	22.67	23.84	25.42
24.34	18.90	22.68	23.85	25.44
24.35	18.91	22.69	23.86	25.45
24.36	18.92	22.70	23.87	25.46
24.37	18.93	22.71	23.88	25.47
24.38	18.94	22.72	23.89	25.48
24.39	18.94	22.73	23.90	25.49
24.40	18.95	22.74	23.91	25.50
24.41	18.96	22.75	23.92	25.51
24.42	18.97	22.76	23.93	25.52
24.43	18.97	22.77	23.94	25.53
24.44	18.98	22.78	23.95	25.54
24.45	18.99	22.78	23.96	25.55
24.46	19.00	22.79	23.97	25.56
24.47	19.01	22.80	23.98	25.57
24.48	19.01	22.81	23.99	25.58
24.49	19.02	22.82	24.00	25.59

100% Price	Equivalent Price As			
	60° Baumé	66° Baumé	98%	104.5%
24.50	19.03	22.83	24.01	25.60
24.51	19.04	22.84	24.02	25.61
24.52	19.04	22.85	24.03	25.62
24.53	19.05	22.86	24.04	25.63
24.54	19.06	22.87	24.05	25.64
24.55	19.07	22.88	24.06	25.65
24.56	19.08	22.89	24.07	25.67
24.57	19.08	22.90	24.08	25.68
24.58	19.09	22.91	24.09	25.69
24.59	19.10	22.92	24.10	25.70
24.60	19.11	22.92	24.11	25.71
24.61	19.11	22.93	24.12	25.72
24.62	19.12	22.94	24.13	25.73
24.63	19.13	22.95	24.14	25.74
24.64	19.14	22.96	24.15	25.75
24.65	19.15	22.97	24.16	25.76
24.66	19.15	22.98	24.17	25.77
24.67	19.16	22.99	24.18	25.78
24.68	19.17	23.00	24.19	25.79
24.69	19.18	23.01	24.20	25.80
24.70	19.18	23.02	24.21	25.81
24.71	19.19	23.03	24.22	25.82
24.72	19.20	23.04	24.23	25.83
24.73	19.21	23.05	24.24	25.84
24.74	19.22	23.06	24.25	25.85
24.75	19.22	23.06	24.26	25.86
24.76	19.23	23.07	24.26	25.87
24.77	19.24	23.08	24.27	25.88
24.78	19.25	23.09	24.28	25.90
24.79	19.25	23.10	24.29	25.91
24.80	19.26	23.11	24.30	25.92
24.81	19.27	23.12	24.31	25.93
24.82	19.28	23.13	24.32	25.94
24.83	19.29	23.14	24.33	25.95
24.84	19.29	23.15	24.34	25.96
24.85	19.30	23.16	24.35	25.97
24.86	19.31	23.17	24.36	25.98
24.87	19.32	23.18	24.37	25.99
24.88	19.32	23.19	24.38	26.00
24.89	19.33	23.19	24.39	26.01
24.90	19.34	23.20	24.40	26.02
24.91	19.35	23.21	24.41	26.03
24.92	19.36	23.22	24.42	26.04
24.93	19.36	23.23	24.43	26.05
24.94	19.37	23.24	24.44	26.06
24.95	19.38	23.25	24.45	26.07
24.96	19.39	23.26	24.46	26.08
24.97	19.39	23.27	24.47	26.09
24.98	19.40	23.28	24.48	26.10
24.99	19.41	23.29	24.49	26.11
25.00	19.42	23.30	24.50	26.13

TABLE XXI. FREIGHT EQUIVALENTS   Factor Reciprocal of Acidity
Factor Times Freight Rate Per Ton= 100% freight/ton

%	Factor	%	Factor	%	Factor	%	Factor	%	Factor	%	Factor
75.0	1.333	80.0	1.250	85.0	1.176	90.0	1.1111	95.0	1.053	100.0	1.000
.1	1.332	.1	1.248	.1	1.175	.1	1.110	.1	1.052	.1	·999
.2	1.330	.2	1.247	.2	1.174	.2	1.109	.2	1.050	.2	.998
.3	1.328	.3	1.245	.3	1.172	.3	1.107	.3	1.049	.3	.997
.4	1.326	.4	1.244	.4	1.171	.4	1.106	.4	1.048	.4	.996
.5	1.324	.5	1.242	.5	1.170	.5	1.105	.5	1.047	.5	.995
.6	1.323	.6	1.241	.6	1.168	.6	1.104	.6	1.046	.6	.994
.7	1.321	.7	1.239	.7	1.167	.7	1.103	.7	1.045	.7	.993
.8	1.319	.8	1.238	.8	1.166	.8	1.101	.8	1.044	.8	.992
.9	1.318	.9	1.236	.9	1.164	.9	1.100	.9	1.043	.9	.991
76.0	1.316	81.0	1.235	86.0	1.163	91.0	1.099	96.0	1.042	101.0	.990
.1	1.314	.1	1.233	.1	1.161	.1	1.098	.1	1.041	.1	.989
.2	1.312	.2	1.232	.2	1.160	.2	1.096	.2	1.040	.2	.988
.3	1.311	.3	1.230	.3	1.159	.3	1.095	.3	1.038	.3	.987
.4	1.309	.4	1.229	.4	1.157	.4	1.094	.4	1.037	.4	.986
.5	1.307	.5	1.227	.5	1.156	.5	1.093	.5	1.036	.5	.985
.6	1.305	.6	1.225	.6	1.155	.6	1.092	.6	1.035	.6	.984
.7	1.304	.7	1.224	.7	1.153	.7	1.091	.7	1.034	.7	.983
.8	1.302	.8	1.222	.8	1.152	.8	1.089	.8	1.033	.8	.982
.9	1.300	.9	1.221	.9	1.151	.9	1.088	.9	1.032	.9	.981
77.0	1.299	82.0	1.220	87.0	1.149	92.0	1.087	97.0	1.031	102.0	.980
.1	1.297	.1	1.218	.1	1.148	.1	1.086	.1	1.030	.1	.979
.2	1.295	.2	1.217	.2	1.147	.2	1.085	.2	1.029	.2	.978
.3	1.294	.3	1.215	.3	1.145	.3	1.083	.3	1.028	.3	.978
.4	1.292	.4	1.214	.4	1.144	.4	1.082	.4	1.027	.4	.977
.5	1.290	.5	1.212	.5	1.143	.5	1.081	.5	1.026	.5	.976
.6	1.289	.6	1.211	.6	1.142	.6	1.080	.6	1.025	.6	.975
.7	1.287	.7	1.209	.7	1.140	.7	1.079	.7	1.024	.7	.974
.8	1.285	.8	1.208	.8	1.139	.8	1.078	.8	1.022	.8	.973
.9	1.284	.9	1.206	.9	1.138	.9	1.076	.9	1.021	.9	.972
78.0	1.282	83.0	1.205	88.0	1.136	93.0	1.075	98.0	1.020	103.0	.971
.1	1.280	.1	1.203	.1	1.135	.1	1.074	.1	1.019	.1	.970
.2	1.279	.2	1.202	.2	1.134	.2	1.073	.2	1.018	.2	.969
.3	1.277	.3	1.200	.3	1.133	.3	1.072	.3	1.017	.3	.968
.4	1.276	.4	1.199	.4	1.131	.4	1.071	.4	1.016	.4	.967
.5	1.274	.5	1.198	.5	1.130	.5	1.070	.5	1.015	.5	.966
.6	1.272	.6	1.196	.6	1.129	.6	1.068	.6	1.014	.6	.965
.7	1.271	.7	1.195	.7	1.127	.7	1.067	.7	1.013	.7	.964
.8	1.269	.8	1.193	.8	1.126	.8	1.066	.8	1.012	.8	.963
.9	1.267	.9	1.192	.9	1.125	.9	1.065	.9	1.011	.9	.962
79.0	1.266	84.0	1.190	89.0	1.124	94.0	1.064	99.0	1.010	104.0	.962
.1	1.264	.1	1.189	.1	1.122	.1	1.063	.1	1.009	.1	.961
.2	1.263	.2	1.188	.2	1.121	.2	1.062	.2	1.008	.2	.960
.3	1.261	.3	1.186	.3	1.120	.3	1.060	.3	1.007	.3	.959
.4	1.259	.4	1.185	.4	1.119	.4	1.059	.4	1.006	.4	.958
.5	1.258	.5	1.183	.5	1.117	.5	1.058	.5	1.005	.5	.957
.6	1.256	.6	1.182	.6	1.116	.6	1.057	.6	1.004		
.7	1.255	.7	1.181	.7	1.115	.7	1.056	.7	1.003		
.8	1.253	.8	1.179	.8	1.114	.8	1.055	.8	1.002		
.9	1.252	.9	1.178	.9	1.112	.9	1.054	.9	1.001		

TABLE XXII. SULFURIC ACID PROPERTIES (0–100%)

° Baumé @60° F	Specific Gravity	Percent H_2SO_4	Weight Lb/Gal	Percent Total H_2O	Percent SO_3	Freezing Pt° F
0.0	1.0000	0.00	8.338	100.00	.00	32.0
1.0	1.0069	1.02	8.395	99.17	.83	31.4
2.0	1.0140	2.08	8.454	98.30	1.70	30.7
3.0	1.0211	3.13	8.514	97.45	2.55	29.8
4.0	1.0284	4.21	8.574	96.56	3.44	28.9
5.0	1.0357	5.28	8.635	95.69	4.31	28.0
6.0	1.0432	6.37	8.698	94.80	5.20	27.1
7.0	1.0507	7.45	8.760	93.92	6.08	26.1
8.0	1.0584	8.55	8.825	93.02	6.98	24.9
9.0	1.0662	9.66	8.890	92.12	7.88	24.0
10.0	1.0741	10.77	8.956	91.21	8.79	22.7
11.0	1.0821	11.89	9.022	90.29	9.71	21.2
12.0	1.0902	13.01	9.090	89.38	10.62	19.7
13.0	1.0985	14.13	9.159	88.47	11.53	18.1
14.0	1.1069	15.25	9.229	87.55	12.45	16.3
15.0	1.1154	16.38	9.300	86.63	13.37	14.6
16.0	1.1240	17.53	9.372	85.69	14.31	12.2
17.0	1.1328	18.71	9.445	84.73	15.27	10.0
18.0	1.1417	19.89	9.519	83.76	16.24	7.3
19.0	1.1508	21.07	9.595	82.80	17.20	4.7
20.0	1.1600	22.25	9.672	81.84	18.16	+ 1.8
21.0	1.1694	23.43	9.750	80.87	19.13	− 1.8
22.0	1.1798	24.61	9.837	79.91	20.09	− 6.2
23.0	1.1885	25.81	9.909	78.93	21.07	− 10.9
24.0	1.1983	27.03	9.991	77.94	22.06	− 15.4
25.0	1.2083	28.28	10.074	76.92	23.08	− 20.9
26.0	1.2185	29.53	10.159	75.89	24.11	− 28.2
27.0	1.2288	30.79	10.245	74.87	25.13	− 35.3
28.0	1.2393	32.05	10.333	73.84	26.16	− 44.7
29.0	1.2500	33.33	10.422	72.79	27.21	− 54.0
30.0	1.2609	34.63	10.513	71.73	28.27	− 66.6
31.0	1.2719	35.93	10.605	70.67	29.33	− 79.1
32.0	1.2832	37.26	10.699	69.58	30.42	− 74.3
33.0	1.2946	38.58	10.794	68.51	31.49	− 70.8
34.0	1.3063	39.92	10.892	67.41	32.59	− 67.3
35.0	1.3182	41.27	10.991	66.31	33.69	− 65.3
36.0	1.3303	42.63	11.092	65.20	34.80	− 63.3
37.0	1.3426	43.99	11.194	64.09	35.91	− 57.4
38.0	1.3551	45.35	11.298	62.98	37.02	− 50.2
39.0	1.3679	46.72	11.405	61.86	38.14	− 44.5
40.0	1.3810	48.10	11.514	60.76	39.26	− 38.0
41.0	1.3942	49.47	11.624	59.62	40.38	− 33.5
42.0	1.4078	50.87	11.738	58.47	41.53	− 29.3
43.0	1.4216	52.26	11.853	57.34	42.66	− 25.4
44.0	1.4356	53.66	11.970	56.20	43.80	− 22.6
45.0	1.4500	55.07	12.090	55.05	44.95	− 20.6
46.0	1.4646	56.48	12.211	53.90	46.10	− 19.4
47.0	1.4796	57.90	12.336	52.74	47.26	− 19.1
48.0	1.4948	59.32	12.463	51.58	48.42	− 19.9
49.0	1.5104	60.75	12.593	50.41	49.59	− 21.8

(cont'd)

TABLE XXII. SULFURIC ACID PROPERTIES (cont'd)

° Baumé @60° F	Specific Gravity	Percent H2SO4	Weight Lb/Gal	Percent Total H2O	Percent SO3	Freezing Pt°F
50.0	1.5263	62.18	12.726	49.23	50.77	− 25.0
51.0	1.5426	63.66	12.862	48.03	51.97	− 27.5
51.9	1.5575	64.98	12.986	46.96	53.04	− 28.9
51.91	1.5577	65.00	12.988	46.94	53.06	− 34.2
51.98	1.5588	65.10	12.997	46.86	53.14	− 34.2
52.05	1.5599	65.20	13.006	46.78	53.22	− 34.2
52.11	1.5610	65.30	13.015	46.70	53.30	− 34.3
52.18	1.5621	65.40	13.024	46.61	53.39	− 34.3
52.25	1.5633	65.50	13.034	46.53	53.47	− 34.4
52.31	1.5644	65.60	13.043	46.45	53.55	− 34.5
52.38	1.5656	65.70	13.054	46.37	53.63	− 34.6
52.45	1.5667	65.80	13.063	46.29	53.71	− 34.6
52.52	1.5679	65.90	13.073	46.21	53.79	− 34.7
52.58	1.5690	66.00	13.082	46.12	53.88	− 34.8
52.65	1.5701	66.10	13.091	46.04	53.96	− 34.9
52.71	1.5712	66.20	13.100	45.96	54.04	− 34.9
52.78	1.5724	66.30	13.110	45.88	54.12	− 35.0
52.84	1.5735	66.40	13.119	45.80	54.20	− 35.1
52.91	1.5746	66.50	13.129	45.72	54.28	− 35.3
52.98	1.5757	66.60	13.138	45.63	54.37	− 35.4
53.05	1.5769	66.70	13.148	45.55	54.45	− 35.5
53.11	1.5780	66.80	13.157	45.47	54.53	− 35.6
53.18	1.5792	66.90	13.167	45.39	54.61	− 35.7
53.24	1.5803	67.00	13.176	45.31	54.69	− 35.9
53.31	1.5814	67.10	13.185	45.23	54.77	− 36.0
53.38	1.5826	67.20	13.195	45.14	54.86	− 36.2
53.45	1.5838	67.30	13.205	45.06	54.94	− 36.3
53.51	1.5850	67.40	13.215	44.98	55.02	− 36.4
53.58	1.5861	67.50	13.224	44.90	55.10	− 36.6
53.64	1.5872	67.60	13.234	44.82	55.18	− 36.7
53.71	1.5884	67.70	13.244	44.74	55.26	− 36.9
53.78	1.5896	67.80	13.254	44.65	55.35	− 37.0
53.85	1.5907	67.90	13.263	44.57	55.43	− 37.2
53.91	1.5919	68.00	13.273	44.49	55.51	− 37.4
53.98	1.5931	68.10	13.283	44.41	55.59	− 37.7
54.04	1.5942	68.20	13.292	44.33	55.67	− 38.0
54.11	1.5954	68.30	13.302	44.25	55.75	− 38.5
54.18	1.5966	68.40	13.312	44.17	55.83	− 39.0
54.24	1.5977	68.50	13.321	44.08	55.92	− 39.5
54.30	1.5988	68.60	13.330	44.00	56.00	− 40.0
54.37	1.600	68.70	13.340	43.92	56.08	− 40.6
54.44	1.6011	68.80	13.349	43.84	56.16	− 41.2
54.51	1.6023	68.90	13.359	43.76	56.24	− 41.7
54.57	1.6035	69.00	13.370	43.68	56.32	− 42.2
54.64	1.6047	69.10	13.380	43.59	56.41	− 42.6
54.70	1.6058	69.20	13.389	43.51	56.49	− 43.0
54.76	1.6069	69.30	13.398	43.43	56.57	− 43.3
54.83	1.6080	69.40	13.407	43.35	56.65	− 43.6
54.90	1.6093	69.50	13.418	43.27	56.73	− 44.0
54.97	1.6105	69.60	13.428	43.19	56.81	− 44.4
55 03	1.6117	69.70	13.438	43.10	56.90	− 44.9
55.10	1.6129	69.80	13.448	43.02	56.98	− 44.5

° Baumé @60° F	Specific Gravity	Percent H_2SO_4	Weight Lb/Gal	Percent Total H_2O	Percent SO_3	Freezing Pt° F
55.17	1.6141	69.90	13.458	42.94	57.06	− 44.2
55.23	1.6153	70.00	13.468	42.86	57.14	− 43.8
55.29	1.6164	70.10	13.477	42.78	57.22	− 43.6
55.36	1.6175	70.20	13.486	42.70	57.30	− 43.3
55.42	1.6187	70.30	13.496	42.61	57.39	− 43.0
55.49	1.6199	70.40	13.506	42.53	57.47	− 42.8
55.56	1.6212	70.50	13.517	42.45	57.55	− 42.5
55.63	1.6224	70.60	13.527	42.37	57.63	− 42.2
55.69	1.6236	70.70	13.537	42.29	57.71	− 42.0
55.75	1.6247	70.80	13.546	42.20	57.80	− 41.7
55.82	1.6259	70.90	13.556	42.12	57.88	− 41.5
55.88	1.6271	71.00	13.566	42.04	57.96	− 41.2
55.95	1.6283	71.10	13.576	41.96	58.04	− 41.0
56.02	1.6295	71.20	13.586	41.88	58.12	− 40.8
56.08	1.6306	71.30	13.595	41.80	58.20	− 40.7
56.14	1.6318	71.40	13.605	41.72	58.28	− 40.5
56.21	1.6330	71.50	13.615	41.63	58.37	− 40.4
56.27	1.6342	71.60	13.625	41.55	58.45	− 40.3
56.34	1.6354	71.70	13.635	41.47	58.53	− 40.1
56.40	1.6366	71.80	13.645	41.39	58.61	− 40.0
56.47	1.6378	71.90	13.655	41.31	58.69	− 39.9
56.53	1.6389	72.00	13.665	41.23	58.77	− 39.8
56.59	1.6400	72.10	13.674	41.14	58.86	− 39.7
56.65	1.6412	72.20	13.684	41.06	58.94	− 39.6
56.71	1.6424	72.30	13.694	40.98	59.02	− 39.5
56.78	1.6436	72.40	13.704	40.90	59.10	− 39.4
56.84	1.6448	72.50	13.714	40.82	59.18	− 39.4
56.91	1.6460	72.60	13.724	40.74	59.26	− 39.3
56.97	1.6471	72.70	13.733	40.65	59.35	− 39.2
57.03	1.6483	72.80	13.743	40.57	59.43	− 39.2
57.09	1.6495	72.90	13.753	40.49	59.51	− 39.1
57.15	1.6506	73.00	13.762	40.41	59.59	− 39.1
57.22	1.6518	73.10	13.772	40.33	59.67	− 39.1
57.28	1.6530	73.20	13.782	40.25	59.75	− 39.2
57.34	1.6542	73.30	13.792	40.17	59.83	− 39.2
57.41	1.6554	73.40	13.802	40.08	59.92	− 39.3
57.47	1.6566	73.50	13.812	40.00	60.00	− 39.4
57.52	1.6576	73.60	13.821	39.92	60.08	− 39.5
57.59	1.6587	73.70	13.830	39.84	60.16	− 39.7
57.65	1.6599	73.80	13.840	39.76	60.24	− 38.0
57.71	1.6611	73.90	13.850	39.68	60.32	− 36.5
57.77	1.6623	74.00	13.860	39.59	60.41	− 35.0
57.84	1.6636	74.10	13.871	39.51	60.49	− 33.5
57.90	1.6648	74.20	13.881	39.43	60.57	− 32.0
57.97	1.6660	74.30	13.891	39.35	60.65	− 30.5
58.03	1.6672	74.40	13.901	39.27	60.73	− 29.0
58.09	1.6683	74.50	13.910	39.19	60.81	− 27.5
58.15	1.6695	74.60	13.920	39.10	60.90	− 26.0
58.21	1.6706	74.70	13.929	39.02	60.98	− 24.5
58.27	1.6718	74.80	13.939	38.94	61.06	− 23.0
58.33	1.6730	74.90	13.949	38.86	61.14	− 21.5
58.40	1.6743	75.00	13.960	38.78	61.22	− 20.0

(cont'd)

TABLE XXII. SULFURIC ACID PROPERTIES (cont'd)

° Baumé @60° F	Specific Gravity	Percent H_2SO_4	Weight Lb/Gal	Percent Total H_2O	Percent SO_3	Freezing Pt° F
58.46	1.6755	75.10	13.970	38.70	61.30	− 18.9
58.52	1.6766	75.20	13.979	38.61	61.39	− 17.7
58.58	1.6778	75.30	13.989	38.53	61.47	− 16.4
58.64	1.6790	75.40	13.999	38.45	61.55	− 15.0
58.70	1.6802	75.50	14.009	38.37	61.63	− 13.8
58.76	1.6814	75.60	14.019	38.29	61.71	− 12.5
58.82	1.6825	75.70	14.028	38.21	61.79	− 11.2
58.88	1.6837	75.80	14.038	38.12	61.88	− 10.0
58.94	1.6849	75.90	14.048	38.04	61.96	− 8.8
59.00	1.6861	76.00	14.058	37.96	62.04	− 7.5
59.06	1.6873	76.10	14.068	37.88	62.12	− 6.2
59.16	1.6885	76.20	14.078	37.80	62.20	− 4.8
59.19	1.6897	76.30	14.088	37.72	62.28	− 3.5
59.25	1.6909	76.40	14.098	37.63	62.37	− 2.4
59.30	1.6920	76.50	14.107	37.55	62.45	− 1.0
59.36	1.6932	76.60	14.117	37.47	62.53	+ .5
59.42	1.6944	76.70	14.127	37.39	62.61	+ 1.6
59.48	1.6956	76.80	14.137	37.31	62.69	+ 2.7
59.54	1.6967	76.90	14.147	37.23	62.77	+ 3.9
59.60	1.6979	77.00	14.157	37.14	62.86	+ 4.3
59.66	1.6991	77.10	14.167	37.06	62.94	+ 5.6
59.72	1.7003	77.20	14.177	36.98	63.02	+ 6.6
59.78	1.7015	77.30	14.187	36.90	63.10	+ 7.7
59.84	1.7027	77.40	14.197	36.82	63.18	+ 8.7
59.90	1.7039	77.50	14.207	36.74	63.26	+ 9.7
59.96	1.7051	77.60	14.217	36.65	63.35	+ 10.8
60.00	1.7059	77.67	14.223	36.60	63.40	+ 11.6
60.02	1.7062	77.70	14.226	36.57	63.43	+ 11.8
60.08	1.7074	77.80	14.236	36.49	63.51	+ 12.8
60.13	1.7085	77.90	14.245	36.41	63.59	+ 13.8
60.18	1.7096	78.00	14.254	36.33	63.67	+ 14.8
60.24	1.7108	78.10	14.264	36.25	63.75	+ 15.8
60.30	1.7119	78.20	14.273	36.17	63.83	+ 16.8
60.36	1.7131	78.30	14.283	36.08	63.92	+ 17.7
60.41	1.7142	78.40	14.292	36.00	64.00	+ 18.7
60.47	1.7154	78.50	14.302	35.92	64.08	+ 19.6
60.53	1.7165	78.60	14.312	35.84	64.16	+ 20.5
60.58	1.7177	78.70	14.322	35.76	64.24	+ 21.4
60.64	1.7188	78.80	14.331	35.68	64.32	+ 22.3
60.70	1.7200	78.90	14.341	35.59	64.41	+ 23.2
60.76	1.7211	79.00	14.350	35.51	64.49	+ 24.1
60.81	1.7223	79.10	14.360	35.43	64.57	+ 24.9
60.87	1.7235	79.20	14.370	35.35	64.65	+ 25.7
60.93	1.7247	79.30	14.380	35.27	64.73	+ 26.6
60.99	1.7259	79.40	14.390	35.19	64.81	+ 27.5
61.04	1.7269	79.50	14.398	35.10	64.90	+ 28.2
61.09	1.7280	79.60	14.408	35.02	64.98	+ 28.9
61.15	1.7292	79.70	14.418	34.94	65.06	+ 29.6
61.20	1.7303	79.80	14.427	34.86	65.14	+ 29.6
61.25	1.7314	79.90	14.436	34.78	65.22	+ 29.6
61.31	1.7325	80.00	14.445	34.70	65.30	+ 29.7
61.36	1.7336	80.10	14.454	34.61	65.39	+ 29.7

°Baumé @60° F	Specific Gravity	Percent H_2SO_4	Weight Lb/Gal	Percent Total H_2O	Percent SO_3	Freezing Pt° F
61.41	1.7347	80.20	14.463	34.53	65.47	+ 29.7
61.47	1.7358	80.30	14.473	34.45	65.55	+ 29.7
61.52	1.7369	80.40	14.482	34.37	65.63	+ 30.7
61.57	1.7380	80.50	14.491	34.29	65.71	+ 31.8
61.62	1.7391	80.60	14.500	34.21	65.79	+ 32.6
61.67	1.7402	80.70	14.509	34.12	65.88	+ 34.3
61.73	1.7413	80.80	14.518	34.04	65.96	+ 35.2
61.78	1.7424	80.90	14.528	33.96	66.04	+ 36.1
61.84	1.7436	81.00	14.538	33.88	66.12	+ 37.0
61.89	1.7447	81.10	14.547	33.80	66.20	+ 37.6
61.95	1.7459	81.20	14.557	33.72	66.28	+ 38.3
62.00	1.7470	81.30	14.566	33.63	66.37	+ 39.0
62.05	1.7480	81.40	14.574	33.55	66.45	+ 39.4
62.10	1.7491	81.50	14.583	33.47	66.53	+ 39.7
62.15	1.7501	81.60	14.592	33.39	66.61	+ 39.9
62.20	1.7511	81.70	14.600	33.31	66.69	+ 40.0
62.25	1.7522	81.80	14.609	33.23	66.77	+ 40.6
62.29	1.7532	81.90	14.618	33.15	66.85	+ 41.2
62.34	1.7542	82.00	14.626	33.06	66.94	+ 41.6
62.39	1.7552	82.10	14.634	32.98	67.02	+ 42.0
62.44	1.7563	82.20	14.644	32.90	67.10	+ 42.5
62.49	1.7574	82.30	14.653	32.82	67.18	+ 42.9
62.54	1.7584	82.40	14.661	32.74	67.26	+ 43.4
62.59	1.7595	82.50	14.670	32.66	67.34	+ 43.7
62.64	1.7606	82.60	14.679	32.57	67.43	+ 44.1
62.69	1.7616	82.70	14.688	32.49	67.51	+ 44.6
62.73	1.7625	82.80	14.695	32.41	67.59	+ 45.0
62.78	1.7636	82.90	14.704	32.33	67.67	+ 45.3
62.83	1.7647	83.00	14.714	32.25	67.75	+ 45.6
62.88	1.7657	83.10	14.722	32.16	67.84	+ 45.8
62.93	1.7668	83.20	14.731	32.08	67.92	+ 46.0
62.98	1.7679	83.30	14.740	32.00	68.00	+ 46.2
63.03	1.7689	83.40	14.749	31.92	68.08	+ 46.5
63.07	1.7699	83.50	14.757	31.84	68.16	+ 46.7
63.12	1.7708	83.60	14.764	31.76	68.24	+ 46.9
63.16	1.7717	83.70	14.772	31.68	68.32	+ 47.1
63.20	1.7726	83.80	14.779	31.59	68.41	+ 47.3
63.24	1.7735	83.90	14.787	31.51	68.49	+ 47.4
63.29	1.7745	84.00	14.795	31.43	68.57	+ 47.4
63.33	1.7754	84.10	14.803	31.35	68.65	+ 47.3
63.47	1.7763	84.20	14.810	31.27	68.73	+ 47.3
63.41	1.7772	84.30	14.818	31.19	68.81	+ 47.3
63.46	1.7782	84.40	14.826	31.10	68.90	+ 47.3
63.50	1.7791	84.50	14.834	31.02	68.98	+ 47.2
63.54	1.7800	84.60	14.841	30.94	69.06	+ 47.1
63.59	1.7810	84.70	14.849	30.86	69.14	+ 47.0
63.63	1.7819	84.80	14.857	30.78	69.22	+ 46.9
63.67	1.7829	84.90	14.865	30.70	69.30	+ 46.7
63.72	1.7839	85.00	14.874	30.61	69.39	+ 46.6
63.76	1.7848	85.10	14.881	30.53	69.47	+ 46.5
63.80	1.7857	85.20	14.889	30.45	69.55	+ 46.2
63.84	1.7866	85.30	14.896	30.37	69.63	+ 46.0
63.89	1.7876	85.40	14.904	30.29	69.71	+ 45.8

(cont'd)

TABLE XXII. SULFURIC ACID PROPERTIES (cont'd)

°Baumé @60° F	Specific Gravity	Percent H_2SO_4	Weight Lb/Gal	Percent Total H_2O	Percent SO_3	Freezing Pt° F
63.93	1.7886	85.50	14.913	30.21	69.79	+ 45.6
63.97	1.7895	85.60	14.920	30.12	69.88	+ 45.4
64.02	1.7905	85.70	14.929	30.04	69.96	+ 45.2
64.06	1.7914	85.80	14.936	29.96	70.04	+ 44.9
64.10	1.7923	85.90	14.944	29.88	70.12	+ 44.7
64.14	1.7932	86.00	14.951	29.80	70.20	+ 44.3
64.18	1.7940	86.10	14.958	29.72	70.28	+ 43.9
64.21	1.7948	86.20	14.965	29.63	70.37	+ 43.6
64.25	1.7957	86.30	14.972	29.55	70.45	+ 43.2
64.29	1.7965	86.40	14.979	29.47	70.53	+ 42.9
64.32	1.7973	86.50	14.985	29.39	70.61	+ 42.5
64.36	1.7981	86.60	14.992	29.31	70.69	+ 42.2
64.39	1.7988	86.70	14.999	29.23	70.77	+ 41.8
64.42	1.7995	86.80	15.004	29.15	70.85	+ 41.5
64.46	1.8003	86.90	15.010	29.06	70.94	+ 41.2
64.49	1.8010	87.00	15.016	28.98	71.02	+ 40.8
64.52	1.8017	87.10	15.022	28.90	71.10	+ 40.2
64.55	1.8024	87.20	15.028	28.82	71.18	+ 39.7
64.59	1.8032	87.30	15.035	28.74	71.26	+ 39.3
64.62	1.8040	87.40	15.041	28.66	71.34	+ 38.8
64.65	1.8047	87.50	15.047	28.57	71.43	+ 38.3
64.69	1.8054	87.60	15.053	28.49	71.51	+ 37.8
64.71	1.8060	87.70	15.058	28.41	71.59	+ 37.3
64.74	1.8066	87.80	15.063	28.33	71.67	+ 36.7
64.76	1.8071	87.90	15.067	28.25	71.75	+ 36.2
64.79	1.8077	88.00	15.072	28.17	71.83	+ 35.7
64.82	1.8084	88.10	15 079	28.08	71.92	+ 35.2
64.85	1.8092	88.20	15.085	28.00	72.00	+ 34.7
64.89	1.8101	88.30	15.092	27.92	72.08	+ 34.1
64.92	1.8108	88.40	15.098	27.84	72.16	+ 33.5
64.96	1.8115	88.50	15.104	27.76	72.24	+ 32.9
64.99	1.8122	88.60	15.110	27.68	72.32	+ 32.3
65.01	1.8128	88.70	15.115	27.59	72.41	+ 31.8
65.04	1.8135	88.80	15.120	27.51	72.49	+ 31.2
65.07	1.8142	88.90	15.126	27.43	72.57	+ 30.4
65.11	1.8149	89.00	15.132	27.35	72.65	+ 29.8
65.14	1.8156	89.10	15.138	27.27	72.73	+ 29.2
65.17	1.8163	89.20	15.144	27.19	72.81	+ 28.5
65.20	1.8170	89.30	15.150	27.10	72.90	+ 27.8
65.22	1.8175	89.40	15.154	27.02	72.98	+ 27.2
65.24	1.8180	89.50	15.158	26.94	73.06	+ 26.5
65.26	1.8185	89.60	15.162	26.86	73.14	+ 25.7
65.29	1.8190	89.70	15.166	26.78	73.22	+ 25.0
65.31	1.8195	89.80	15.170	26.70	73.30	+ 24.3
65.33	1,8201	89.90	15.175	26.61	73.39	+ 23.5
65.36	1.8206	90.00	15.180	26.53	73.47	+ 22.5
65.38	1.8212	90.10	15.185	26.45	73,55	+ 21.4
65.41	1.8218	90.20	15.190	26.37	73.63	+ 20.3
65.43	1.8223	90.30	15.194	26.29	73.71	+ 19.2
65.45	1.8228	90.40	15.198	26.21	73.79	+ 18.2
65.48	1.8234	90.50	15.203	26.12	73.88	+ 17.2
65.50	1.8239	90.60	15.207	26.04	73.96	+ 16.1
65.52	1.8244	90.70	15.211	25.96	74.04	+ 15.0

° Baumé @60° F	Specific Gravity	Percent H_2SO_4	Weight Lb/Gal	Percent Total H_2O	Percent SO_3	Freezing Pt° F
65.54	1.8249	90.80	15.215	25.88	74.12	+ 14.0
65.57	1.8254	90.90	15.220	25.80	74.20	+ 13.1
65.59	1.8259	91.00	15.224	25.72	74.28	+ 11.9
65.61	1.8264	91.10	15.228	25.64	74.36	+ 10.8
65.63	1.8269	91.20	15.232	25.55	74.45	+ 9.7
65.65	1.8274	91.30	15.236	25.47	74.53	+ 8.5
65.67	1.8278	91.40	15.240	25.39	74.61	+ 7.3
65.69	1.8283	91.50	15.244	25.31	74.69	+ 6.1
65.71	1.8288	91.60	15.248	25.23	74.77	+ 4.8
65.73	1.8292	91.70	15.251	25.15	74.85	+ 3.5
65.75	1.8296	91.80	15.255	25.06	74.94	+ 2.3
65.77	1.8301	91.90	15.259	24.98	75.02	+ 1.1
65.79	1.8305	92.00	15.262	24.90	75.10	− .3
65.81	1.8309	92.10	15.265	24.82	75.18	− 1.5
65.83	1.8314	92.20	15.270	24.74	75.26	− 2.9
65.84	1.8318	92.30	15.273	24.66	75.34	− 4.3
65.86	1.8322	92.40	15.276	24.57	75.43	− 5.9
65.88	1.8327	92.50	15.281	24.49	75.51	− 7.6
65.90	1.8331	92.60	15.284	24.41	75.59	− 9.5
65.92	1.8335	92.70	15.287	24.33	75.67	− 11.1
65.93	1.8339	92.80	15.291	24.25	75.75	− 12.6
65.95	1.8343	92.90	15.294	24.17	75.83	− 14.5
65.97	1.8347	93.00	15.297	24.08	75.92	− 16.6
65.98	1.8350	93.10	15.300	24.00	76.00	− 18.8
66.00	1.8354	93.19	15.303	23.93	76.07	− 20.0
	1.8354	93.20	15.303	23.92	76.08	− 20.2
	1.8357	93.30	15.306	23.84	76.16	− 21.7
	1,8360	93.40	15.308	23.76	76.24	− 23.8
	1,8364	93.50	15.311	23.68	76.32	− 25.8
	1.8367	93.60	15.314	23.59	76.41	− 27.5
	1.8371	93.70	15.317	23.51	76.49	− 29.3
	1.8374	93.80	15.320	23.43	76.57	− 30.3
	1.8378	93.90	15.323	23.35	76.65	− 27.8
	1.8381	94.00	15.326	23.27	76.73	− 25.0
	1.8384	94.10	15.328	23.19	76.81	− 22.5
	1.8386	94.20	15.330	23.10	76.90	− 20.0
	1.8389	94.30	15.332	23.02	76.98	− 17.5
	1.8391	94.40	15.334	22.94	77.06	− 15.0
	1.8394	94.50	15.336	22.86	77.14	− 13.0
	1.8397	94.60	15.339	22.78	77.22	− 17.3
	1.8399	94.70	15.341	22.70	77.30	− 9.5
	1.8302	94.80	15.343	22.61	77.39	− 7.8
	1.8304	94.90	15.345	22.53	77.47	− 6.5
	1.8407	95.00	15.347	22.45	77.55	− 5.3
	1.8409	95.10	15.349	22.37	77.63	− 4.8
	1.8411	95.20	15.351	22.29	77.71	− 4.0
	1.8413	95.30	15.352	22.21	77.79	− 3.3
	1.8415	95.40	15.354	22.12	77.88	− 2.3
	1.8417	95.50	15.356	22.04	77.96	− 1.3
	1.8419	95.60	15.357	21.96	78.04	0.0
	1.8421	95.70	15.358	21.88	78.12	+ 1.2
	1.8423	95.80	15.361	21.80	78.20	+ 2.5
	1.8425	95.90	15.362	21.72	78.28	+ 4.0

(cont'd)

TABLE XXII. SULFURIC ACID PROPERTIES (cont'd)

Specific Gravity	Percent H_2SO_4	Weight Lb/Gal	Percent Total H_2O	Percent SO_3	Freezing Pt° F
1.8427	96.00	15.364	21.64	78.36	+ 5.5
1.8428	96.10	15.365	21.55	78.45	+ 7.0
1.8429	96.20	15.366	21.47	78.53	+ 8.6
1.8430	96.30	15.366	21.39	78.61	+ 10.6
1.8431	96.40	15.367	21.31	78.69	+ 12.5
1.8432	96.50	15.368	21.23	78.77	+ 14.4
1.8433	96.60	15.369	21.15	78.85	+ 16.1
1.8434	96.70	15.370	21.06	78.94	+ 17.5
1.8435	96.80	15.371	20.98	79.02	+ 18.8
1.8436	96.90	15.371	20.90	79.10	+ 19.9
1.8437	97.00	15.372	20.82	79.18	+ 20.7
1.8437	97.10	15.372	20.74	79.26	+ 21.3
1.8438	97.20	15.373	20.66	79.34	+ 22.0
1.8439	97.30	15.374	20.57	79.43	+ 22.5
1.8439	97.40	15.374	20.49	79.51	+ 23.5
1.8439	97.50	15.374	20.41	79.59	+ 24.4
1.8439	97.60	15.374	20.33	79.67	+ 25.3
1.8438	97.70	15.373	20.25	79.75	+ 26.5
1.8438	97.80	15.373	20.17	79.83	+ 28.4
1.8437	97.90	15.372	20.08	79.92	+ 29.4
1.8437	98.00	15.372	20.00	80.00	+ 30.0
1.8436	98.10	15.371	19.92	80.08	+ 30.6
1.8435	98.20	15.371	19.84	80.16	+ 31.5
1.8434	98.30	15.370	19.76	80.24	+ 32.3
1.8433	98.40	15.369	19.68	80.32	+ 32.8
1.8431	98.50	15.367	19.59	80.41	+ 34.4
1.8430	98.60	15.366	19.51	80.49	+ 36.0
1.8429	98.70	15.366	19.43	80.57	+ 37.1
1.8428	98.80	15.365	19.35	80.65	+ 38.3
1.8426	98.90	15.363	19.27	80.73	+ 39.4
1.8424	99.00	15.361	19.19	80.81	+ 40.1
1.8422	99.10	15.360	19.10	80.90	+ 41.2
1.8420	99.20	15.358	19.02	80.98	+ 42.2
1.8417	99.30	15.356	18.94	81.06	+ 43.2
1.8415	99.40	15.354	18.86	81.14	+ 44.1
1.8412	99.50	15.351	18.78	81.22	+ 45.0
1.8409	99.60	15.349	18.70	81.30	+ 46.0
1.8405	99.70	15.346	18.61	81.39	+ 47.1
1.8401	99.80	15.342	18.53	81.47	+ 48.1
1.8396	99.90	15.338	18.45	81.55	+ 49.4
1.8391	100.00	15.334	18.37 ·	81.63	+ 50.7

ALLOWANCE FOR TEMPERATURE

At 10° Bé, .029° Bé or .00023 Sp. Gr. = 1° F

At 20° Bé, .036° Bé or .00034 Sp. Gr. = 1° F

At 30° Bé, .035° Bé or .00039 Sp. Gr. = 1° F

At 40° Bé, .031° Bé or .00041 Sp. Gr. = 1° F

At 50° Bé, .028° Bé or .00045 Sp. Gr. = 1° F

At 60° Bé, .026° Bé or .00053 Sp. Gr. = 1° F

At 63° Bé, .026° Bé or .00057 Sp. Gr. = 1° F

At 66° Bé, .0235° Bé or .00054 Sp. Gr. = 1° F

Specific Gravity determinations were made at 60° F, compared with water at 60° F.

From the Specific Gravities, the corresponding degrees Baumé were calculated by the following formula.

$$Baumé = 145 - \frac{145}{Sp. Gr.}$$

Baumé Hydrometers for use with this table must be graduated by the above formula, which formula should always be printed on the scale.

66° Baumé = Sp. Gr. 1.8354
1 cu. ft. water at 60° F weighs
62.37 lbs. avoirdupois

Reproduced by permission from the standards adopted and published by the Manufacturing Chemists Association. Manual Sheet T-7.

TABLE XXIII. OLEUM (FUMING SULFURIC ACID) PROPERTIES

Percent Equiv. H_2SO_4	Specific Gravity	Weight Lb/Gal	Percent Actual H_2SO_4	Percent Free SO_3	Percent Comb'd H_2O	Percent Total SO_3	Approx. Freezing Pt° F
100.0	1.839	15.333	100.00	0.00	18.37	81.63	50.7
.1	1.842	15.358	99.56	.44	18.29	81.71	50.3
.2	1.845	15.383	99.11	.89	18.21	81.79	49.7
.23	1.846	15.391	99.00	1.00	18.19	81.81	49.5
.30	1.847	15.400	98.67	1.33	18.13	81.87	48.8
.40	1.850	15.425	98.22	1.78	18.04	81.96	48.0
.45	1.851	15.433	98.00	2.00	18.00	82.00	47.5
.50	1.852	15.441	97.78	2.22	17.96	82.04	47.1
.60	1.853	15.450	97.33	2.67	17.88	82.12	46.1
.68	1.855	15.466	97.00	3.00	17.82	82.18	47.5
.70	1.855	15.466	96.89	3.11	17.80	82.20	47.4
.80	1.857	15.483	96.44	3.56	17.72	82.28	46.6
.90	1.858	15.491	96.00	4.00	17.64	82.36	45.5
101.0	1.860	15.508	95.56	4.44	17.55	82.45	45.0
.1	1.861	15.516	95.11	4.89	17.47	82.53	43.9
.13	1.862	15.525	95.00	5.00	17.45	82.55	43.4
.2	1.863	15.533	94.67	5.33	17.39	82.61	42.6
.3	1.864	15.541	94.22	5.78	17.31	82.69	41.5
.35	1.865	15.550	94.00	6.00	17.27	82.73	40.8
.4	1.866	15.558	93.78	6.22	17.23	82.77	40.1
.5	1.868	15.575	93.33	6.67	17.14	82.86	38.5
.58	1.869	15.583	93.00	7.00	17.08	82.92	37.6
.6	1.870	15.591	92.89	7.11	17.06	82.94	37.4
.7	1.871	15.600	92.44	7.56	16.98	83.02	35.7
.8	1.873	15.616	92.00	8.00	16.90	83.10	34.5
.9	1.875	15.633	91.56	8.44	16.82	83.18	33.2
102.0	1.876	15.642	91.11	8.89 ✓	16.74	83.26	32.0
.03	1.877	15.650	91.00	9.00	16.72	83.28	31.8
.1	1.878	15.658	90.67	9.33	16.66	83.34	31.0
.2	1.879	15.667	90.22	9.78	16.57	83.43	30.0
.25	1.880	15.675	90.00	10.00	16.53	83.47	29.3
.3	1.881	15.683	89.78	10.22	16.49	83.51	28.8
.4	1.883	15.700	89.33	10.67	16.41	83.59	27.7
.48	1.884	15.708	89.00	11.00	16.35	83.65	27.0
.5	1.884	15.708	88.89	11.11	16.33	83.67	26.8
.6	1.885	15.717	88.44	11.56	16.25	83.75	25.9
.7	1.887	15.733	88.00	12.00	16.17	83.83	25.0
.8	1.889	15.750	87.56	12.44	16.08	83.92	24.0
.9	1.891	15.767	87.11	12.89	16.00	84.00	23.8
.93	1.891	15.767	87.00	13.00 ✓	15.98	84.02	22.7
103.0	1.893	15.783	86.67	13.33 ✓	15.92	84.08	22.0
.1	1.894	15.792	86.22	13.78	15.84	84.16	21.0
.15	1.895	15.800	86.00	14.00	15.80	84.20	20.0
.2	1.896	15.808	85.78	14.22	15.76	84.24	18.9
.3	1.897	15.817	85.33	14.67	15.68	84.32	17.0
.38	1.899	15.833	85.00	15.00	15.61	84.39	15.7
.4	1.899	15.833	84.89	15.11	15.59	84.41	15.0
.5	1.900	15.842	84.44	15.56	15.51	84.49	13.8
103.6	1.902	15.858	84.00	16.00	15.43	84.57	15.3
.7	1.903	15.867	83.56	16.44	15.35	84.65	16.4
.8	1.905	15.883	83.11	16.89	15.27	84.73	19.7

(cont'd)

TABLE XXIII. OLEUM PROPERTIES (cont'd)

Percent Equiv H2SO4	Specific Gravity	Weight Lb/Gal	Percent Actual H2SO4	Percent Free SO3	Percent Comb'd H2O	Percent Total SO3	Approx Freezing Pt°F
.82	1.905	15.833	83.00	17.00	15.25	84.75	21.8
.9	1.907	15.900	82.67	17.33	15.19	84.81	25.2
104.0	1.908	15.908	82.22	17.78✓	15.10	84.90	26.8
.05	1.909	15.917	82.00	18.00	15.06	84.94	27.8
.1	1.910	15.925	81.78	18.22	15.02	84.98	28.4
.2	1.911	15.933	81.33	18.67	14.94	85.06	29.7
.28	1.912	15.942	81.00	19.00	14.88	85.12	30.9
.3	1.913	15.950	80.89	19.11	14.86	85.14	31.3
.4	1.914	15.958	80.44	19.56	14.78	85.22	32.7
.5	1.916	15.975	80.00	20.00	14.70	85.30	34.2
.6	1.918	15.992	79.56	20.44	14.62	85.38	35.8
.7	1.919	16.000	79.11	20.89	14.53	85.47	37.8
.73	1.920	16.008	79.00	21.00	14.51	85.49	38.2
.8	1.921	16.017	78.67	21.33	14.45	85.55	39.2
.9	1.922	16.025	78.22	21.78	14.37	85.63	40.9
.95	1.923	16.033	78.00	22.00	14.33	85.67	42.1
105.0	1.924	16.042	77.78	22.22	14.29	85.71	42.9
.1	1.925	16.050	77.33	22.67	14.21	85.79	44.7
.18	1.927	16.067	77.00	23.00	14.14	85.86	46.1
.2	1.927	16.067	76.89	23.11	14.13	85.87	46.7
.3	1.929	16.083	76.44	23.56	14.04	85.96	48.4
.4	1.931	16.100	76.00	24.00	13.96	86.04	52.8
.5	1.933	16.117	75.56	24.44	13.88	86.12	54.7
.6	1.934	16.125	75.11	24.89	13.80	86.20	56.4
.63	1.935	16.133	75.00	25.00	13.78	86.22	56.8
.7	1.936	16.142	74.67	25.33	13.72	86.28	57.7
.8	1.938	16.158	74.22	25.78	13.64	86.36	58.8
.85	1.939	16.167	74.00	26.00	13.59	86.41	59.9
.9	1.940	16.175	73.78	26.22	13.55	86.45	60.5
106.0	1.942	16.192	73.33	26.67	13.47	86.53	61.7
.08	1.943	16.200	73.00	27.00	13.41	86.59	62.9
.1	1.943	16.200	72.89	27.11	13.39	86.61	63.2
.2	1.945	16.217	72.44	27.56	13.31	86.69	64.6
.3	1.946	16.225	72.00	28.00	13.23	86.77	66.0
.4	1.947	16.234	71.56	28.44	13.15	86.85	66.6
.5	1.949	16.250	71.11	28.89	13.06	86.94	67.8
.53	1.949	16.250	71.00	29.00	13.04	86.96	68.3
.6	1.950	16.259	70.67	29.33	12.98	87.02	69.2
.7	1.952	16.275	70.22	29.78	12.90	87.10	70.7
.75	1.952	16.275	70.00	30.00	12.86	87.14	71.4
.8	1.953	16.284	69.78	30.22	12.82	87.18	72.0
.9	1.954	16.292	69.33	30.67	12.74	87.26	73.3
.98	1.956	16.309	69.00	31.00	12.67	87.33	74.3
107.0	1.956	16.309	68.89	31.11	12.66	87.34	74.6
.1	1.957	16.317	68.44	31.56	12.57	87.43	75.7
.2	1.958	16.325	68.00	32.00	12.49	87.51	76.9
.3	1.960	16.342	67.56	32.44	12.41	87.59	78.1
.4	1.961	16.350	67.11	32.89	12.33	87.67	79.3
107.5	1.963	16.367	66.67	33.33	12.25	87.75	80.4
.6	1.964	16.375	66.22	33.78	12.17	87.83	81.5
.65	1.965	16.384	66.00	34.00	12.12	87.88	82.2
.7	1.966	16.391	65.78	34.22	12.08	87.92	82.7
.8	1.967	16.400	65.33	34.67	12.00	88.00	83.8
.87	1.968	16.409	65.00	35.00	11.94	88.06	84.7

Percent Equiv H$_2$SO$_4$	Specific Gravity	Weight Lb/Gal	Percent Actual H$_2$SO$_4$	Percent Free SO$_3$	Percent Comb'd H$_2$O	Percent Total SO$_3$	Approx Freezing Pt°F
.9	1.968	16.409	64.89	35.11	11.92	88.08	85.0
108.0	1.970	16.425	64.44	35.56	11.84	88.16	85.9
.1	1.972	16.442	64.00	36.00	11.76	88.24	87.0
.2	1.974	16.459	63.56	36.44	11.68	88.32	87.9
.3	1.975	16.466	63.11	36.89	11.59	88.41	88.9
.33	1.976	16.475	63.00	37.00	11.57	88.43	89.1
.4	1.977	16.484	62.67	37.33	11.51	88.49	89.8
.5	1.978	16.492	62.22	37.78	11.43	88.57	90.4
.55	1.979	16.500	62.00	38.00	11.39	88.61	90.9
.6	1.980	16.509	61.78	38.22	11.35	88.65	91.2
.7	1.980	16.509	61.33	38.67	11.27	88.73	91.8
.77	1.981	16.517	61.00	39.00	11.21	88.79	92.3
.8	1.981	16.517	60.89	39.11	11.19	88.81	92.4
.9	1.982	16.525	60.44	39.56	11.10	88.90	92.8
109.0	1.983	16.534	60.00	40.00	11.02	88.98	93.3
.1	1.984	16.542	59.56	40.44	10.94	89.06	93.6
.2	1.985	16.550	59.11	40.89	10.86	89.14	93.8
.22	1.985	16.550	59.00	41.00	10.84	89.16	93.9
.3	1.986	16.559	58.67	41.33	10.78	89.22	94.2
.4	1.987	16.567	58.22	41.78	10.70	89.30	94.3
.45	1.987	16.567	58.00	42.00	10.65	89.35	94.5
.5	1.988	16.575	57.78	42.22	10.61	89.39	94.6
.6	1.988	16.575	57.33	42.67	10.53	89.47	94.7
.68	1.989	16.584	57.00	43.00	10.47	89.53	94.8
.7	1.989	16.584	56.89	43.11	10.45	89.55	94.9
.8	1.990	16.592	56.44	43.56	10.37	89.63	95.1
.9	1.991	16.600	56.00	44.00	10.29	89.71	95.2
110.00	1.992	16.608	56.56	44.44	10.39	89.61	95.2
110.13	1.993	16.617	55.00	45.00	10.29	89.71	95.3
110.35	1.994	16.625	54.00	46.00	10.10	89.90	95.1
110.58	1.996	16.642	53.00	47.00	9.92	90.08	94.6
110.80	1.998	16.659	52.00	48.00	9.74	90.26	93.9
111.00	1.999	16.667	51.11	48.89	9.55	90.45	93.2
111.03	1.999	16.667	51.00	49.00	9.37	90.63	93.0
111.25	2.001	16.684	50.00	50.00	9.19	90.81	92.8
111.48	2.002	16.692	49.00	51.00	9.00	91.00	89.2
111.70	2.003	16.700	48.00	52.00	8.82	91.18	85.2
111.93	2.004	16.709	47.00	53.00	8.63	91.37	83.3
112.00	2.004	16.709	46.67	53.33	8.57	91.43	82.4
112.15	2.005	16.717	46.00	54.00	8.45	91.55	80.3
112.38	2.005	16.717	45.00	55.00	8.27	91.73	77.6
112.60	2.005	16.717	44.00	56.00	8.08	91.92	74.4
112.83	2.004	16.709	43.00	57.00	7.90	92.10	71.2
113.00	2.004	16.709	42.22	57.78	7.76	92.24	68.8
113.05	2.004	16.709	42.00	58.00	7.72	92.28	68.0
113.28	2.003	16.700	41.00	59.00	7.53	92.47	65.3
113.50	2.002	16.692	40.00	60.00	7.35	92.65	62.1
113.73	2.000	16 675	39.00	61.00	7.16	92.84	59.0
113.95	1.999	16.667	38.00	62.00	6.98	93.02	55.4
114.00	1.998	16.659	37.78	62.22	6.94	93.06	54.5
114.18	1.996	16.642	37.00	63.00	6.80	93.20	51.5
114.40	1.994	16.625	36.00	64.00	6.61	93.39	37.6
114.63	1.992	16.608	35.00	65.00	6.43	93.57	33.3

(cont'd)

TABLE XXIII. OLEUM PROPERTIES (cont'd)

Percent Equiv H_2SO_4	Specific Gravity	Weight Lb/Gal	Percent Actual H_2SO_4	Percent Free SO_3	Percent Comb'd H_2O	Percent Total SO_3	Approx Freezing Pt° F
114.85	1.990	16.592	34.00	66.00	6.25	93.75	30.0
115.00	1.989	16.584	33.33	66.67	6.12	93.88	35.0
115.08	1.988	16.575	33.00	67.00	6.06	93.94	38.0
115.30	1.986	16.559	32.00	68.00	5.88	94.12	45.0
115.53	1.984	16.542	31.00	69.00	5.69	94.31	50.0
115.75	1.982	16.525	30.00	70.00	5.51	94.49	55.0
115.98	1.979	16.500	29.00	71.00	5.33	94.67	58.0
116.00	1.979	16.500	28.88	71.12	5.31	94.69	58.5
116.20	1.976	16.475	28.00	72.00	5.14	94.86	61.3
116.43	1.973	16.450	27.00	73.00	4.96	95.04	64.2
116.65	1.969	16.417	26.00	74.00	4.78	95.22	66.4
116.88	1.966	16.392	25.00	75.00	4.59	95.41	68.8
117.00	1.964	16.375	24.46	75.56	4.49	95.51	70.2
117.10	1.963	16.367	24.00	76.00	4.41	95.59	71.6
117.33	1.959	16.334	23.00	77.00	4.23	95.77	72.8
117.55	1.956	16.309	22.00	78.00	4.04	95.96	74.8
117.78	1.954	16.292	21.00	79.00	3.86	96.14	76.2
118.00	1.949	16.250	20.00	80.00	3.67	96.33	77.5
118.23	1.946	16.225	19.00	81.00	3.49	96.51	79.0
118.45	1.942	16.192	18.00	82.00	3.31	96.69	80.0
118.68	1.938	16.158	17.00	83.00	3.12	96.88	81.5
118.90	1.934	16.125	16.00	84.00	2.94	97.06	82.1
119.00	1.933	16.117	15.56	84.44	2.86	97.14	82.9
119.13	1.931	16.100	15.00	85.00	2.76	97.24	82.8
119.35	1.927	16.067	14.00	86.00	2.57	97.43	
119.58	1.923	16.033	13.00	87.00	2.39	97.61	
119.80	1.919	16.000	12.00	88.00	2.20	97.80	
120.00	1.915	15.967	11.11	88.89	2.04	97.96	
120.03	1.915	15.967	11.00	89.00	2.02	97.98	
120.25	1.911	15.933	10.00	90.00	1.84	98.16	
120.48	1.907	15.900	9.00	91.00	1.65	98.35	
120.70	1.903	15.867	8.00	92.00	1.47	98.53	
120.93	1.898	15.825	7.00	93.00	1.29	98.71	
121.00	1.897	15.817	6.67	93.33	1.23	98.77	
121.15	1.894	15.792	6.00	94.00	1.10	98.90	
121.38	1.889	15.750	5.00	95.00	.92	99.08	96.8
121.60	1.884	15.708	4.00	96.00	.73	99.27	
121.83	1.879	15.667	3.00	97.00	.55	99.45	
122.00	1.875	15.633	2.22	97.78	.41	99.59	
122.05	1.873	15.617	2.00	98.00	.36	99.64	
122.28	1.866	15.558	1.00	99.00	.18	99.82	
122.50	1.857	15.483	0.00	100.00	.00	100.00	104.0

Freezing Points Extrapolated from Phase Equilibrium "SO_3–Water"
C.M. Gable, H.F. Betz   S.H. Maron J ACS Vol. 72 (Jan–Apr '50) p. 1445-1448

TABLE XXIV. DENSITY OF SULFURIC ACID SOLUTIONS lb./cu. ft.

Wt. % H₂O	°F	-40	-20	0	20	40	60	80	100	120	140	160	180	200	220	240	260	280	300
	°C	-40	-28.9	-17.8	-6.7	4.4	15.5	26.7	37.8	48.9	60	71.1	82.2	93.3	104.4	115.6	126.7	137.8	148.9
0		*	*	*	*	*	114.6	113.9	113.2	112.5	111.9	111.3	110.6	110.0	109.3	108.6	107.9	107.3	106.6
10		*	*	*	*	114.4	113.6	112.9	112.1	111.4	110.7	110.0	109.3	108.6	107.9	107.2	106.6	106.0	105.4
20		*	*	*	*	108.9	108.1	107.4	106.7	106.0	105.3	104.6	104.0	103.4	102.7	102.0	101.3	100.7	100.0
30		104.0	103.4	102.8	102.1	101.5	100.8	100.1	99.5	99.0	98.4	97.8	97.2	96.6	96.0	95.4	94.8	94.2	93.6
40		*	96.2	95.6	95.0	94.4	93.8	93.2	92.6	92.0	91.5	91.0	90.4	89.9	89.4	88.8	88.2	87.7	87.2
50		*	89.4	88.9	88.4	87.8	87.3	86.8	86.3	85.7	85.2	84.6	84.1	83.6	83.1	82.6	82.1	81.6	81.2
60		84.2	83.6	83.1	82.6	82.0	81.5	81.0	80.5	80.0	79.5	79.0	78.5	78.0	77.5	77.0	76.5	76.0	75.5
70		*	78.4	77.8	77.3	76.7	76.2	75.8	75.3	74.8	74.4	73.9	73.4	72.9	72.5	72.0	71.6	71.1	70.6
80		*	*	*	72.0	71.6	71.3	70.9	70.4	70.0	69.6	69.2	68.7	68.2	67.8	67.3	66.9	66.4	66.0
90		*	*	*	*	66.9	66.6	66.3	66.0	65.7	65.3	64.8	64.4	64.0	63.5	63.1	62.6	62.2	61.8
100		*	*	*	*	62.4	62.4	62.2	62.0	61.8	61.4	61.0	60.6	60.2	59.6	59.1	58.6	58.0	57.3

Wt. % Free SO₃	-40	-20	0	20	40	60	80	100	120	140	160	180	200	220	240	260	280	300
10	*	*	*	*	117.5	116.9	116.2	115.5	114.9	114.2	113.5	112.8	112.1	111.5	110.8	110.1	109.4	108.8
20	*	*	*	*	119.7	119.0	118.3	117.6	116.9	116.1	115.4	114.7	114.0	113.3	112.6	111.9	111.1	110.4
30	*	*	*	*	*	*	120.6	119.9	119.1	118.3	117.5	116.7	115.9	115.1	114.3	113.5	112.6	111.8
40	*	*	*	*	*	*	*	121.6	120.7	119.9	119.0	118.0	117.1	116.3	115.4	114.5	113.5	112.6

*Below freezing point.

TABLE XXV. ELECTROLYTE CONVERSION TABLES

Specific Gravity		Percent	° Baumé	Lb/gal.
@ 80° F	@ 60° F	H₂SO₄	@ 80° F	@ 80° F
1.250	1.258	34.28	29.00	10.39
1.255	1.263	34.88	29.46	10.43
1.260	1.268	35.47	29.92	10.48
1.265	1.273	36.06	30.37	10.52
1.270	1.278	36.65	30.83	10.56
1.275	1.283	37.23	31.27	10.60
1.280	1.288	37.82	31.72	10.64
1.285	1.293	38.39	32.16	10.68
1.290	1.298	38.98	32.60	10.73
1.295	1.303	39.55	33.03	10.77
1.300	1.308	40.11	33.46	10.81
1.310	1.318	41.25	34.31	10.89
1.320	1.328	42.38	35.15	10.97
1.325	1.333	42.93	35.57	11.02
1.330	1.338	43.49	35.98	11.06
1.340	1.348	44.58	36.79	11.14
1.350	1.358	45.66	37.59	11.22
1.360	1.368	46.73	38.38	11.31
1.365	1.373	47.26	38.77	11.35
1.370	1.378	47.79	39.16	11.39
1.375	1.383	48.31	39.55	11.43
1.380	1.388	48.83	39.93	11.47
1.385	1.393	49.35	40.31	11.51
1.390	1.398	49.86	40.68	11.56
1.395	1.403	50.38	41.06	11.60
1.400	1.408	50.89	41.43	11.64
1.410	1.418	51.90	42.16	11.72
1.420	1.428	52.90	42.89	11.81
1.425	1.433	53.40	43.25	11.85
1.430	1.438	53.90	43.60	11.89
1.440	1.449	54.98	44.31	11.97
1.450	1.459	55.95	45.00	12.06
1 460	1.469	56.90	45.68	12.14
1.470	1.479	57.85	46.36	12.22
1.475	1.484	58.32	46.69	12.26
1.480	1.489	58.79	47.03	12.30
1.490	1.499	59.71	47.68	12.39
1.500	1.509	60.63	48.33	12.47
1.510	1.519	61.55	48.97	12.55
1.520	1.529	62.46	49.61	12.64
1.525	1.534	62.90	49.92	12.68
1.530	1.539	63.35	50.23	12.72
1.540	1.549	64.24	50.84	12.80
1.550	1.559	65.12	51.45	12.89
1.560	1.569	66.00	52.05	12.97
1.570	1.579	66.89	52.64	13.05
1.575	1.584	67.34	52.94	13.09
1.580	1.590	67.83	53.23	13.14
1.590	1.600	68.71	53.81	13.22
1.600	1.610	69.57	54.37	13.30
1.610	1.620	70.41	54.94	13.39
1.620	1.630	71.27	55.49	13.47
1.625	1.635	71.69	55.77	13.51

TABLE XXV. ELECTROLYTE CONVERSION TABLE (cont'd)

Specific Gravity @80° F	@ 60° F	Percent H_2SO_4	° Baumé @ 80° F	Lb/gal. @ 80° F
1.630	1.640	72.11	56.04	13.55
1.640	1.650	72.95	56.58	13.64
1.650	1.660	73.81	57.12	13.72
1.660	1.670	74.64	57.65	13.80
1.670	1.680	75.48	58.17	13.88
1.675	1.685	75.91	58.43	13.93
1.680	1.690	76.33	58.69	13.97
1.690	1.700	77.18	59.20	14.05
1.700	1.711	78.31	59.71	14.13
1.710	1.721	78.99	60.21	14.22
1.720	1.731	79.86	60.70	14.30
1.725	1.736	80.32	60.94	14.34
1.730	1.741	80.77	61.18	14.38
1.740	1.751	81.69	61.67	14.47
1.750	1.761	82.65	62.14	14.55
1.760	1.771	83.62	62.61	14.63
1.770	1.781	84.70	63.08	14.72
1.775	1.786	85.23	63.31	14.76
1.780	1.791	85.76	63.54	14.80
1.790	1.801	87.01	63.99	14.88
1.800	1.811	88.43	64.44	14.97
1.810	1.821	90.70	64.89	15.05
1.820	1.831	92.12	65.33	15.13
1.823	1.835	93.19	65.50	15.16
1.830	1.841	95.20	65.77	15.21

Water = 8.314 Lbs/Gallon @ 80° F

TABLE XXVI. FACTORS FOR CORRECTING VOLUME TO 60° F

Flow Temp. ° F.	Wt. % H_2SO_4				
	60.0 - 69.2	69.3-76.5	76.6-81.3	81.4-95.0	95.1-100.0
50	1.00296	1.00304	1.00315	1.00304	1.00291
51	1.00266	1.00274	1.00284	1.00274	1.00262
52	1.00237	1.00243	1.00252	1.00243	1.00233
53	1.00207	1.00213	1.00221	1.00213	1.00204
54	1.00178	1.00182	1.00189	1.00182	1.00175
55	1.00148	1.00152	1.00158	1.00152	1.00146
56	1.00118	1.00122	1.00126	1.00122	1.00116
57	1.00089	1.00091	1.00095	1.00092	1.00087
58	1.00059	1.00061	1.00063	1.00061	1.00058
59	1.00030	1.00030	1.00032	1.00030	1.00029
60	1.00000	1.00000	1.00000	1.00000	1.00000
61	.99970	.99970	.99969	.99970	.99971
62	.99941	.99939	.99937	.99939	.99942
63	.99911	.99909	.99906	.99909	.99913
64	.99882	.99878	.99874	.99878	.99884
65	.99852	.99848	.99843	.99848	.99855
66	.99822	.99818	.99811	.99818	.99825
67	.99793	.99787	.99780	.99787	.99796

(cont'd)

TABLE XXVI. FACTORS FOR CORRECTING VOLUME TO 60° F (cont'd)

Flow Temp. °F.	Wt. % H$_2$SO$_4$				
	60.0 - 69.2	69.3-76.5	76.6-81.3	81.4-95.0	95.1-100.0
68	.99763	.99757	.99748	.99757	.99767
69	.99734	.99726	.99717	.99726	.99738
70	.99704	.99696	.99685	.99696	.99709
71	.99674	.99666	.99654	.99666	.99680
72	.99645	.99635	.99622	.99635	.99651
73	.99615	.99605	.99591	.99605	.99622
74	.99586	.99574	.99559	.99574	.99593
75	.99556	.99544	.99528	.99544	.99564
76	.99526	.99514	.99496	.99514	.99534
77	.99497	.99483	.99465	.99483	.99505
78	.99467	.99453	.99433	.99453	.99476
79	.99438	.99422	.99402	.99422	.99447
80	.99408	.99392	.99370	.99392	.99418
81	.99378	.99362	.99339	.99362	.99390
82	.99349	.99331	.99307	.99331	.99360
83	.99319	.99301	.99276	.99301	.99331
84	.99290	.99270	.99244	.99270	.99302
85	.99260	.99240	.99213	.99240	.99273
86	.99230	.99210	.99181	.99210	.99243
87	.99201	.99179	.99150	.99179	.99214
88	.99171	.99149	.99118	.99149	.99185
89	.99142	.99118	.99087	.99118	.99156
90	.99112	.99088	.99055	.99088	.99127
91	.99082	.99058	.99024	.99058	.99098
92	.99053	.99027	.98992	.99027	.99069
93	.99023	.98997	.98961	.98997	.99040
94	.98994	.98966	.98929	.98966	.99011
95	.98964	.98936	.98898	.98936	.98982
96	.98934	.98906	.98866	.98906	.98952
97	.98905	.98875	.98835	.98875	.98923
98	.98875	.98845	.98803	.98845	.98894
99	.98846	.98814	.98772	.98814	.98865
100	.98816	.98784	.98740	.98784	.98836
101	.98786	.98754	.98709	.98754	.98807
102	.98757	.98723	.98677	.98723	.98778
103	.98727	.98693	.98646	.98693	.98749
104	.98698	.98662	.98614	.98662	.98720
105	.98668	.98632	.98583	.98632	.98691
106	.98638	.98602	.98551	.98602	.98661
107	.98609	.98571	.98520	.98571	.98632
108	.98579	.98541	.98488	.98541	.98603
109	.98550	.98510	.98457	.98510	.98574
110	.98520	.98480	.98425	.98480	.98545
111	.98490	.98450	.98394	.98450	.98516
112	.98461	.98419	.98362	.98419	.98487
113	.98431	.98389	.98331	.98389	.98458
114	.98402	.98358	.98299	.98358	.98429
115	.98372	.98328	.98268	.98328	.98400
116	.98342	.98298	.98236	.98298	.98370
117	.98313	.98267	.98205	.98267	.98341
118	.98283	.98237	.98173	.98237	.98312
119	.98254	.98206	.98142	.98206	.98283
120	.98224	.98176	.98110	.98176	.98254

TABLE XXVII. CORRECTIONS FOR HYDROMETER READINGS

Use this table to convert hydrometer readings to 60° F basis. Subtract corrections when
acid is below 60° F, and add when above.

Temp °F	Baumé 15° to 25°	Sp. Gr. 1.154 to 1.2083	Baumé 25° to 35°	Sp. Gr. 1.2083 to 1.3182	Baumé 35° to 45°	Sp. Gr. 1.3182 to 1.4500	Baumé 45° to 55°	Sp. Gr. 1.4500 to 1.6111	Baumé 55° to 63°	Sp. Gr. 1.6111 to 1.7683	Baumé 63° to 66°	Sp. Gr. 1.7683 to 1.8354
31	-1.04	-.0099	-1.01	-.0113	-.90	-.0119	-.81	-.0154	-.75	-.0165	-.68	-.0157
32	-1.01	-.0095	-.98	-.0109	-.87	-.0115	-.78	-.0148	-.73	-.0160	-.66	-.0151
33	-.98	-.0092	-.94	-.0105	-.84	-.0111	-.76	-.0143	-.70	-.0154	-.63	-.0146
34	-.94	-.0088	-.91	-.0101	-.81	-.0107	-.73	-.0138	-.68	-.0148	-.61	-.0140
35	-.90	-.0085	-.87	-.0098	-.77	-.0103	-.70	-.0133	-.65	-.0143	-.59	-.0135
36	-.85	-.0082	-.84	-.0094	-.74	-.0098	-.67	-.0127	-.62	-.0137	-.56	-.0130
37	-.83	-.0078	-.80	-.0094	-.71	-.0094	-.64	-.0122	-.60	-.0131	-.54	-.0124
38	-.79	-.0075	-.77	-.0086	-.68	-.0090	-.62	-.0117	-.57	-.0125	-.52	-.0119
39	-.76	-.0071	-.73	-.0082	-.65	-.0086	-.59	-.0113	-.55	-.0120	-.49	-.0113
40	-.72	-.0068	-.70	-.0078	-.62	-.0082	-.56	-.0106	-.52	-.0114	-.47	-.0108
41	-.68	-.0065	-.66	-.0074	-.59	-.0078	-.53	-.0101	-.49	-.0108	-.45	-.0103
42	-.65	-.0061	-.63	-.0070	-.56	-.0074	-.50	-.0095	-.47	-.0103	-.42	-.0097
43	-.61	-.0058	-.59	-.0066	-.53	-.0070	-.48	-.0090	-.44	-.0097	-.40	-.0092
44	-.58	-.0054	-.56	-.0062	-.50	-.0066	-.45	-.0085	-.42	-.0091	-.38	-.0086
45	-.54	-.0051	-.52	-.0059	-.46	-.0062	-.42	-.0080	-.39	-.0086	-.35	-.0081
46	-.50	-.0048	-.49	-.0055	-.43	-.0057	-.39	-.0074	-.36	-.0080	-.33	-.0076
47	-.47	-.0044	-.45	-.0051	-.40	-.0053	-.36	-.0069	-.34	-.0074	-.31	-.0070
48	-.43	-.0041	-.42	-.0047	-.37	-.0049	-.34	-.0064	-.31	-.0068	-.28	-.0065
49	-.40	-.0037	-.38	-.0043	-.34	-.0045	-.31	-.0058	-.29	-.0063	-.26	-.0059
50	-.36	-.0034	-.34	-.0039	-.31	-.0041	-.28	-.0053	-.26	-.0057	-.24	-.0054
51	-.32	-.0031	-.31	-.0035	-.28	-.0037	-.25	-.0048	-.23	-.0051	-.21	-.0049
52	-.29	-.0027	-.28	-.0031	-.25	-.0033	-.22	-.0042	-.21	-.0046	-.19	-.0043
53	-.25	-.0024	-.24	-.0027	-.22	-.0029	-.20	-.0037	-.18	-.0040	-.16	-.0038
54	-.22	-.0020	-.21	-.0023	-.19	-.0025	-.17	-.0032	-.16	-.0034	-.14	-.0032
55	-.18	-.0017	-.17	-.0020	-.15	-.0021	-.14	-.0027	-.13	-.0029	-.12	-.0027
56	-.14	-.0014	-.14	-.0016	-.12	-.0016	-.11	-.0021	-.10	-.0023	-.09	-.0022
57	-.11	-.0010	-.10	-.0012	-.09	-.0012	-.08	-.0016	-.08	-.0017	-.07	-.0016
58	-.07	-.0007	-.07	-.0008	-.06	-.0008	-.06	-.0011	-.05	-.0011	-.05	-.0011
59	-.04	-.0003	-.03	-.0004	-.03	-.0004	-.03	-.0005	-.02	-.0006	-.02	-.0005
60	0.00	0.0000	0.00	0.0000	0.00	0.0000	0.00	0.0000	0.00	0.0000	0.00	0.0000
61	.04	.0003	.03	.0004	.03	.0004	.03	.0005	.02	.0006	.02	.0005
62	.07	.0007	.07	.0008	.06	.0008	.06	.0011	.05	.0011	.05	.0011
63	.11	.0010	.10	.0012	.09	.0012	.08	.0016	.08	.0017	.07	.0016
64	.14	.0014	.14	.0016	.12	.0016	.11	.0021	.10	.0023	.09	.0022
65	.18	.0017	.17	.0020	.15	.0021	.14	.0027	.13	.0029	.12	.0027
66	.22	.0020	.21	.0023	.19	.0025	.17	.0032	.16	.0034	.14	.0032
67	.25	.0024	.24	.0027	.22	.0029	.20	.0037	.18	.0040	.16	.0038
68	.29	.0027	.28	.0031	.25	.0033	.22	.0042	.21	.0046	.19	.0043

(cont'd)

TABLE XXVII. CORRECTIONS FOR HYDROMETER READINGS (cont'd)

Temp °F	Baumé 15° to 25°	Sp. Gr. 1.154 to 1.2083	Baumé 25° to 35°	Sp. Gr. 1.2083 to 1.3182	Baumé 35° to 45°	Sp. Gr. 1.3182 to 1.4500	Baumé 45° to 55°	Sp. Gr. 1.4500 to 1.6111	Baumé 55° to 63°	Sp. Gr. 1.6111 to 1.7683	Baumé 63° to 66°	Sp. Gr. 1.7683 to 1.8354
69	.32	.0031	.31	.0035	.28	.0037	.25	.0048	.23	.0051	.21	.0049
70	.36	.0034	.34	.0039	.31	.0041	.28	.0053	.26	.0057	.24	.0054
71	.40	.0037	.38	.0043	.34	.0045	.31	.0058	.29	.0063	.26	.0059
72	.43	.0041	.42	.0047	.37	.0049	.34	.0064	.31	.0068	.28	.0065
73	.47	.0044	.45	.0051	.40	.0053	.36	.0069	.34	.0074	.31	.0070
74	.50	.0048	.49	.0055	.43	.0057	.39	.0074	.36	.0080	.33	.0076
75	.54	.0051	.52	.0059	.46	.0062	.42	.0080	.39	.0086	.35	.0081
76	.58	.0054	.56	.0062	.50	.0066	.45	.0085	.42	.0091	.38	.0086
77	.61	.0058	.59	.0066	.53	.0070	.48	.0090	.44	.0097	.40	.0092
78	.65	.0061	.63	.0070	.56	.0074	.50	.0095	.47	.0103	.42	.0097
79	.68	.0065	.66	.0074	.59	.0078	.53	.0101	.49	.0108	.45	.0103
80	.72	.0068	.70	.0078	.62	.0082	.56	.0106	.52	.0114	.47	.0108
81	.76	.0071	.73	.0082	.65	.0086	.59	.0111	.55	.0120	.49	.0113
82	.79	.0075	.77	.0086	.68	.0090	.62	.0117	.57	.0125	.52	.0119
83	.83	.0078	.80	.0090	.71	.0094	.64	.0122	.60	.0131	.54	.0124
84	.86	.0082	.84	.0094	.74	.0098	.67	.0127	.62	.0137	.56	.0130
85	.90	.0085	.87	.0098	.77	.0103	.70	.0133	.65	.0143	.59	.0135
86	.94	.0088	.91	.0101	.81	.0107	.73	.0138	.68	.0148	.61	.0140
87	.97	.0092	.94	.0105	.84	.0111	.76	.0143	.70	.0154	.63	.0146
88	1.01	.0095	.98	.0109	.87	.0115	.78	.0148	.73	.0160	.66	.0151
89	1.04	.0099	1.01	.0113	.90	.0119	.81	.0154	.75	.0165	.68	.0157
90	1.08	.0102	1.05	.0117	.93	.0123	.84	.0159	.78	.0171	.70	.0162
91	1.12	.0105	1.08	.0121	.96	.0127	.87	.0164	.81	.0177	.73	.0167
92	1.15	.0109	1.12	.0125	.99	.0131	.90	.0170	.83	.0182	.75	.0173
93	1.19	.0112	1.15	.0129	1.02	.0135	.92	.0175	.86	.0188	.78	.0178
94	1.22	.0116	1.19	.0133	1.05	.0139	.95	.0180	.88	.0194	.80	.0184
95	1.26	.0119	1.22	.0137	1.08	.0144	.98	.0186	.91	.0200	.82	.0189
96	1.30	.0122	1.26	.0140	1.12	.0148	1.01	.0191	.94	.0205	.85	.0194
97	1.33	.0126	1.29	.0144	1.15	.0152	1.04	.0196	.96	.0211	.87	.0200
98	1.37	.0129	1.33	.0148	1.18	.0156	1.06	.0201	.99	.0217	.90	.0205
99	1.40	.0133	1.36	.0152	1.21	.0160	1.09	.0207	1.01	.0222	.92	.0211
100	1.44	.0136	1.40	.0156	1.24	.0164	1.12	.0212	1.04	.0228	.94	.0216
101	1.48	.0139	1.43	.0160	1.27	.0168	1.15	.0217	1.07	.0234	.96	.0221
102	1.51	.0143	1.47	.0164	1.30	.0172	1.18	.0223	1.09	.0239	.99	.0227
103	1.55	.0146	1.50	.0168	1.33	.0176	1.20	.0228	1.12	.0245	1.01	.0232
104	1.58	.0150	1.54	.0172	1.36	.0180	1.23	.0233	1.14	.0251	1.03	.0238
105	1.62	.0153	1.57	.0176	1.39	.0185	1.26	.0239	1.17	.0257	1.06	.0243
106	1.66	.0156	1.61	.0179	1.43	.0189	1.29	.0244	1.20	.0262	1.08	.0248
107	1.69	.0160	1.64	.0183	1.46	.0193	1.32	.0249	1.22	.0268	1.10	.0254
108	1.73	.0163	1.68	.0187	1.49	.0197	1.34	.0254	1.25	.0274	1.13	.0259
109	1.76	.0167	1.71	.0191	1.52	.0201	1.37	.0260	1.27	.0279	1.15	.0265

Temp °F	Baumé 15° to 25°	Sp. Gr. 1.154 to 1.2083	Baumé 25° to 35°	Sp. Gr. 1.2083 to 1.3182	Baumé 35° to 45°	Sp. Gr. 1.3182 to 1.4500	Baumé 45° to 55°	Sp. Gr. 1.4500 to 1.6111	Baumé 55° to 63°	Sp. Gr. 1.6111 to 1.7683	Baumé 63° to 66°	Sp. Gr. 1.7683 to 1.8354
110	1.80	.0170	1.75	.0195	1.55	.0205	1.40	.0265	1.30	.0285	1.18	.0270
111	1.84	.0173	1.78	.0199	1.58	.0209	1.43	.0270	1.33	.0291	1.20	.0275
112	1.87	.0177	1.82	.0203	1.61	.0213	1.46	.0276	1.35	.0296	1.22	.0281
113	1.91	.0180	1.85	.0207	1.64	.0217	1.48	.0281	1.38	.0302	1.25	.0286
114	1.94	.0184	1.89	.0211	1.67	.0221	1.51	.0286	1.40	.0308	1.27	.0292
115	1.98	.0187	1.92	.0215	1.70	.0226	1.54	.0292	1.43	.0314	1.29	.0297
116	2.02	.0190	1.96	.0218	1.74	.0230	1.57	.0297	1.46	.0319	1.32	.0302
117	2.05	.0194	1.99	.0222	1.77	.0234	1.60	.0302	1.48	.0325	1.34	.0308
118	2.09	.0197	2.03	.0226	1.80	.0238	1.62	.0307	1.51	.0331	1.36	.0313
119	2.12	.0201	2.06	.0230	1.83	.0242	1.65	.0313	1.53	.0336	1.39	.0319
120	2.16	.0204	2.10	.0234	1.86	.0246	1.68	.0318	1.56	.0342	1.41	.0324
121	2.20	.0207	2.13	.0238	1.89	.0250	1.71	.0323	1.59	.0348	1.43	.0329
122	2.23	.0211	2.17	.0242	1.92	.0254	1.74	.0329	1.61	.0353	1.46	.0335
123	2.27	.0214	2.20	.0246	1.95	.0258	1.76	.0334	1.64	.0359	1.48	.0340
124	2.30	.0218	2.24	.0250	1.98	.0262	1.79	.0339	1.66	.0365	1.50	.0346
125	2.34	.0221	2.27	.0254	2.01	.0267	1.82	.0345	1.69	.0371	1.53	.0351
126	2.38	.0224	2.31	.0257	2.05	.0271	1.85	.0350	1.72	.0376	1.55	.0356
127	2.41	.0228	2.34	.0261	2.08	.0275	1.88	.0355	1.74	.0382	1.57	.0362
128	2.45	.0231	2.38	.0265	2.11	.0279	1.90	.0360	1.77	.0388	1.60	.0367
129	2.48	.0235	2.41	.0269	2.14	.0283	1.93	.0366	1.79	.0393	1.62	.0373
130	2.52	.0238	2.45	.0273	2.17	.0287	1.96	.0371	1.82	.0399	1.64	.0378
131	2.56	.0241	2.48	.0277	2.20	.0291	1.99	.0376	1.85	.0405	1.67	.0383
132	2.59	.0245	2.52	.0281	2.23	.0295	2.02	.0382	1.87	.0410	1.69	.0389
133	2.63	.0248	2.55	.0285	2.26	.0299	2.04	.0387	1.90	.0416	1.72	.0394
134	2.66	.0252	2.59	.0289	2.29	.0303	2.07	.0392	1.92	.0422	1.74	.0400
135	2.70	.0255	2.62	.0293	2.32	.0308	2.10	.0398	1.95	.0428	1.76	.0405
136	2.74	.0258	2.66	.0296	2.36	.0312	2.13	.0403	1.98	.0433	1.79	.0410
137	2.77	.0262	2.69	.0300	2.39	.0316	2.16	.0408	2.00	.0439	1.81	.0416
138	2.81	.0265	2.73	.0304	2.42	.0320	2.18	.0413	2.03	.0445	1.83	.0421
139	2.84	.0269	2.76	.0308	2.45	.0324	2.21	.0419	2.05	.0450	1.86	.0427
140	2.88	.0272	2.80	.0312	2.48	.0328	2.24	.0424	2.08	.0456	1.88	.0432
141	2.92	.0275	2.83	.0316	2.51	.0332	2.27	.0429	2.11	.0462	1.90	.0437
142	2.95	.0279	2.87	.0320	2.54	.0336	2.30	.0434	2.13	.0467	1.93	.0443
143	2.99	.0282	2.90	.0324	2.57	.0340	2.32	.0440	2.16	.0473	1.95	.0448
144	3.02	.0286	2.94	.0328	2.60	.0344	2.35	.0445	2.18	.0479	1.97	.0453
145	3.06	.0289	2.97	.0332	2.63	.0349	2.38	.0451	2.21	.0485	2.00	.0459
146	3.10	.0292	3.01	.0335	2.67	.0353	2.41	.0456	2.24	.0490	2.02	.0464
147	3.13	.0296	3.04	.0339	2.70	.0357	2.44	.0461	2.26	.0496	2.04	.0470
148	3.17	.0299	3.08	.0343	2.73	.0361	2.46	.0466	2.29	.0502	2.07	.0475
149	3.20	.0303	3.11	.0347	2.76	.0365	2.49	.0472	2.31	.0507	2.09	.0481
150	3.24	.0306	3.15	.0351	2.79	.0369	2.52	.0477	2.34	.0513	2.12	.0486

(cont'd)

TABLE XXVII. CORRECTIONS FOR HYDROMETER READINGS (cont'd)

Temp °F	Baumé 15° to 25°	Sp. Gr. 1.154 to 1.2083	Baumé 25° to 35°	Sp. Gr. 1.2083 to 1.3182	Baumé 35° to 45°	Sp. Gr. 1.3182 to 1.4500	Baumé 45° to 55°	Sp. Gr. 1.4500 to 1.6111	Baumé 55° to 63°	Sp. Gr. 1.6111 to 1.7683	Baumé 63° to 66°	Sp. Gr. 1.7683 to 1.8354
151	3.28	.0309	3.18	.0355	2.82	.0373	2.55	.0482	2.37	.0519	2.14	.0491
152	3.31	.0313	3.22	.0359	2.85	.0377	2.58	.0488	2.39	.0524	2.16	.0497
153	3.35	.0316	3.26	.0363	2.88	.0381	2.60	.0493	2.42	.0530	2.19	.0502
154	3.38	.0320	3.29	.0367	2.91	.0385	2.63	.0498	2.44	.0536	2.21	.0508
155	3.42	.0323	3.32	.0371	2.94	.0390	2.66	.0504	2.47	.0542	2.23	.0513
156	3.46	.0326	3.36	.0374	2.98	.0394	2.69	.0509	2.50	.0547	2.26	.0518
157	3.49	.0330	3.39	.0378	3.01	.0398	2.72	.0514	2.52	.0553	2.28	.0524
158	3.53	.0333	3.43	.0382	3.04	.0402	2.74	.0519	2.55	.0559	2.30	.0529
159	3.56	.0337	3.46	.0386	3.07	.0406	2.77	.0525	2.57	.0564	2.33	.0535
160	3.60	.0340	3.50	.0390	3.10	.0410	2.80	.0530	2.60	.0570	2.35	.0540
161	3.64	.0343	3.53	.0394	3.13	.0414	2.83	.0535	2.63	.0576	2.37	.0545
162	3.67	.0347	3.57	.0398	3.16	.0418	2.86	.0541	2.65	.0581	2.40	.0551
163	3.71	.0350	3.60	.0402	3.19	.0422	2.88	.0546	2.68	.0587	2.42	.0556
164	3.74	.0354	3.64	.0406	3.22	.0426	2.91	.0551	2.70	.0593	2.44	.0562
165	3.78	.0357	3.67	.0410	3.25	.0431	2.94	.0557	2.73	.0599	2.47	.0567
166	3.82	.0360	3.71	.0413	3.29	.0435	2.97	.0562	2.76	.0604	2.49	.0572
167	3.85	.0364	3.74	.0417	3.32	.0439	3.00	.0567	2.78	.0610	2.51	.0578
168	3.89	.0367	3.78	.0421	3.35	.0443	3.02	.0572	2.81	.0616	2.54	.0583
169	3.92	.0371	3.81	.0425	3.38	.0447	3.05	.0578	2.83	.0621	2.56	.0589
170	3.96	.0374	3.85	.0429	3.41	.0451	3.08	.0583	2.86	.0627	2.58	.0594
171	4.00	.0377	3.88	.0433	3.44	.0455	3.11	.0588	2.89	.0633	2.61	.0599
172	4.03	.0381	3.92	.0437	3.47	.0459	3.14	.0594	2.91	.0638	2.63	.0605
173	4.07	.0384	3.95	.0441	3.50	.0463	3.16	.0599	2.94	.0644	2.66	.0610
174	4.10	.0388	3.99	.0445	3.53	.0467	3.19	.0604	2.96	.0650	2.68	.0616
175	4.14	.0391	4.02	.0449	3.56	.0472	3.22	.0610	2.99	.0656	2.70	.0621
176	4.18	.0394	4.06	.0452	3.60	.0476	3.25	.0615	3.02	.0661	2.73	.0626
177	4.21	.0398	4.09	.0456	3.63	.0480	3.27	.0620	3.04	.0667	2.75	.0632
178	4.25	.0401	4.13	.0460	3.66	.0484	3.30	.0625	3.07	.0673	2.77	.0637
179	4.28	.0405	4.16	.0464	3.69	.0488	3.33	.0631	3.09	.0678	2.80	.0643
180	4.32	.0408	4.20	.0468	3.72	.0492	3.36	.0636	3.12	.0684	2.82	.0648
181	4.35	.0411	4.23	.0472	3.75	.0496	3.39	.0641	3.15	.0690	2.84	.0653
182	4.39	.0415	4.27	.0476	3.78	.0500	3.42	.0647	3.17	.0695	2.87	.0658
183	4.43	.0418	4.30	.0480	3.81	.0504	3.44	.0652	3.20	.0701	2.89	.0664
184	4.46	.0422	4.34	.0484	3.84	.0508	3.47	.0657	3.22	.0707	2.91	.0669
185	4.50	.0425	4.37	.0488	3.87	.0513	3.50	.0663	3.25	.0713	2.94	.0675
186	4.54	.0428	4.41	.0491	3.91	.0517	3.53	.0668	3.28	.0718	2.96	.0680
187	4.57	.0432	4.44	.0495	3.94	.0521	3.56	.0673	3.30	.0724	2.98	.0686
188	4.61	.0435	4.48	.0499	3.97	.0525	3.58	.0678	3.33	.0730	3.01	.0691
189	4.64	.0439	4.51	.0503	4.00	.0529	3.61	.0684	3.35	.0735	3.03	.0697
190	4.68	.0442	4.55	.0507	4.03	.0533	3.64	.0689	3.38	.0741	3.05	.0702

TABLE XXVIII. BOILING POINTS (°F) OF SULFURIC ACID SOLUTIONS

Deg. Bé	% H₂SO₄	Spec. Grav.	ABSOLUTE PRESSURE AND VACUUM										
			29.92"	3.92"	2.92"	2.42"	1.92"	1.42"	.92"	.72"	.52"	.32"	.12"
			0"	26"	27"	27.5"	28"	28.5"	29"	29.2"	29.4"	29.6"	29.8"
26	29.53	1.2185	227	135	125	117	109	99	83	76	67	60	20
28	32.05	1.2393	229	137	126	118	110	100	84	77	68	61	21
30	34.63	1.2609	232	139	127	119	111	101	85	78	69	62	22
32	37.26	1.2832	236	142	129	122	113	104	89	80	71	63	24
34	39.92	1.3063	240	145	131	125	116	107	90	82	73	64	27
36	42.63	1.3303	244	148	134	129	120	110	93	86	76	65	30
38	45.35	1.3551	248	152	139	133	124	113	97	90	79	67	33
40	48.10	1.3810	253	157	144	138	129	118	102	95	84	70	37
42	50.87	1.4078	260	163	150	144	135	124	107	101	90	75	42
44	53.66	1.4356	267	170	157	151	142	131	114	107	97	82	48
46	56.48	1.4646	275	178	165	159	150	138	122	114	104	90	55
48	59.32	1.4948	283	186	173	167	158	146	130	122	112	98	62
50	62.18	1.5263	291	195	182	176	167	155	138	130	120	106	70
52	65.13	1.5591	304	206	193	186	177	165	148	141	130	115	80
54	68.13	1.5934	318	219	207	199	190	178	161	154	143	128	93
56	71.17	1.6292	334	236	223	215	206	194	177	169	159	143	108
58	74.36	1.6667	352	254	241	233	224	212	194	186	175	160	123
59	75.99	1.6860	365	264	251	243	233	221	204	196	185	169	133
60	77.67	1.7059	378	274	261	253	243	231	214	206	195	179	143
61	79.43	1.7262	388	285	271	263	254	241	223	215	204	188	151
62	81.30	1.7470	406	299	285	277	267	255	236	228	217	200	162
63	83.34	1.7683	423	315	301	293	283	269	251	242	231	214	175
64	85.60	1.7901	442	335	320	312	302	288	269	261	249	232	192
64.5	87.04	1.8012	459	350	335	326	316	302	283	275	262	245	204
65	88.65	1.8125	477	365	350	341	331	317	297	289	276	259	217
65.5	90.60	1.8239	500	387	372	363	352	338	318	310	297	279	237
66	93.19	1.8354	529	417	402	393	381	367	347	337	324	306	263

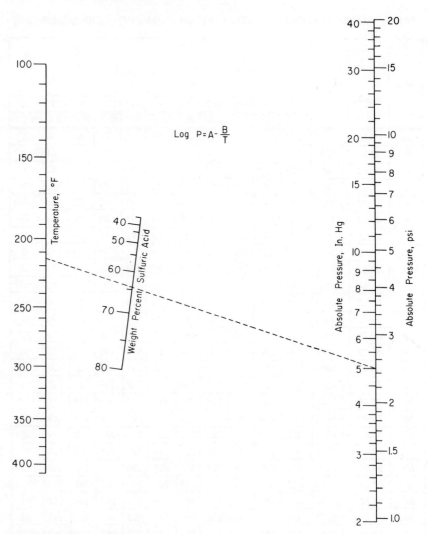

Fig. 59. Boiling temperatures of sulfuric acid. (*Chemical Processing, August 1960, Copyright Putman Publishing Company.*)

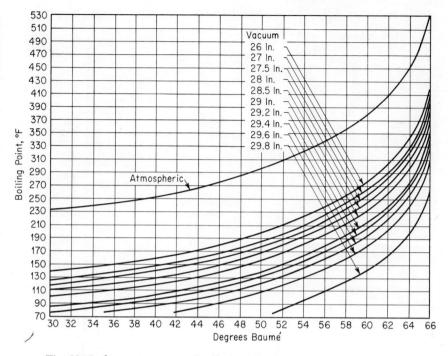

Fig. 60. Boiling-point curves of sulfuric acid solutions at various pressures.

TABLE XXIX. STRENGTH OF H_2SO_4 REQUIRED TO GIVE DEFINITE HUMIDITIES

Relative Humidity %	Percent H2SO4 Required at:			
	0° C	25° C	50° C	75° C
10	63.1	64.8	66.6	68.3
25	54.3	55.9	57.5	59.0
35	49.4	50.9	52.5	54.0
50	42.1	43.4	44.8	46.2
65	34.8	36.0	37.1	38.3
75	29.4	30.4	31.4	32.4
90	17.8	18.5	19.2	20.0

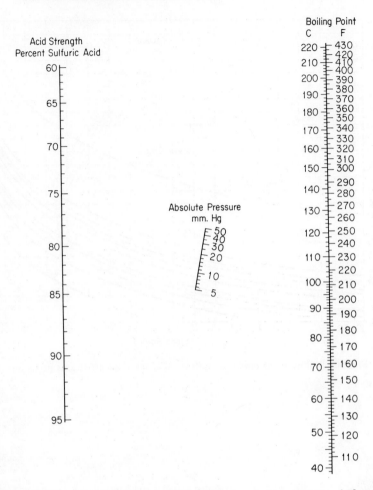

Fig. 61. Boiling points of strong sulfuric acid at vacuum pressures. (*Chemical Engineering Progress, Vol. 43, No. 5, Copyright American Institute of Chemical Engineers.*)

TABLE XXX. CALCULATED VALUES FOR RELATIVE VAPOR PRESSURE OF DILUTE SULFURIC ACID @ 25° C

%H_2SO_4	Temp. t°C	Vapor Pressure mm.	Relative Vapor Pressure at t°C	Calculated Relative Vapor Pressure @25°
5.62	0	4.535	98.0	98.1
9.24	0	4.452	96.4	96.6
15.73	0	4.284	92.7	93.1
20.8	0	4.065	87.9	88.6
27.2	0	3.664	79.3	80.3
32.8	0	3.200	69.3	71.2
35.4	0	2.952	63.9	66.2
40.5	0	2.435	52.7	55.2
47.3	0	1.748	37.8	40.8
53.4	0	1.206	26.1	29.1
61.3	0	0.569	12.3	14.7
62.8	75	45.9	15.9	11.6
68.5	0	0.164	3.5	4.6
70.8	100	57.0	7.5	3.7
74.0	75	12.1	4.2	2.3
77.5	100	20.2	2.66	0.94
78.0	75	7.0	2.4	1.14
79.2	100	14.3	1.88	0.61

TABLE XXXI. BEST VALUES FROM VAPOR PRESSURE CURVES FOR SULFURIC ACID SOLUTIONS

Relative Vapor Pressure Values at:

%H_2SO_4	0° C Percent	25° C Percent	50° C Percent	75° C Percent
0	100.0	100.0	100.0	100.0
5	98.4	98.5	98.5	98.6
10	95.9	96.1	96.3	96.5
15	92.4	92.9	93.4	93.8
20	87.8	88.5	89.3	90.0
25	81.7	82.9	84.0	85.0
30	73.8	75.6	77.2	78.6
35	64.6	66.8	68.9	70.8
40	54.2	56.8	59.3	61.6
45	44.0	46.8	49.5	52.0
50	33.6	36.8	39.9	42.8
55	23.5	26.8	30.0	33.0
60	14.6	17.2	20.0	22.8
65	7.8	9.8	12.0	14.2
70	3.9	5.2	6.7	8.3
75	1.6	2.3	3.2	4.4
80	0.5	0.8	1.2	1.8

TABLE XXXII. VAPOR PRESSURE OF SULFURIC ACID SOLUTIONS, lb./sq. in. abs.

Wt. % H2O	-40° F / -40° C	-20 / -28.9	0 / -17.8	20 / -6.7	Temperature 40 / 4.4	60 / 15.5	80 / 26.7	100 / 37.8	120 / 48.9
0	*	*	*	*	*	*	.000003	.000008	.000023
10	*	*	*	*	.000022	.000065	.000174	.000435	.00102
20	*	*	*	*	.000422	.00110	.00267	.00632	.0135
30	.000062	.000203	.000604	.00168	.00433	.0101	.0222	.0466	.0932
40	*	.00108	.00296	.00778	.0186	.0406	.0851	.164	.319
50	*	.00290	.00735	.0180	.0420	.0890	.190	.348	.654
60	.00159	.00457	.0120	.0296	.0683	.143	.286	.542	.986
70	*	.00615	.0161	.0400	.0915	.191	.383	.716	1.30
80	*	*	*	.0470	.106	.226	.451	.847	1.50
90	*	*	*	*	.116	.242	.480	.900	1.60
100	*	*	*	*	.122	.256	.507	.949	1.69

Wt. % Free SO3									
10	*	*	*	*	.00716	.0155	.0313	.0600	.110
20	*	*	*	*	.00928	.0222	.0503	.104	.219
30	*	*	*	*	*	*	.120	.253	.462
40	*	*	*	*	*	*	*	.574	1.16
50	*	*	*	*	*	*	*	1.53	2.86
60	*	*	*	*	*	*	2.09	3.81	6.58
70	*	*	*	.518	1.16	2.46	4.84	8.60	15.1

*Below freezing point

TABLE XXXII. VAPOR PRESSURE OF SULFURIC ACID SOLUTIONS, lb./sq. in. abs.

Wt. % H_2O	*140 60	160 71.1	180 82.2	Temperature 200 93.3	220 104.4	240 115.6	260 126.7	280 137.8	300° F 148.9° C
0	.000056	.000133	.000296	.000652	.00126	.00238	.00441	.00760	.0128
10	.00232	.00486	.00986	.0194	.0366	.0648	.112	.188	.319
20	.0284	.0548	.102	.184	.333	.567	.948	1.49	2.30
30	.178	.319	.572	.967	1.59	2.51	3.91	5.88	8.70
40	.567	1.01	1.66	2.65	4.22	6.32	9.34	13.5	19.4
50	1.12	1.91	3.10	4.89	7.41	11.2	16.4	23.2	32.5
60	1.70	2.80	4.55	7.06	10.8	15.7	22.4	32.1	44.9
70	2.22	3.60	5.76	8.80	13.3	19.4	27.5	38.3	52.8
80	2.57	4.22	6.62	10.2	15.5	22.2	31.7	43.9	59.0
90	2.77	4.45	7.06	11.0	16.4	23.8	33.5	47.0	65.2
100	2.89	4.74	7.51	11.5	17.2	25.0	35.4	49.2	67.0

Wt. % Free SO_3									
10	.194	.323	.503	.758	1.20	1.88	2.88	4.31	6.28
20	.387	.716	1.22	1.99	3.23	5.03	7.74	11.4	16.6
30	.890	1.61	2.90	4.95	8.32	13.2	20.7	31.7	46.8
40	2.22	3.91	6.81	11.4	18.2	28.4	43.5	64.6	92.8
50	4.97	8.86	14.7	23.6	36.4	54.2	81.2	116	162
60	11.2	19.4	30.9	47.8	71.0	104	151	211	284
70	25.3	40.6	63.8	95.4	139	199	277	381	513

*Below freezing point

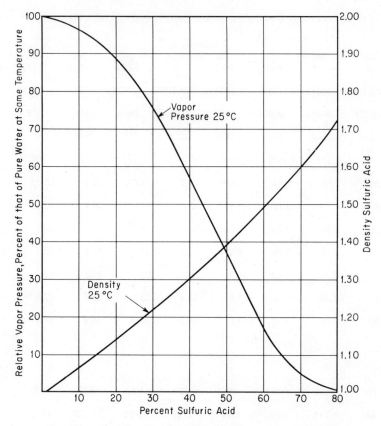

Fig. 62. Aqueous vapor pressure and density of sulfuric acid.

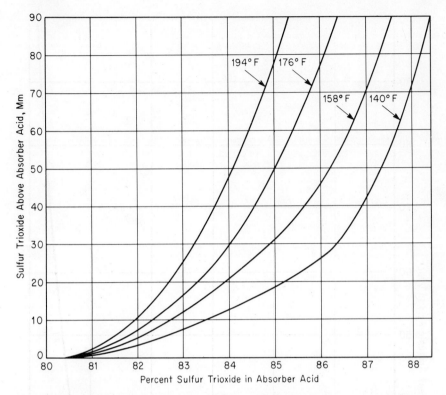

Fig. 63. Vapor pressure of SO₃ over sulfuric acid in absorber at various temperatures. (*Courtesy Olin-Mathieson Chemical Corporation.*)

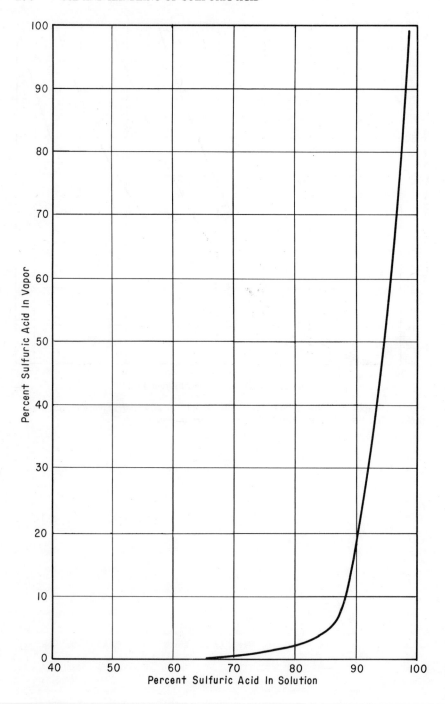

Fig. 64. Composition of vapors in equilibrium with boiling sulfuric acid solutions at 760 mm.

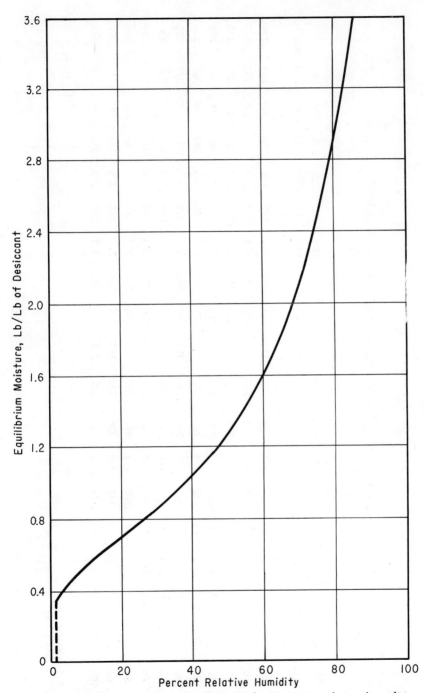

Fig. 65. Equilibrium moisture of sulfuric acid at various relative humidities. (*Perry, "Chemical Engineering Handbook," Copyright 1963 McGraw-Hill Book Company.*)

TABLE XXXIII. THERMAL CONDUCTIVITY OF SULFURIC ACID SOLUTIONS

B.t.u./(hr.)(sq. ft.)(° F/ft.)

Wt. % H₂O	Temperature																	
°F	-40	-20	0	20	40	60	80	100	120	140	160	180	200	220	240	260	280	300
°C	-40	-28.9	-17.8	-6.7	4.4	15.5	26.7	37.8	48.9	60	71.1	82.2	93.3	104.4	115.6	126.7	137.8	148.9
0	*	*	*	*	*	.170	.174	.177	.180	.183	.187	.190	.193	.196	.200	.203	.206	.210
10	*	*	*	*	.203	.208	.213	.218	.223	.228	.232	.236	.240	.244	.247	.250	.252	.253
20	*	*	*	*	.225	.231	.236	.242	.248	.254	.259	.264	.268	.271	.274	.276	.278	.280
30	.211	.217	.223	.230	.236	.242	.248	.254	.261	.267	.272	.277	.281	.285	.288	.290	.291	.292
40	*	.228	.235	.242	.248	.255	.262	.269	.276	.282	.287	.292	.296	.299	.302	.304	.305	.306
50	*	.241	.248	.256	.263	.271	.278	.286	.293	.299	.304	.309	.313	.317	.320	.321	.322	.322
60	.244	.252	.260	.268	.276	.284	.292	.300	.307	.314	.320	.325	.329	.332	.334	.335	.336	.336
70	*	.264	.272	.281	.289	.298	.306	.314	.322	.329	.335	.340	.344	.348	.350	.351	.351	.351
80	*	*	*	.294	.303	.312	.321	.329	.337	.344	.350	.355	.360	.364	.366	.366	.366	.366
90	*	*	*	*	.316	.326	.336	.345	.353	.360	.366	.372	.376	.379	.381	.381	.381	.381
100	*	*	*	*	.331	.341	.351	.360	.368	.376	.382	.388	.392	.395	.396	.396	.396	.395

*Below freezing point

TABLE XXXIV. SPECIFIC HEAT OF SULFURIC ACID SOLUTIONS B.t.u./(lb.)/(°F)

Temperature

Wt. % H2O (°F)	-40	-20	0	20	40	60	80	100	120	140	160	180	200	220	240	260	280	300
(°C)	-40	-28.9	-17.8	-6.7	4.4	15.5	26.7	37.8	48.9	60	71.1	82.2	93.3	104.4	115.6	126.7	137.8	148.9
0	*	*	*	*	*	.333	.338	.343	.347	.351	.355	.360	.364	.368	.372	.376	.380	.384
10	*	*	*	*	.384	.392	.399	.404	4.08	.412	.416	.421	.425	.429	.434	.438	.442	.447
20	*	*	*	*	.441	.447	.453	.457	.460	.462	.468	.475	.481	.488	.494	.500	.507	.513
30	.451	.456	.460	.465	.470	.474	.478	.483	.489	.495	.501	.508	.514	.520	.527	.533	.539	.545
40	*	.513	.516	.520	.523	.526	.529	.532	.537	.543	.546	.549	.552	.556	.559	.562	.565	.568
50	*	.579	.583	.586	.590	.594	.598	.602	.604	.606	.608	.609	.611	.613	.614	.616	.618	.620
60	.646	.653	.660	.667	.674	.680	.684	.684	.684	.684	.685	.685	.686	.686	.687	.687	.688	.688
70	*	.730	.738	.747	.755	.764	.768	.766	.766	.767	.763	.758	.754	.749	.744	.740	.735	.730
80	*	*	*	.844	.844	.844	.842	.842	.841	.840	.836	.833	.829	.825	.822	.818	.814	.811
90	*	*	*	*	.916	.916	.916	.916	.916	.917	.915	.912	.910	.908	.905	.902	.900	.898
100	*	*	*	*	1.004	1.000	.998	.998	.998	.999	1.001	1.003	1.005	1.010	1.014	1.019	1.024	1.029

*Below freezing point

TABLE XXXV. CALCULATED HEATS OF SOLUTION AND RESULTING
TEMPERATURE RISE FOR VARIOUS MIXTURES OF SULFURIC ACID

Lbs. Strong Acid	Strength Strong Acid	Lbs. Weak Acid Added	Strength Weak Acid	Lbs. of Mixed Acid Made	Strength Mixed Acid	Heat Evolved B.T.U. ΔH	Average Sp.Heat 20°-B.P.	Temp. Rise Deg. F.
100	106.08	35.11	100.0	135.11	104.5	-494	@20° C .34	10.8°
100	–	24.31	98.0	124.31	–	-717	.34	17.0°
100	–	13.97	93.19	113.97	–	-1184	.34	30.6°
100	–	10.90	90.00	110.90	–	-1351'	.34	35.8°
100	–	8.10	85.00	108.10	–	-1545	.34	42.0°
100	–	5.90	77.67	105.90	–	-1764	.34	49.0°
100	–	1.51	H_2O	101.51	–	-2832	.34	82.1°
100	104.5	290.00	85.0	390.00	90.00	-6936	20° to BP .45	39.5°
100	–	224.50	98.0	324.50	100.00	-2564	.39	20.3°
100	–	65.93	93.19	165.93	–	-3513	–	54.3°
100	–	44.90	90.00	144.90	–	-3767	–	66.7°
100	–	29.93	85.00	129.93	–	-4090	–	80.8°
100	–	20.10	77.67	120.10	–	-4528	–	96.7°
100	–	4.49	H_2O	104.49	–	-7111	–	174.4°
100	100.0	41.58	93.19	141.58	98.0	-591	.40	10.4°
100	–	25.00	90.00	125.00	–	-661	–	13.2°
100	–	15.39	85.00	115.39	–	-779	–	16.9°
100	–	9.84	77.67	109.84	–	-932	–	21.2°
100	–	2.04	H_2O	102.04	–	-2058	–	50.4°
100	98.0	150.78	90.00	250.78	93.19	-424	.43	3.9°
100	–	58.73	85.00	158.73	–	-715	–	10.5°
100	–	30.99	77.67	130.99	–	-1152	–	20.4°
100	–	5.16	H_2O	105.16	–	-3710	–	82.1°
100	93.19	63.80	85.0	163.80	90.00	-317	.45	4.3°
100	–	25.87	77.67	125.87	–	-606	–	10.7°
100	–	3.54	H_2O	103.54	–	-2257	–	39.8°
100	90.00	68.21	77.67	168.20	85.00	-1811	.47	22.9°
100	–	5.88	H_2O	105.88	–	-3224	–	64.8°
100	85.0	9.44	H_2O	109.44	77.67	-3938	.48	75.0°

TABLE XXXVI. PARTIAL MOLAL HEATS OF SOLUTION OF
SULFUR TRIOXIDE (Liq.) IN WATER (Liq.)

(Temperature - 18° C.; for H_2O(Liq), $\bar{H}_1$ = 0; for SO_3(Liq), $\bar{H}_2$ = 0

% Free SO_3	100% Equiv. H_2SO_4	% H_2O	% SO_3	Mols H_2O Per 100 lb.	Mols SO_3 Per 100 lb.	Total Mols SO_3+H_2O	Mol Fraction SO_3 $\overline{SO_3+H_2O}$	$\bar{H}_1$ BTU Per lb. MolH_2O	$\bar{H}_2$ BTU Per lb. MolSO_3	Avg Specific Heat 20° -BP
	66.13	45.61	54.39	2.5334	.6799	3.2133	.2116	-2850	-48800	.53
	68.13	44.38	55.62	2.4646	.6953	3.1609	.2199	-3170	-47360	.52
	69.65	43.14	56.86	2.3967	.7108	3.1075	.2287	-3600	-45950	.51
	71.17	41.90	58.10	2.3278	.7263	3.0541	.2378	-4060	.44420	.505
	72.75	40.61	59.39	2.2561	.7424	2.9985	.2475	-4540	-42800	.50
	74.36	39.30	60.70	2.1833	.7588	2.9421	.2579	-5060	-41410	.50
	75.99	37.97	62.03	2.1094	.7754	2.8848	.2687	-5590	-40000	.49
	77.67	36.60	63.40	2.0333	.7925	2.8258	.2805	-6190	-38400	.48
	78.00	36.33	63.67	2.0183	.7959	2.8142	.2829	-6310	-38081	.48
	79.43	35.16	64.84	1.9533	.8105	2.7638	.2933	-6830	-36700	.48
	81.30	33.63	66.37	1.8683	.8296	2.6979	.3074	-7490	-34820	.48
	83.34	31.97	68.03	1.7761	.8504	2.6265	.3237	-8150	-33790	.47
	85.00	30.62	69.38	1.7010	.8673	2.5683	.3378	-8758	-32566	.47
	85.66	30.08	69.92	1.6711	.8740	2.5451	.3434	-9000	-32080	.46
	86.33	29.53	70.47	1.6406	.8809	2.5215	.3494	-9240	-31540	.46
	87.04	28.95	71.05	1.6083	.8881	2.4964	.3558	-9510	-31000	.46
	87.81	28.32	71.68	1.5733	.8960	2.4693	.3629	-9810	-30580	.45
	88.65	27.63	72.37	1.5350	.9046	2.4396	.3708	-10160	-29990	.45
	89.55	26.90	73.10	1.4944	.9138	2.4082	.3795	-10520	-29360	.45
	90.00	26.53	73.47	1.4740	.9184	2.3923	.3840	-10713	-29034	.45
	90.60	26.04	73.96	1.4467	.9245	2.3712	.3899	-10970	-28600	.44
	91.80	25.06	74.94	1.3922	.9368	2.3290	.4022	-11510	-27700	.43
	93.19	23.93	76.07	1.3294	.9509	2.2803	.4170	-12300	-26600	.43
	94.00	23.27	76.73	1.2928	.9591	2.2519	.4259	-12880	-26070	.42
	95.00	22.45	77.55	1.2472	.9694	2.2166	.4373	-13390	-25300	.42
	96.00	21.64	78.36	1.2022	.9795	2.1817	.4490	-14000	-24540	.41
	97.00	20.82	79.18	1.1567	.9898	2.1465	.4611	-15170	-23290	.41
	97.50	20.41	79.59	1.1339	.9949	2.1288	.4674	-15800	-22600	.41
	98.00	20.00	80.00	1.1111	1.0000	2.1111	.4689	-15950	-22420	.40
	99.00	19.19	80.81	1.0661	1.0101	2.0762	.4865	-17710	-20520	.40

(cont'd)

TABLE XXXVI. PARTIAL MOLAL HEATS OF SOLUTION OF
SULFUR TRIOXIDE (Liq.) IN WATER (Liq.) (cont'd)

% Free SO₃	100% Equiv H₂SO₄	% H₂O	% SO₃	Mols H₂O Per 100 lb.	Mols SO₃ Per 100 lb.	Total Mols SO₃+H₂O	Mol Fraction SO₃ SO₃+H₂O	H̄₁ BTU Per lb MolH₂O	H̄₂ BTU Per lb MolSO₃	Avg. Specific Heat 20° -BP
0	100.00	18.37	81.63	1.0206	1.0204	2.0410	.5000	-19060	-19060	.39
1	100.22	18.19	81.81	1.0106	1.0223	2.0329	.5029	-20380	-17810	@ 20°C .34
2	100.45	18.00	82.00	1.000	1.0250	2.0250	.5062	-22000	-16200	.34
3	100.67	17.82	82.18	.9900	1.0273	2.0173	.5092	-23400	-14840	.34
4	100.89	17.64	82.36	.9800	1.0295	2.0095	.5123	-25000	-13360	.34
5	101.13	17.45	82.55	.9694	1.0319	2.0013	.5156	-26420	-11840	.34
6	101.35	17.27	82.73	.9594	1.0341	1.9935	.5187	-28000	-10300	.34
7	101.58	17.08	82.92	.9489	1.0365	1.9854	.5221	-28820	- 9490	.34
8	101.80	16.90	83.10	.9389	1.0388	1.9777	.5253	-29070	- 9380	.34
9	102.02	16.72	83.28	.9289	1.0410	1.9699	.5285	-29300	- 9220	.34
10	102.25	16.57	83.47	.9206	1.0434	1.9640	.5313	-29410	- 8980	.34
11	102.47	16.35	83.65	.9083	1.0456	1.9539	.5351	-29810	- 8720	.34
12	102.71	16.17	83.83	.8983	1.0479	1.9462	.5384	-30040	- 8400	.34
13	102.92	15.98	84.02	.8878	1.0503	1.9381	.5419	-30300	- 8280	.34
14	103.15	15.80	84.20	.8778	1.0525	1.9303	.5453	-30570	- 8030	.34
15	103.38	15.61	84.39	.8672	1.0549	1.9221	.5488	-30820	- 7810	.34
16	103.60	15.43	84.57	.8572	1.0571	1.9143	.5522	-31130	- 7490	.34
17	103.82	15.25	84.75	.8472	1.0594	1.9066	.5556	-31410	- 7390	.34
18	104.05	15.06	84.94	.8367	1.0618	1.8985	.5593	-31720	- 7160	.34
19	104.28	14.88	85.12	.8267	1.0640	1.8907	.5628	-32010	- 6930	.34
20	104.49	14.70	85.30	.8167	1.0663	1.8830	.5647	-32160	- 6820	.34
21	104.73	14.51	85.49	.8061	1.0686	1.8747	.5700	-32610	- 6400	.34
22	104.95	14.33	85.67	.7961	1.0709	1.8670	.5736	-32910	- 6280	.34
23	105.18	14.14	85.86	.7856	1.0733	1.8589	.5774	-33230	- 6030	.34
24	105.40	13.96	86.04	.7756	1.0755	1.8511	.5810	-33520	- 5810	.34
25	105.62	13.78	86.22	.7656	1.0778	1.8434	.5852	-33900	- 5460	.34
26	105.85	13.59	86.41	.7550	1.0801	1.8351	.5886	-34160	- 5360	.34
27	106.08	13.41	86.59	.7450	1.0824	1.8274	.5923	-34470	- 5110	.34

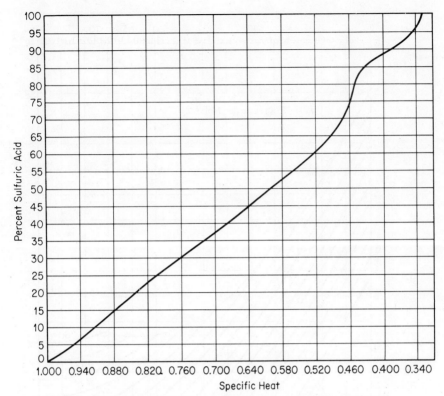

Fig. 66. Specific heat of aqueous solutions of sulfuric acid at 20°C.

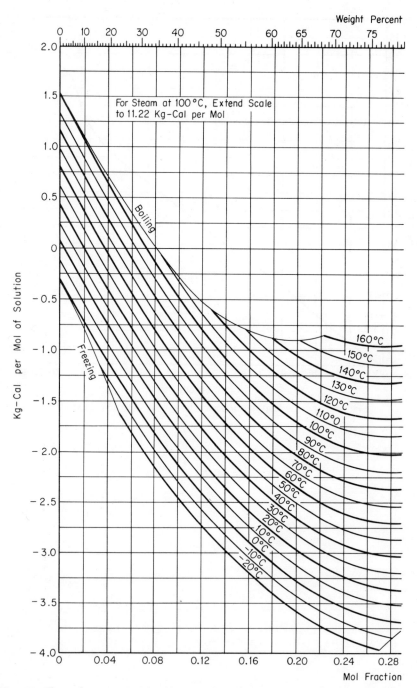

Fig. 67. Thermal properties of sulfuric acid and oleum. (Basis: one mol of solu-

Sulfuric Acid

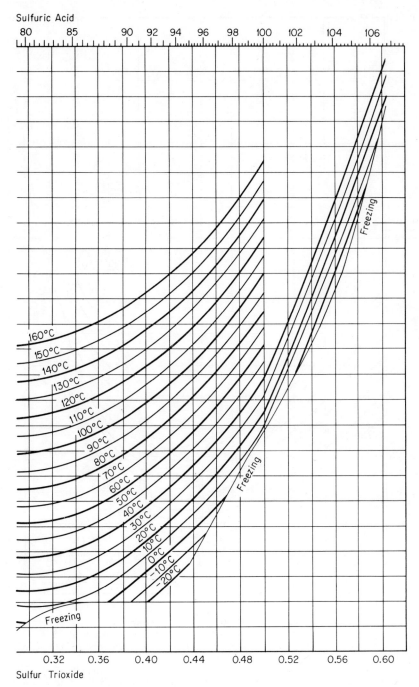

Sulfur Trioxide

tion equals N mol of SO_3 plus $(1-N)$ mol of H_2O.)

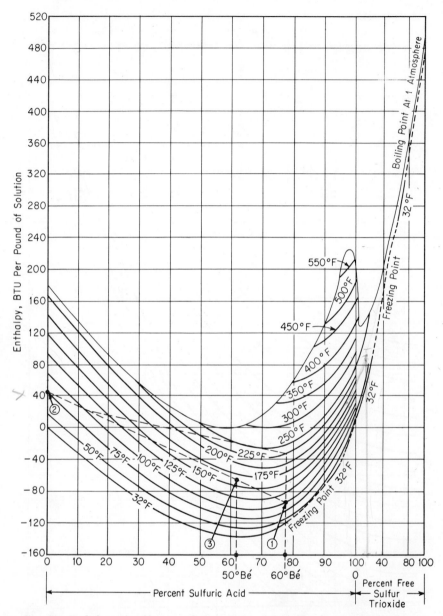

Fig. 68. Enthalpy of sulfuric acid and oleum. (Example: In the production of superphosphate, suppose 60° Bé acid at 100°F. is cut with water at 75°F. Connect Point (1) in chart—where acid strength intersects temperature curve—with Point (2)—where water (0% acid) intersects the 75°F. curve. This line crosses the 50° Bé axis at Point (3) on the 165°F. curve. Thus, approximately 45 BTU/lb. of solution must be dissipated to reduce the temperature to 75°F.) (*Ross, Chem. Eng. Progress 48 (1952); Miles, Trans. Faraday Soc. 40 (1944); Morgen, Ind. Eng. Chemistry 34 (1942); and Broughton, Chem. & Met. 52 (1945).*)

TABLE XXXVII. PRANDTL MODULUS OF SULFURIC ACID SOLUTIONS

Wt. % H2O	-40°F / -40°C	-20 / -28.9	0 / -17.8	20 / -6.7	40 / 4.4	60 / 15.5	80 / 26.7	100 / 37.8	120 / 48.9	140 / 60	160 / 71.1	180 / 82.2	200 / 93.3	220 / 104.4	240 / 115.6	260 / 126.7	280 / 137.8	300° F / 148.9° C
0	*	*	*	*	*	173	109	75.9	54.6	40.0	30.8	24.8	20.3	16.8	14.1	12.0	10.30	8.85
10	*	*	*	*	183	123	85.2	61.4	44.3	33.2	26.0	20.7	16.8	13.9	11.7	10.0	8.66	7.65
20	*	*	*	*	169	112	77.1	54.4	39.5	29.5	23.2	18.8	15.5	13.1	11.2	9.69	8.52	7.54
30	724	361	198	121	78.6	54.0	39.2	29.9	23.1	18.4	15.0	12.5	10.5	8.92	7.75	6.85	6.14	5.56
40	*	218	120	71.8	47.0	33.4	24.9	19.1	15.3	12.6	10.6	9.10	7.94	7.05	6.32	5.72	5.23	4.81
50	*	118	70.6	44.8	30.9	22.6	17.2	13.6	11.2	9.36	8.04	7.03	6.28	5.66	5.15	4.75	4.42	4.14
60	184	94.7	54.6	34.9	24.2	17.5	13.2	10.2	8.25	6.85	5.80	5.00	4.39	3.90	3.48	3.13	2.86	2.63
70	*	77.0	44.7	28.0	19.3	14.0	10.5	8.15	6.50	5.36	4.52	3.86	3.34	2.92	2.58	2.30	2.08	1.91
80	*	*	*	23.7	16.0	11.3	8.38	6.50	5.20	4.26	3.58	3.07	2.65	2.30	2.01	1.78	1.61	1.50
90	*	*	*	*	13.0	9.24	6.86	5.34	4.27	3.51	2.97	2.55	2.23	1.96	1.73	1.55	1.43	1.31
100	*	*	*	*	11.4	7.94	5.92	4.59	3.67	3.02	2.54	2.17	1.89	1.67	1.49	1.36	1.25	1.17

*Below freezing point.

TABLE XXXVIII. VISCOSITY OF SULFURIC ACID SOLUTIONS (CENTIPOISES)

Wt. % H_2SO_4	Temperature																	
°F	-40	-20	0	20	40	60	80	100	120	140	160	180	200	220	240	260	280	300
°C	-40	-28.9	-17.8	-6.7	4.4	15.5	26.7	37.8	48.9	60	71.1	82.2	93.3	104.4	115.6	126.7	137.8	148.9
100	*	*	*	*	*	36.5	23.3	16.0	11.7	8.8	6.8	5.4	4.44	3.70	3.13	2.67	2.30	2.00
90	*	*	*	*	40.0	27.0	18.9	13.7	10.0	7.6	6.0	4.80	3.93	3.28	2.76	2.36	2.04	1.79
80	*	*	*	*	35.6	24.0	16.6	11.9	8.8	6.7	5.3	4.32	3.57	3.00	2.56	2.21	1.93	1.70
70	140	71	39.6	24.8	16.3	11.4	8.4	6.5	5.1	4.10	3.37	2.81	2.37	2.02	1.75	1.54	1.37	1.23
60	*	40.0	22.5	13.8	9.2	6.7	5.1	4.00	3.24	2.70	2.31	2.00	1.76	1.57	1.41	1.28	1.17	1.07
50	*	20.3	12.4	8.1	5.7	4.25	3.30	2.67	2.23	1.91	1.66	1.47	1.33	1.21	1.11	1.02	.95	.89
40	28.8	15.1	8.9	5.8	4.10	3.02	2.32	1.85	1.53	1.30	1.12	.98	.87	.78	.70	.63	.58	.53
30	*	11.5	6.8	4.35	3.05	2.25	1.73	1.38	1.13	.95	.82	.72	.63	.56	.50	.45	.41	.38
20	*	*	*	3.41	2.38	1.73	1.32	1.05	.86	.72	.62	.54	.47	.42	.37	.33	.30	.28
10	*	*	*	*	1.85	1.36	1.04	.83	.68	.57	.49	.43	.38	.34	.30	.27	.25	.23
0	*	*	*	*	1.55	1.12	.86	.68	.56	.47	.40	.35	.31	.27	.24	.22	.20	.19

Wt. % Free SO_3	Temperature																	
°F	-40	-20	0	20	40	60	80	100	120	140	160	180	200	220	240	260	280	300
°C	-40	-28.9	-17.8	-6.7	4.4	15.5	26.7	37.8	48.9	60	71.1	82.2	93.3	104.4	115.6	126.7	137.8	148.9
10	*	*	*	*	66	39.0	25.0	17.0	12.4	9.3	7.2	5.7	4.66	3.87	3.27	2.78	2.40	2.10
20	*	*	*	*	73	43.8	27.5	19.0	13.7	10.4	8.1	6.4	5.2	4.38	3.71	3.17	2.74	2.39
30	*	*	*	*	*	*	36.0	23.8	16.4	12.0	9.1	7.1	5.7	4.67	3.88	3.26	2.78	2.40
40	*	*	*	*	*	*	*	28.6	19.0	13.4	10.0	7.7	6.0	4.78	3.90	3.26	2.78	2.40

*Below freezing point.

TABLE XXXIX. KINEMATIC VISCOSITY OF SULFURIC ACID SOLUTIONS, sq.ft./hr.

Wt. % H₂O	Temperature																	
°F	-40	-20	0	20	40	60	80	100	120	140	160	180	200	220	240	260	280	300
°C	-40	-28.9	-17.8	-6.7	4.4	15.5	26.7	37.8	48.9	60	71.1	82.2	93.3	104.4	115.6	126.7	137.8	148.9
0	*	*	*	*	*	.771	.495	.342	.252	.190	.148	.118	.0976	.0820	.0697	.0599	.0519	.0454
10	*	*	*	*	.846	.575	.405	.296	.217	.166	.131	.106	.0875	.0735	.0624	.0536	.0466	.0411
20	*	*	*	*	.791	.537	.374	.270	.201	.155	.123	.100	.0836	.0707	.0607	.0528	.0464	.0411
30	3.26	1.66	.932	.588	.389	.274	.203	.158	.125	.101	.0834	.0700	.0593	.0509	.0444	.0393	.0352	.0318
40	*	1.01	.570	.351	.236	.173	.132	.105	.0854	.0714	.0614	.0536	.0474	.0424	.0384	.0351	.0323	.0297
50	*	.550	.338	.222	.157	.118	.0921	.0748	.0630	.0542	.0475	.0424	.0384	.0352	.0325	.0301	.0282	.0265
60	.828	.437	.259	.170	.121	.0896	.0693	.0556	.0463	.0396	.0343	.0302	.0270	.0244	.0220	.0200	.0184	.0170
70	*	.355	.212	.136	.0962	.0714	.0552	.0442	.0361	.0309	.0268	.0236	.0209	.0187	.0168	.0152	.0139	.0129
80	*	*	*	.115	.0804	.0587	.0450	.0361	.0297	.0250	.0217	.0190	.0168	.0149	.0133	.0119	.0109	.0103
90	*	*	*	*	.0669	.0494	.0380	.0304	.0250	.0211	.0183	.0162	.0144	.0129	.0115	.0104	.0097	.0090
100	*	*	*	*	.0601	.0434	.0335	.0267	.0219	.0185	.0159	.0139	.0123	.0110	.0099	.0090	.0083	.0078
Wt. % Free SO₃																		
10	*	*	*	*	1.36	.808	.520	.356	.261	.197	.153	.122	.100	.0840	.0713	.0611	.0531	.0467
20	*	*	*	*	1.48	.890	.562	.391	.284	.217	.170	.135	.111	.0936	.0797	.0686	.0596	.0524
30	*	*	*	*	*	*	.722	.481	.333	.246	.187	.147	.119	.0982	.0822	.0695	.0598	.0520
40	*	*	*	*	*	*	*	.569	.381	.271	.203	.158	.124	.0995	.0818	.0689	.0593	.0516

*Below freezing point.

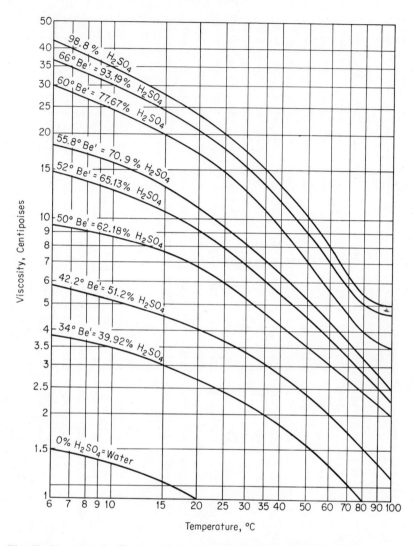

Fig. 69. Viscosity of sulfuric acid at various temperatures (used for friction calculations.) (*Courtesy Chas. S. Lewis & Company, St. Louis, Mo.*)

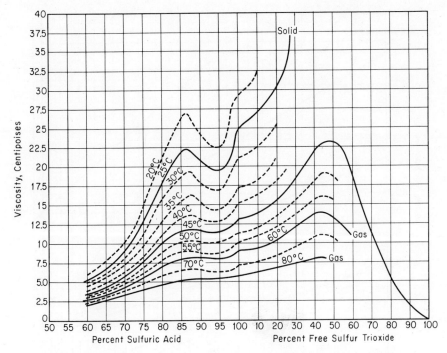

Fig. 70. Viscosity of sulfuric acid and oleum at various temperatures.

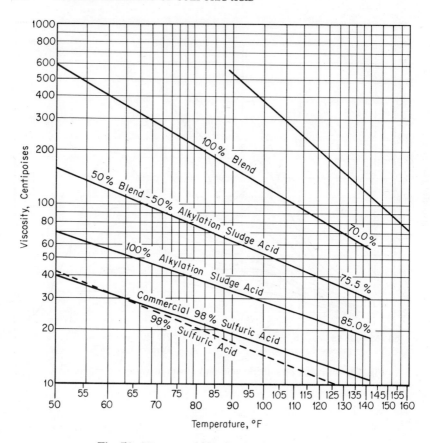

Fig. 71. Viscosity of blends of spent sulfuric acid.

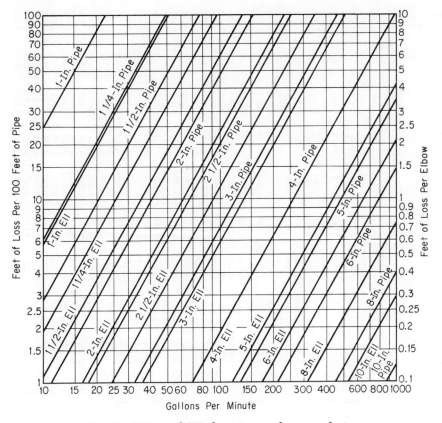

Fig. 72. Friction of 40% oleum in extra heavy steel pipe.

TABLE XI. DESICCATING AND/OR DILUTING TABLE

Pounds of Water Absorbed Per Pound Strong Acid When Diluting to Various Strengths.

	98.0	98.1	98.2	98.3	98.4	98.5	98.6	98.7	98.8	98.9	99.0	99.1	99.2	99.3	99.4	99.5
70.0	0.400	0.401	0.403	0.404	0.406	0.407	0.409	0.410	0.411	0.413	0.414	0.416	0.417	0.419	0.420	0.421
70.2	0.396	0.397	0.399	0.400	0.402	0.403	0.405	0.406	0.407	0.409	0.410	0.412	0.413	0.415	0.416	0.417
70.4	0.392	0.394	0.395	0.396	0.398	0.399	0.401	0.402	0.403	0.405	0.406	0.408	0.409	0.411	0.412	0.413
70.6	0.388	0.390	0.391	0.392	0.394	0.395	0.397	0.398	0.399	0.401	0.402	0.404	0.405	0.407	0.408	0.409
70.8	0.384	0.386	0.387	0.388	0.390	0.391	0.393	0.394	0.395	0.397	0.398	0.400	0.401	0.403	0.404	0.405
71.0	0.380	0.382	0.383	0.385	0.386	0.387	0.389	0.390	0.392	0.393	0.394	0.396	0.397	0.399	0.400	0.401
71.2	0.376	0.378	0.379	0.381	0.382	0.383	0.385	0.386	0.388	0.389	0.390	0.392	0.393	0.395	0.396	0.397
71.4	0.373	0.374	0.375	0.377	0.378	0.380	0.381	0.382	0.384	0.385	0.387	0.388	0.389	0.391	0.392	0.394
71.6	0.369	0.370	0.371	0.373	0.374	0.376	0.377	0.378	0.380	0.381	0.383	0.384	0.385	0.387	0.388	0.390
71.8	0.365	0.366	0.368	0.369	0.371	0.372	0.373	0.375	0.376	0.377	0.379	0.380	0.382	0.383	0.384	0.386
72.0	0.361	0.363	0.364	0.365	0.367	0.368	0.369	0.371	0.372	0.374	0.375	0.376	0.378	0.379	0.381	0.382
72.2	0.357	0.359	0.360	0.361	0.363	0.364	0.366	0.367	0.368	0.370	0.371	0.373	0.374	0.375	0.377	0.378
72.4	0.354	0.355	0.356	0.357	0.359	0.360	0.362	0.363	0.365	0.366	0.367	0.369	0.370	0.372	0.373	0.374
72.6	0.350	0.351	0.353	0.354	0.355	0.357	0.358	0.359	0.361	0.362	0.364	0.365	0.366	0.368	0.369	0.371
72.8	0.346	0.348	0.349	0.350	0.352	0.353	0.354	0.356	0.357	0.358	0.360	0.361	0.363	0.364	0.365	0.367
73.0	0.343	0.344	0.345	0.347	0.348	0.349	0.351	0.352	0.353	0.355	0.356	0.358	0.359	0.360	0.362	0.363
73.2	0.339	0.340	0.342	0.343	0.344	0.346	0.347	0.348	0.350	0.351	0.352	0.354	0.355	0.357	0.358	0.359
73.4	0.335	0.337	0.338	0.339	0.341	0.342	0.343	0.345	0.346	0.347	0.349	0.350	0.352	0.353	0.354	0.356
73.6	0.332	0.333	0.334	0.336	0.337	0.338	0.340	0.341	0.342	0.344	0.345	0.346	0.348	0.349	0.351	0.352
73.8	0.328	0.329	0.331	0.332	0.333	0.335	0.336	0.337	0.339	0.340	0.341	0.343	0.344	0.346	0.347	0.348
74.0	0.324	0.326	0.327	0.328	0.330	0.331	0.332	0.334	0.335	0.337	0.338	0.339	0.341	0.342	0.343	0.345
74.2	0.321	0.322	0.323	0.325	0.326	0.327	0.329	0.330	0.332	0.333	0.334	0.336	0.337	0.338	0.340	0.341
74.4	0.317	0.319	0.320	0.321	0.322	0.324	0.325	0.327	0.328	0.329	0.331	0.332	0.333	0.335	0.336	0.337
74.6	0.314	0.315	0.316	0.318	0.319	0.320	0.322	0.323	0.324	0.326	0.327	0.328	0.330	0.331	0.332	0.334
74.8	0.310	0.311	0.313	0.314	0.316	0.317	0.318	0.320	0.321	0.322	0.324	0.325	0.326	0.328	0.329	0.330
75.0	0.307	0.308	0.309	0.311	0.312	0.313	0.315	0.316	0.317	0.319	0.320	0.321	0.323	0.324	0.325	0.327
75.2	0.303	0.305	0.306	0.307	0.309	0.310	0.311	0.313	0.314	0.315	0.317	0.318	0.319	0.320	0.322	0.323
75.4	0.300	0.301	0.302	0.304	0.305	0.306	0.308	0.309	0.310	0.312	0.313	0.314	0.316	0.317	0.318	0.320
75.6	0.296	0.298	0.299	0.300	0.302	0.303	0.304	0.306	0.307	0.308	0.310	0.311	0.312	0.314	0.315	0.316
75.8	0.293	0.294	0.296	0.297	0.298	0.300	0.301	0.302	0.303	0.305	0.306	0.307	0.309	0.310	0.311	0.313
76.0	0.289	0.291	0.292	0.293	0.295	0.296	0.297	0.299	0.300	0.301	0.303	0.304	0.305	0.307	0.308	0.309
76.2	0.286	0.287	0.289	0.290	0.291	0.293	0.294	0.295	0.297	0.298	0.299	0.300	0.302	0.303	0.304	0.306
76.4	0.283	0.284	0.285	0.287	0.288	0.289	0.291	0.292	0.293	0.295	0.296	0.297	0.298	0.300	0.301	0.302
76.6	0.279	0.281	0.282	0.283	0.285	0.286	0.287	0.289	0.290	0.291	0.292	0.294	0.295	0.296	0.298	0.299
76.8	0.276	0.277	0.279	0.280	0.281	0.283	0.284	0.285	0.286	0.288	0.289	0.290	0.292	0.293	0.294	0.296
77.0	0.273	0.274	0.275	0.277	0.278	0.279	0.281	0.282	0.283	0.284	0.286	0.287	0.288	0.290	0.291	0.292
77.2	0.269	0.271	0.272	0.273	0.275	0.276	0.277	0.278	0.280	0.281	0.282	0.284	0.285	0.286	0.288	0.289
77.4	0.266	0.267	0.269	0.270	0.271	0.273	0.274	0.275	0.276	0.278	0.279	0.280	0.282	0.283	0.284	0.286
77.6	0.263	0.264	0.266	0.267	0.268	0.269	0.271	0.272	0.273	0.275	0.276	0.277	0.278	0.280	0.281	0.282

TABLE XL. DESICCATING AND/OR DILUTING TABLE (cont'd)

	98.0	98.1	98.2	98.3	98.4	98.5	98.6	98.7	98.8	98.9	99.0	99.1	99.2	99.3	99.4	99.5
77.8	0.260	0.261	0.262	0.263	0.265	0.266	0.267	0.269	0.270	0.271	0.272	0.274	0.275	0.276	0.278	0.279
78.0	0.256	0.258	0.259	0.260	0.261	0.263	0.264	0.265	0.267	0.268	0.269	0.270	0.272	0.273	0.274	0.276
78.2	0.253	0.255	0.256	0.257	0.258	0.260	0.261	0.262	0.263	0.265	0.266	0.267	0.269	0.270	0.271	0.272
78.4	0.250	0.251	0.253	0.254	0.255	0.256	0.258	0.259	0.260	0.261	0.263	0.264	0.265	0.267	0.268	0.269
78.6	0.247	0.248	0.249	0.251	0.252	0.253	0.254	0.256	0.257	0.258	0.260	0.261	0.262	0.263	0.265	0.266
78.8	0.244	0.245	0.246	0.247	0.249	0.250	0.251	0.253	0.254	0.255	0.256	0.258	0.259	0.260	0.261	0.263
79.0	0.240	0.242	0.243	0.244	0.246	0.247	0.248	0.249	0.251	0.252	0.253	0.254	0.256	0.257	0.258	0.259
79.2	0.237	0.239	0.240	0.241	0.242	0.244	0.245	0.246	0.247	0.249	0.250	0.251	0.252	0.254	0.255	0.256
79.4	0.234	0.235	0.237	0.238	0.239	0.241	0.242	0.243	0.244	0.246	0.247	0.248	0.249	0.251	0.252	0.253
79.6	0.231	0.232	0.234	0.235	0.236	0.237	0.239	0.240	0.241	0.242	0.244	0.245	0.246	0.247	0.249	0.250
79.8	0.228	0.229	0.231	0.232	0.233	0.234	0.236	0.237	0.238	0.239	0.241	0.242	0.243	0.244	0.246	0.247
80.0	0.225	0.226	0.228	0.229	0.230	0.231	0.233	0.234	0.235	0.236	0.238	0.239	0.240	0.241	0.243	0.244
80.2	0.222	0.223	0.224	0.226	0.227	0.228	0.229	0.231	0.232	0.233	0.234	0.236	0.237	0.238	0.239	0.241
80.4	0.219	0.220	0.221	0.223	0.224	0.225	0.226	0.228	0.229	0.230	0.231	0.233	0.234	0.235	0.236	0.238
80.6	0.216	0.217	0.218	0.220	0.221	0.222	0.223	0.225	0.226	0.227	0.228	0.230	0.231	0.232	0.233	0.234
80.8	0.213	0.214	0.215	0.217	0.218	0.219	0.220	0.222	0.223	0.224	0.225	0.226	0.228	0.229	0.230	0.231
81.0	0.210	0.211	0.212	0.214	0.215	0.216	0.217	0.219	0.220	0.221	0.222	0.223	0.225	0.226	0.227	0.228
81.2	0.207	0.208	0.209	0.211	0.212	0.213	0.214	0.216	0.217	0.218	0.219	0.220	0.222	0.223	0.224	0.225
81.4	0.204	0.205	0.206	0.208	0.209	0.210	0.211	0.213	0.214	0.215	0.216	0.217	0.219	0.220	0.221	0.222
81.6	0.201	0.202	0.203	0.205	0.206	0.207	0.208	0.210	0.211	0.212	0.213	0.214	0.216	0.217	0.218	0.219
81.8	0.198	0.199	0.200	0.202	0.203	0.204	0.205	0.207	0.208	0.209	0.210	0.211	0.213	0.214	0.215	0.216
82.0	0.195	0.196	0.198	0.199	0.200	0.201	0.202	0.204	0.205	0.206	0.207	0.209	0.210	0.211	0.212	0.213
82.2	0.192	0.193	0.195	0.196	0.197	0.198	0.199	0.201	0.202	0.203	0.204	0.206	0.207	0.208	0.209	0.210
82.4	0.189	0.191	0.192	0.193	0.194	0.195	0.197	0.198	0.199	0.200	0.201	0.203	0.204	0.205	0.206	0.208
82.6	0.186	0.188	0.189	0.190	0.191	0.193	0.194	0.195	0.196	0.197	0.199	0.200	0.201	0.202	0.203	0.205
82.8	0.184	0.185	0.186	0.187	0.188	0.190	0.191	0.192	0.193	0.194	0.196	0.197	0.198	0.199	0.200	0.202
83.0	0.181	0.182	0.183	0.184	0.186	0.187	0.188	0.189	0.190	0.192	0.193	0.194	0.195	0.196	0.198	0.199
83.2	0.178	0.179	0.180	0.181	0.183	0.184	0.185	0.186	0.187	0.189	0.190	0.191	0.192	0.193	0.195	0.196
83.4	0.175	0.176	0.177	0.179	0.180	0.181	0.182	0.183	0.185	0.186	0.187	0.188	0.189	0.191	0.192	0.193
83.6	0.172	0.173	0.175	0.176	0.177	0.178	0.179	0.181	0.182	0.183	0.184	0.185	0.187	0.188	0.189	0.190
83.8	0.169	0.171	0.172	0.173	0.174	0.175	0.177	0.178	0.179	0.180	0.181	0.183	0.184	0.185	0.186	0.187
84.0	0.167	0.168	0.169	0.170	0.171	0.173	0.174	0.175	0.176	0.177	0.179	0.180	0.181	0.182	0.183	0.185
84.2	0.164	0.165	0.166	0.167	0.169	0.170	0.171	0.172	0.173	0.174	0.176	0.177	0.178	0.179	0.180	0.182
84.4	0.161	0.162	0.163	0.165	0.166	0.167	0.168	0.169	0.171	0.172	0.173	0.174	0.175	0.177	0.178	0.179
84.6	0.158	0.160	0.161	0.162	0.163	0.164	0.165	0.167	0.168	0.169	0.170	0.171	0.173	0.174	0.175	0.176
84.8	0.156	0.157	0.158	0.159	0.160	0.162	0.163	0.164	0.165	0.166	0.167	0.169	0.170	0.171	0.172	0.173
85.0	0.153	0.154	0.155	0.156	0.158	0.159	0.160	0.161	0.162	0.164	0.165	0.166	0.167	0.168	0.169	0.171
85.2	0.150	0.151	0.153	0.154	0.155	0.156	0.157	0.158	0.160	0.161	0.162	0.163	0.164	0.165	0.167	0.168
85.4	0.148	0.149	0.150	0.151	0.152	0.153	0.155	0.156	0.157	0.158	0.159	0.160	0.161	0.163	0.164	0.165
85.6	0.145	0.146	0.147	0.148	0.150	0.151	0.152	0.153	0.154	0.155	0.157	0.158	0.159	0.160	0.161	0.162
85.8	0.142	0.143	0.145	0.146	0.147	0.148	0.149	0.150	0.152	0.153	0.154	0.155	0.156	0.157	0.159	0.160

(cont'd)

TABLE XI. DESICCATING AND/OR DILUTING TABLE (Con'd)

	98.0	98.1	98.2	98.3	98.4	98.5	98.6	98.7	98.8	98.9	99.0	99.1	99.2	99.3	99.4	99.5
86.0	0.140	0.141	0.142	0.143	0.144	0.145	0.147	0.148	0.149	0.150	0.151	0.152	0.153	0.155	0.156	0.157
86.2	0.137	0.138	0.139	0.140	0.141	0.143	0.144	0.145	0.146	0.147	0.148	0.150	0.151	0.152	0.153	0.154
86.4	0.134	0.135	0.137	0.138	0.139	0.140	0.141	0.142	0.144	0.145	0.146	0.147	0.148	0.149	0.150	0.152
86.6	0.132	0.133	0.134	0.135	0.136	0.137	0.139	0.140	0.141	0.142	0.143	0.144	0.145	0.147	0.148	0.149
86.8	0.129	0.130	0.131	0.133	0.134	0.135	0.136	0.137	0.138	0.139	0.141	0.142	0.143	0.144	0.145	0.146
87.0	0.126	0.128	0.129	0.130	0.131	0.132	0.133	0.134	0.136	0.137	0.138	0.139	0.140	0.141	0.143	0.144
87.2	0.124	0.125	0.126	0.127	0.128	0.130	0.131	0.132	0.133	0.134	0.135	0.136	0.138	0.139	0.140	0.141
87.4	0.121	0.122	0.124	0.125	0.126	0.127	0.128	0.129	0.130	0.132	0.133	0.134	0.135	0.136	0.137	0.138
87.6	0.119	0.120	0.121	0.122	0.123	0.124	0.126	0.127	0.128	0.129	0.130	0.131	0.132	0.134	0.135	0.136
87.8	0.116	0.117	0.118	0.120	0.121	0.122	0.123	0.124	0.125	0.126	0.128	0.129	0.130	0.131	0.132	0.133
88.0	0.114	0.115	0.116	0.117	0.118	0.119	0.120	0.122	0.123	0.124	0.125	0.126	0.127	0.128	0.130	0.131
88.2	0.111	0.112	0.113	0.115	0.116	0.117	0.118	0.119	0.120	0.121	0.122	0.124	0.125	0.126	0.127	0.128
88.4	0.109	0.110	0.111	0.112	0.113	0.114	0.115	0.116	0.118	0.119	0.120	0.121	0.122	0.123	0.124	0.126
88.6	0.106	0.107	0.108	0.110	0.111	0.112	0.113	0.114	0.115	0.116	0.117	0.119	0.120	0.121	0.122	0.123
88.8	0.104	0.105	0.106	0.107	0.108	0.109	0.110	0.111	0.113	0.114	0.115	0.116	0.117	0.118	0.119	0.120
89.0	0.101	0.102	0.103	0.104	0.106	0.107	0.108	0.109	0.110	0.111	0.112	0.113	0.115	0.116	0.117	0.118
89.2	0.099	0.100	0.101	0.102	0.103	0.104	0.105	0.107	0.108	0.109	0.110	0.111	0.112	0.113	0.114	0.115
89.4	0.096	0.097	0.098	0.100	0.101	0.102	0.103	0.104	0.105	0.106	0.107	0.109	0.110	0.111	0.112	0.113
89.6	0.094	0.095	0.096	0.097	0.098	0.099	0.100	0.102	0.103	0.104	0.105	0.106	0.107	0.108	0.109	0.111
89.8	0.091	0.092	0.094	0.095	0.096	0.097	0.098	0.099	0.100	0.101	0.102	0.104	0.105	0.106	0.107	0.108
90.0	0.089	0.090	0.091	0.092	0.093	0.094	0.096	0.097	0.098	0.099	0.100	0.101	0.102	0.103	0.104	0.106
90.2	0.086	0.088	0.089	0.090	0.091	0.092	0.093	0.094	0.095	0.096	0.098	0.099	0.100	0.101	0.102	0.103
90.4	0.084	0.085	0.086	0.087	0.089	0.090	0.091	0.092	0.093	0.094	0.095	0.096	0.097	0.098	0.100	0.101
90.6	0.082	0.083	0.084	0.085	0.086	0.087	0.088	0.089	0.091	0.092	0.093	0.094	0.095	0.096	0.097	0.098
90.8	0.079	0.080	0.081	0.083	0.084	0.085	0.086	0.087	0.088	0.089	0.090	0.091	0.092	0.094	0.095	0.096
91.0	0.077	0.078	0.079	0.080	0.081	0.082	0.084	0.085	0.086	0.087	0.088	0.089	0.090	0.091	0.092	0.093
91.2	0.075	0.076	0.077	0.078	0.079	0.080	0.081	0.082	0.083	0.084	0.086	0.087	0.088	0.089	0.090	0.091
91.4	0.072	0.073	0.074	0.076	0.077	0.078	0.079	0.080	0.081	0.082	0.083	0.084	0.085	0.086	0.088	0.089
91.6	0.070	0.071	0.072	0.073	0.074	0.075	0.076	0.078	0.079	0.080	0.081	0.083	0.084	0.085	0.086	0.087
91.8	0.068	0.069	0.070	0.071	0.072	0.073	0.074	0.075	0.076	0.077	0.078	0.079	0.081	0.082	0.083	0.084
92.0	0.065	0.066	0.067	0.069	0.070	0.071	0.072	0.073	0.074	0.075	0.076	0.077	0.078	0.079	0.080	0.081
92.2	0.063	0.064	0.065	0.066	0.067	0.068	0.069	0.071	0.072	0.073	0.074	0.075	0.076	0.077	0.078	0.079
92.4	0.061	0.062	0.063	0.064	0.065	0.066	0.067	0.068	0.069	0.070	0.071	0.073	0.074	0.075	0.076	0.077
92.6	0.058	0.059	0.060	0.062	0.063	0.064	0.065	0.066	0.067	0.068	0.069	0.070	0.071	0.072	0.073	0.075
92.8	0.056	0.057	0.058	0.059	0.060	0.061	0.063	0.064	0.065	0.066	0.067	0.068	0.069	0.070	0.071	0.072
93.0	0.054	0.055	0.056	0.057	0.058	0.059	0.060	0.061	0.062	0.063	0.064	0.066	0.067	0.068	0.069	0.070
93.2	0.052	0.053	0.054	0.055	0.056	0.057	0.058	0.059	0.060	0.061	0.062	0.063	0.064	0.065	0.067	0.068

Determination of amount of water absorbed when one pound of 98% acid is diluted to 70.0%

$\dfrac{98}{70}$ = 1.400 Lbs of Dilute 70% Acid

Water Absorbed = 1.400 − 1.000 = .400 lbs/lb 98% used

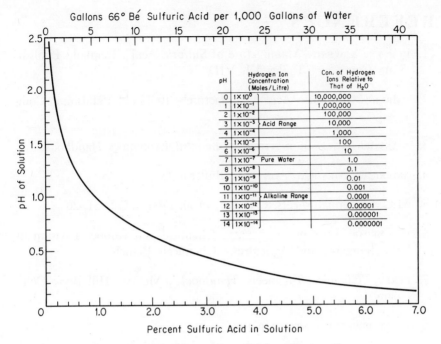

Fig. 73. pH concentration curve for sulfuric acid.

REFERENCES

1. DUECKER & WEST, "Manufacture of Sulfuric Acid", Reinhold Publishing Company (Tables VI, VII)

2. FAIRLIE, "Sulphuric Acid Manufacture", Reinhold Publishing Company

3. STANFORD RESEARCH INSTITUTE, Chemical Economics Handbook

4. AMERICAN CHEMICAL PAINT CO., Bulletin 13

5. M.C.A. Manual Sheets, C-1, C-2, D-30, D-31, TC-1, SD-20

6. U.S. DEPARTMENT OF COMMERCE, Chemical and Rubber Division of the Inorganic and Agricultural Chemicals Branch

7. PERRY, "Chemical Engineers' Handbook", McGraw-Hill Book Company

8. SHELL DEVELOPMENT COMPANY

9. R. L. ROSCHACH, Chemical Engineering, April 1952

10. SULLIVAN, "Sulphuric Acid Handbook", McGraw-Hill Book Company

11. Federal Specifications O-S-809a and O-S-801a

12. CHARLES S. LEWIS CO. (Tables XVII, XVIII)

13. T. R. BUMP AND W. L. SIBBITT, IEC 47,1665 (Tables XXIV, XXXII-XXXVII)

14. Simonson-Mantius Vacuum Process

15. FONTANA, "Corrosion", (Tables V, VIII-XI)

16. HOUGEN AND WATSON, "Industrial Chemical Calculations", John Wiley & Sons (1936). Partial heats of solution and integral heats of solution. (Table XXXVIII)

17. MORGEN, Industrial and Engineering Chemistry, May 1942. (Partial molal heats.) Fairlie, "Sulfuric Acid Manufacture," Reinhold Publishing Co. (1936). (Specific heats). (Table XXXIX)

INDEX

313

O-S-809a

JUNE 6, 1960

SUPERSEDING
Int. Fed. Spec. O-S-00809(GSA-FSS)
September 14, 1959, and
Fed. Spec. O-A-115
August 22, 1945

FEDERAL SPECIFICATION

SULFURIC ACID, TECHNICAL

This specification was approved by the Commissioner, Federal Supply Service, General Services Administration, for the use of all Federal agencies.

1. SCOPE AND CLASSIFICATION

1.1 Scope.—This specification is intended to establish requirements for a technical grade of sulfuric acid (see 6.1 and 6.6).

1.2 Classification.

1.2.1 *Types and classes.* — Sulfuric acid covered by this specification shall be furnished in the following types and classes as specified (see 6.2 and 6.4):

Type I.—66° Baume (93.19 percent).
Type II.—60° Baume (77.67 percent).
Class 1.—For galvanizing and plating.
Class 2.—For general use.

2. APPLICABLE SPECIFICATIONS, STANDARDS, AND OTHER PUBLICATIONS

2.1 Specifications and standards.—The following specifications and standards, of the issues in effect on date of invitation for bids, form a part of this specification:

Federal Specifications:

U-M-186—Medicinal Products and Clinical Laboratory Reagents; General Specification for Containers (Packaging and Packing).

PPP-B-621—Boxes, Wood, Nailed and Lock-Corner.

PPP-B-636—Box, Fiberboard.

PPP-D-700—Drums; Metal, 55-Gallon (For Acid and Corrosive Liquids).

Federal Standards:

Fed. Std. No. 102—Preservation, Packaging, and Packing Levels.

Fed. Std. No. 123—Marking for Domestic Shipment (Civilian Agencies).

(Activities outside the Federal Government may obtain copies of Federal Specifications, Standards, and Handbooks as outlined under General Information in the Index of Federal Specifications, Standards, and Handbooks and at the prices indicated in the Index. The Index, which includes cumulative monthly supplements as issued, is for sale on a subscription basis by the Superintendent of Documents, U. S. Government Printing Office, Washington 25, D. C.

(Single copies of this specification and other product specifications required by activities outside the Federal Government for bidding purposes are available without charge at the General Services Administration Regional Offices in Boston, New York, Atlanta, Chicago, Kansas City, Mo., Dallas, Denver, San Francisco, Los Angeles, Seattle, and Washington, D. C.

(Federal Government activities may obtain copies of Federal Specifications, Standards, and Handbooks and the Index of Federal Specifications, Standards, and Handbooks from established distribution points in their agencies.)

Military Specifications:

MIL-T-4239 — Tape, Pressure-Sensitive Adhesive, Vinyl Plastic Opaque, Photographic

1

Military Standards:

MIL–STD–105 — Sampling Procedures and Tables for Inspection by Attributes.

MIL–STD–129 — Marking for Shipment and Storage.

(Copies of Military Specifications and Standards required by contractors in connection with specific procurement functions should be obtained from the procuring activity or as directed by the contracting officer.)

2.2 Other publications.—The following documents form a part of this specification. Unless otherwise specified, the issue in effect on date of invitation for bids shall apply.

Governmental:

The Federal Caustic Poison Act.

(Information as to the availability of the above Act may be obtained from the Department of Health, Education, and Welfare, Washington 25, D. C.)

Uniform Freight Classification Rules.

(Application for copies should be addressed to the Official Classification Committee, 1 Park Avenue at 33rd Street, New York 16, New York.)

46 CFR 146.01–1—Coast Guard, Department of the Treasury; Transportation or Storage of Explosives or Other Dangerous Articles or Substances, and Combustible Liquids on Board Vessels.

49 CFR 71.1—Interstate Commerce Commission; Explosives and Other Dangerous Articles.

(The above Governmental regulations are now parts of the Code of Federal Regulations and are available from the Superintendent of Documents, Government Printing Office, Washington 25, D. C. Orders for these publications should cite the title and code number as listed above. Prices may be obtained from the Superintendent of Documents.)

Nongovernmental:

ASTM Standards—Part 5

Designation: E 1—Specifications for ASTM Thermometers.

(Copies may be obtained from the American Society for Testing Materials, 1916 Race Street, Philadelphia, Pennsylvania.)

(Technical society and technical association specifications and standards are generally available for reference from libraries. They are also widely distributed among technical groups and using Federal agencies.)

3. REQUIREMENTS

3.1 The sulfuric acid shall be a colorless clear to cloudy liquid, and shall conform to the requirements shown in table I when tested as specified therein.

3.2 Labeling.—The labeling shall be in conformance with the requirements of the Federal Caustic Poison Act. Appropriate warning or caution statements required by the act or

TABLE I.—*Requirements*

	Type I		Type II		Test paragraph
	Class 1	Class 2	Class 1	Class 2	
Sulfuric acid, percent by weight, minimum	93.0	93.0	77.5	77.5	4.3.1 or 4.3.1.1
Specific gravity at 60°/60° F., minimum	1.835	1.835	1.704	1.704	4.3.2
Residue after ignition, percent by weight, maximum, (see 6.5)	0.025	0.025	0.050	0.050	4.3.3
Arsenic test, maximum/165 ml.	0.01 mg.	Not applicable	0.01 mg.	Not applicable	4.3.4

required to insure safe usage of the material shall be included (see 5.3.1).

4. SAMPLING, INSPECTION, AND TEST PROCEDURES

4.1 Unless otherwise specified herein the supplier is responsible for the performance of all inspection requirements prior to submission for Government inspection and acceptance. Except as otherwise specified, the supplier may utilize his own facilities or any commercial laboratory acceptable to the Government. Inspection records of the examinations and tests shall be kept complete and available to the Government as specified in the contract or order.

4.1.1 *Lot.*—For the purposes of sampling, a lot shall consist of all the sulfuric acid of the same type and class manufactured as one batch and offered for delivery at one time.

4.1.1.1 *Batch.*—A batch shall be that quantity of the chemical manufactured at the same time. When practicable, all sulfuric acid of the same type and class supplied on one order shall be from the same manufacturer's batch.

4.1.2 *Sampling for inspection of filled containers.*—A random sample of filled containers shall be selected from each lot in accordance with Military Standard MIL–STD–105 at inspection level I with the lot size expressed in units of containers and acceptable quality level (AQL) = 2.5 percent defective to verify compliance with all stipulations of this specification regarding fill, closure, marking, and other requirements not involving tests.

4.1.2.1 If the material is shipped in containers, select 10 percent but in no case more than ten containers, of the containers comprising the lot, so as to be representative of the entire lot. From each selected container remove sufficient material by means of a thief to form a composite sample of approximately one quart when the portions removed from the selected containers are united. Fill a 16-ounce screw-capped bottle with an acid-impervious liner with the composite sample.

4.1.2.2 If the material is shipped in tank cars or tank trucks, remove the sample (approximately one quart) by means of a thief or a clean, weighed, small-neck glass bottle. The bottle shall have a capacity of approximately one quart and shall be rinsed with the material being sampled. Lower the unstoppered bottle by means of a cord, chain, or rod to the bottom of the tank, and immediately withdraw to the surface. In order to obtain a representative cross-section sample of the material, the speed of lowering and raising the bottle shall be of uniform rate and regulated so that the bottle is just filled as it reaches the surface of the liquid.

4.2 Inspection.

4.2.1 *Inspection of filled containers.*—Each sample filled container selected in accordance with 4.1.2 shall be examined by the inspector for defects of the container and closure, for evidence of leakage, and for unsatisfactory markings. Each sample filled container shall also be weighed to determine the amount of the contents. Any container in the sample having one or more defects, or under fill shall be rejected, and if the number of defective containers in any sample exceeds the acceptance number for the appropriate sampling plan of Military Standard MIL–STD–105, the lot represented by the sample shall be rejected. Rejected lots may be resubmitted for examination provided that the contractor has removed or repaired all nonconforming containers.

4.2.2 *Inspection tests.* — The sample selected in accordance with 4.1.3 shall be subjected to the tests specified in 4.3. If the sample fails in one or more of these tests, the entire lot represented by the sample shall be rejected. Rejected lots may be resubmitted for acceptance provided the contractor has removed or reworked all nonconforming products. Two determinations shall be performed for each characteristic tested.

4.3 Tests.

4.3.1 *Sulfuric acid content.*—Tare a small glass-stoppered Erlenmeyer flask containing 30 ml. of distilled water. Add 1 ml. of the sulfuric acid sample, cool, and weigh. Titrate with 1 N sodium hydroxide using phenolphthalein indicator.

Sulfuric acid, percent by wt. =
$$\frac{0.04904 \times N \times V \times 100}{S}$$
where:
N = normality of NaOH
V = volume of NaOH in ml
S = weight of sample, grams

4.3.1.1 *Alternate method.*—Determine the specific gravity of the acid sample in air at 60°F. in accordance with the method specified in 4.3.2, protecting the solution from contact with air. Determine the percent sulfuric acid from table II. (Acids stronger than 93.19 percent sulfuric acid shall be determined in accordance with the method specified in 4.3.1).

TABLE II.—*Conversion table*[1]

Specific gravity 60°/60° F.	Percent sulfuric acid
1.6667	74.36
1.6860	75.99
1.7059	77.67
1.7262	79.43
1.7470	81.30
1.8125	88.65
1.8182	89.55
1.8239	90.60
1.8297	91.80
1.8354	93.19

Note 1.—The figures given in table II have been taken from the table approved and adopted as a standard by the Manufacturing Chemists' Association, Inc.

4.3.2 *Specific gravity.*

4.3.2.1 *Apparatus.*

4.3.2.1.1 *Pycnometer.*—A pycnometer of 25 ml. capacity with a ground-glass stopper having a capillary opening, a chamber to provide for expansions up to room temperature, and a cap to prevent evaporation.

4.3.2.1.2 *Water bath.*—A water bath capable of maintaining a temperature of 60° ± 1° F. during the test.

4.3.2.1.3 *Thermometer.* — An ASTM low softening point thermometer having a range of 30° to 180°F. and conforming to the requirements for thermometer 15F–39 as prescribed in the Standard Specifications for Thermometers, ASTM Designation: E–1.

4.3.2.2 *Procedure.*

4.3.2.2.1 Fill a thoroughly cleaned pycnometer with freshly boiled distilled water, stopper, and immerse in the water bath maintained at 60° ± 1°F. with the bath level above the graduation mark on the pycnometer. After immersion in the bath for at least 30 minutes, remove the stopper and adjust the level of the liquid with a capillary tube to the proper point on the pycnometer. Put the stopper in place, remove from the bath, wipe dry and weigh. Empty the pycnometer, rinse with acetone, and dry thoroughly in air with suction. Immerse the empty, stoppered pycnometer in the water bath and bring the temperature to 60°F. as above. Remove from the water bath, wipe dry, and weigh. Calculate the weight of the contained water (at 60°F.) in air by subtracting the weight of the empty pycnometer from the weight when filled with water.

4.3.2.2.2 Fill the thoroughly cleaned and dried pycnometer with the sample specimen and bring the temperature to 60°F. as above. After immersion in the water bath for at least 30 minutes, remove the stopper and adjust the level of the acid with a capillary tube. Put the stopper in place, remove from the bath, wipe dry and weigh. Calculate the weight of the contained acid at 60°F. by subtracting the weight of the empty pycnometer from the weight when filled with the sample.

Specific gravity at 60°/60° F. =

$$\frac{\text{Weight of the contained acid}}{\text{Weight of the contained water.}}$$

4.3.3 *Residue after ignition.*

4.3.3.1 A platinum or fused silica dish is heated to red heat with a Meker burner for 30 minutes, cooled in a desiccator for 30 minutes, and weighed to a constant weight.

4.3.3.2 A 10- to 20-gram sample of the sulfuric acid is weighed in a weighing bottle or Lunge weighing pipette. The acid is then placed in the platinum or fused silica dish and the weighing bottle or weighing pipette reweighed. The dish is slowly heated until the acid coagulates or until fumes are no longer evolved. The dish is then heated to red heat with a Meker burner for 30 minutes or until all of the carbon, if any, has been decomposed. The dish is then cooled for 30 minutes in a desiccator and weighed. The increased weight of the dish is due to the ash, composed of substances not volatile at red heat and generally containing iron oxide.

(*Note.*—Blasting is not recommended as the magnetic oxide, Fe_3O_4, will form.)

4.3.4 *Arsenic test (for class 1 only).*

4.3.4.1 *Reagents and apparatus.*

4.3.4.1.1 *Standard arsenic solution, 0.001 mg. arsenous oxide (As_2O_3) per milliliter.*

4.3.4.1.2 *Reagent grade lead acetate, 1 percent solution.*

4.3.4.1.3 *Reagent grade mercuric chloride (or mercuric bromide), 5 percent solution in ethyl (or methyl) alcohol.*

4.3.4.1.4 *Reagent grade stannous chloride, 45 percent solution.*

4.3.4.1.5 *Reagent grade ferric oxide.*

4.3.4.1.6 *Reagent grade concentrated nitric acid.*

4.3.4.1.7 *Reagent grade concentrated sulfuric acid.*

4.3.4.1.8 *Reagent grade zinc, arsenic-free, granulated, 3 to 6 mesh.*

4.3.4.1.9 *Lead acetate paper.*

4.3.4.1.10 *Mercuric chloride (bromide) paper strips.* — Sheets of precut paper are commercially available. These strips are produced in sheets of 32 strips (9 cm. by 2.5 mm.) and have been devised for insuring maximum uniformity and convenience in handling. To sensitize these strips, place a sheet (loosely folded longitudinally) in a 100-ml. graduated cylinder filled with the mercuric chloride (bromide) solution and allow to stand for one hour. Remove the sheet from the solution, and, holding it by the longitudinal ends, wave rapidly in the air until almost dry. (Do not suspend for drying). Place between clean sheets of paper under pressure (as in a book) for straightening. Finally, cut the sheet in two across the center guide marks. Free ends are now all from the same area on the sheet and are uniformly impregnated, so use these ends for the deposition of the stain. The stain varies with the age of impregnation, therefore, it is essential to prepare the sensitized strips immediately prior to use. (Do not use later than 2 hours after preparation.)

4.3.4.1.11 *Gutzeit generators.*—Use 2-ounce wide mouth bottles of uniform capacity and design as generators. Fit each by means of a perforated rubber stopper with a glass tube, 1 cm. in diameter and 6 to 7 cm. long, with an additional constricted end to facilitate connection. Place a small wad of glass wool in the constricted bottom end of the tube and add 3.5 to 4.0 grams of sand, taking care to have the same quantity in each tube. Moisten the sand with 10 percent lead acetate solution and remove the excess by suction. Clean the sand when necessary by treatment (do not remove sand from tube) with nitric acid followed by a water rinse and suction. Treat with the lead acetate solution. If the sand has dried through disuse, clean and remoisten as directed. Connect this tube by means of a rubber stopper with a narrow glass tube of 2.6 to 2.7 mm. internal diameter and 10 to 12 cm. long, and introduce the clean end of the strip of mercuric chloride (bromide) paper (see note "c"). Clean and dry the tube before inserting the mercuric chloride (bromide) paper. Ordinary pipe cleaners may be used for drying the tubes.

4.3.4.1.12 Constant temperature water bath (20° to 25°C.), of such depth that the water reaches to within an inch of the top of the constricted tube of the Gutzeit generator when the generator is in operation.

4.3.4.2 *Procedure.*—Since the small Gutzeit apparatus is limited to stains of arsenous oxide from 0.001 mg. to 0.02 mg., the size of the sample of sulfuric acid must be varied in proportion to the arsenic content to insure stains that will fall within these limits. If the arsenic content is between 0.000001 percent and 0.000005 percent As_2O_3, then a sample of 165 ml. (300 grams of 1.84 specific gravity) must be taken. For higher concentrations of arsenic, the size of the sample may be decreased proportionally. For a sample whose range of arsenic is unknown, a series of samples must be taken to include the above limits.

4.3.4.2.1 For sulfuric acid whose arsenic concentration is within the limits specified in 4.3.4.2, add 3 ml. of concentrated nitric acid (4.3.4.1.6) to 165 ml. of the specimen sample and evaporate to about 10 ml. Cool the residue, dilute with 20 ml. of distilled water, and evaporate to about 5 ml. Cool the sample and dilute with 10 ml. of distilled water. The sample is now ready for the Gutzeit determination.

4.3.4.2.2 Place 0.1 gram of ferric oxide (4.3.4.1.5) in the generator bottle and add 1 ml. of stannous chloride solution (4.3.4.1.4). Wash the sample into the generator bottle, adding the washings, and dilute to 50 ml.

Roll the lead acetate paper (4.3.4.1.9) and insert into the large glass tube. Insert the sensitized mercuric chloride (bromide) paper strip into the small glass tube and connect the two tubes together. Add 5 ml. of arsenic-free zinc (4.3.4.1.8) to the solution in the generator bottle and immediately connect the apparatus together. Shake the apparatus gently and allow to stand for one hour in the water bath with the apparatus immersed to within one inch of the top of the constricted tube of the generator. The mercuric chloride (bromide) paper strip is then removed, dipped in molten paraffin, and the length of the stains on both sides of the paper averaged. Compare with standard stains prepared in the same manner (see 4.3.4.2.3). Due to the degeneration of stains upon long standing and the possible differences in the reagents, test papers, and controls applied from one determination to the next, it is advisable to prepare standard stains in conjunction with each determination.

4.3.4.2.3 *Preparation of standard stains.*— Treat 2 ml., 6 ml., and 10 ml. of the standard arsenic solution (4.3.4.1.1) as directed for the specimen sample of sulfuric acid. The same quantities of all reagents must be used. Add 10 ml. of reagent grade sulfuric acid (4.3.4.1.7) to provide the same acidity as in the sample. The stains thus produced will represent 0.002 mg., 0.006 mg., and 0.01 mg. As_2O_3.

Notes.—

(a) Nitric acid must be added to the sample to prevent possible volatilization of the unoxidized arsenic compounds upon heating. After adding the nitric acid to the sulfuric acid, it is necessary to heat the sulfuric acid to dense fumes of sulfur trioxide to expel the nitric acid.

(b) Interferences from sulfurous acid or hydrogen sulfide in the sulfuric acid are prevented by boiling the sulfuric acid.

(c) The internal diameter of the small tube must not be large enough to permit curling of the paper strip. A 3-mm. bore will permit the strip to curl, resulting in an uneven stain and poor end point.

(d) Lead acetate paper must be used to remove any trace of hydrogen sulfide generated, since this will react with the mercury in the test paper strip and interfere with the arsine stain.

(e) Ferric oxide, reduced by stannous chloride, is used to prevent polarization between the zinc and the acid and thus aids in the evolution of arsine.

(f) The temperature of the reaction in the generator bottle should be maintained between 20° to 25°C. High temperatures cause frothing of the sample, and may cause it to boil over, ruining the determination.

5. PREPARATION FOR DELIVERY

For civil agency procurement, the definitions and applications of the levels of packaging and packing shall be in accordance with Federal Standard No. 102.

5.1 Packaging.—Packaging shall be level A or C as specified (see 6.4).

5.1.1 *Level A.*—When specified, sulfuric acid shall be packaged in glass bottles of 1 or 9 pint capacity conforming to type I, class B, Federal Specification U–M–186. The bottles shall be furnished with plastic screw caps complying with the closure requirements of the bottle specification. Closures shall be sealed with an overlapping band of tape conforming to Military Specification MIL–T–4239. The tape shall be of sufficient width to extend well down on the neck of the bottle and slightly over the top edge of the cap. The tape shall adhere tightly to the cap and the bottle.

5.1.1.1 *Intermediate packaging.*—Each bottle shall be packaged in a fiber box conforming to type I, class 1, style RSC, of Federal Specification PPP–B–636. One-pint bottles shall be cushioned with either 1 pound (minimum) of vermiculite or 3 pounds (minimum) of shredded asbestos and 9 pint bottles with either 5 pounds (minimum) of vermiculite or 13 pounds (minimum) of shredded asbestos. The cushioning shall surround the bottle on all surfaces. Boxes shall be of minimum practical size and shall be closed in accordance with the appendix of the box specification.

5.1.2 *Level C.*—Sulfuric acid shall be packaged in standard commercial containers of

the size and kind commonly used, which will afford the degree of protection required for shipment.

5.2 Packing.—Packing shall be level A, B, or C as specified (see 6.4).

5.2.1 *Level A.*

5.2.1.1 *Bottles.* — Unless otherwise specified, twenty-four 1-pint bottles or four 9-pint bottles packaged in accordance with 5.1.1 and 5.1.1.1 shall be overpacked in exterior shipping containers conforming to Federal Specification PPP–B–621, class 2. Closure and strapping shall be in accordance with the appendix to the box specification. Gross weight of shipping containers shall not exceed 200 pounds.

5.2.1.2 *Bulk.*

5.2.1.2.1 *Carboys.*—Sulfuric acid shall be delivered in 6½-, or 13-gallon glass carboys conforming to Interstate Commerce Commission Specification ID or IA respectively, and shall be overpacked as specified therein. Cushioning shall meet the requirements of section 78.1–7(g) of the ICC regulations. When approved by the procuring activity, polyethylene carboys may be used.

5.2.1.2.2 *Pails and drums.*—Sulfuric acid shall be delivered in 5-gallon metal pails with polyethylene liners, or in 55-gallon drums conforming to Federal Specification PPP–D–700, type I. No further packing shall be required.

5.2.1.2.3 *Tank cars and tank trucks.*—Sulfuric acid shall be delivered in tank cars or tank trucks conforming to ICC specification 103A or 103AW, or MC 310, respectively.

5.2.2 *Level B.*

5.2.2.1 *Bottles.* — Sulfuric acid shall be packed as specified in 5.2.1.1 except that boxes shall conform to Federal Specification PPP–B–621, class 1.

5.2.3 *Level C.* — Sulfuric acid shall be packed in substantial commercial containers of the type, size, and kind commonly used for the purpose, so constructed as to insure compliance with Uniform Freight Classification Rules and regulations applicable to the mode of transportation and shall also comply with the applicable ICC requirements.

5.3 Marking.

5.3.1 *Special labeling.* — Each container, bottle, drum or carboy shall be labeled in accordance with the Federal Caustic Poison Act. In addition, each container shall be provided with a label containing the following information:

Carboy label:

SULFURIC ACID

DANGER! CAUSES SEVERE BURNS

Do not get in eyes, on skin, on clothing.

In case of contact, immediately flush skin or eyes with plenty of water for at least 15 minutes; for eyes, get medical attention.

Do not add water to contents while in a container because of violent reaction.

CARBOY HANDLING AND STORAGE

Before moving carboy be sure closure is securely fastened.

Loosen closure carefully.

Keep out of sun and away from heat.

Never use pressure to empty.

Completely drain carboy before returning.

In case of spillage, flush with plenty of water.

6. NOTES

6.1 Intended use.—Sulfuric acid as covered by this specification is a technical grade. Class 1 material is intended for use in galvanizing and plating ferrous metals and may also be used for general purposes. Class 2 material is intended for general use except in the cleaning of ferrous metal for galvanizing and plating. Type I (66° Baume), class 2 acid is the strength generally used in soda-acid fire extinguishers.

6.1.1 Type I acid has a lower freezing point than type II acid and also may be stored more safely in iron or steel containers. Concentrated sulfuric acid should not be stored in lead containers.

6.2 Designation changes.—Type I and type II sulfuric acid were designated as a class A and class B acid, respectively in Federal Specification O–A–115. Class 1 and class 2 were formerly designated as grades 1 and 2 acid.

6.3 Hazardous properties.—Sulfuric acid is very corrosive and is dangerous when improperly handled. Contact with the body results in rapid destruction of tissues and severe burns. Adequate protection against any contact should be provided for all parts of the body. Although the acid itself is not flammable, it may cause ignition by contact with combustible materials. A highly flammable gas (hydrogen) is generated by the action of the acid on most metals.

6.3.1 Air pressure should never be used to empty carboys. Stored drums should have their plugs loosened weekly, or more often in hot weather, to release pressure that may build up in the drums.

6.4 Ordering data.—Purchasers should exercise any desired options offered herein and procurement documents should specify the following:

(*a*) Number, title, and date of this specification.

(*b*) Type and class of acid required (see 1.2.1).

(*c*) Total weight required and size of individual containers.

(*d*) Level of packaging and packing required (see 5.1 and 5.2).

6.5 The limits on residue after ignition as given in this specification apply to deliveries made in carboys, drums, tank cars, and tank trucks.

6.6 Other publications.

6.6.1 When sulfuric acid is required as a reagent in chemical analyses or for pharmaceutical purposes, reference should be made to the specifications of the American Chemical Society or the National Formulary.

6.6.2 When sulfuric acid is required for use in storage batteries, reference should be made to Federal Specification O–S–801, Sulfuric Acid, Electrolyte; For Storage Batteries.

6.6.3 When sulfuric acid is required for use as a fire extinguisher charge, reference should be made to Federal Specification O–C–240, Charge, Fire Extinguisher, Antifreeze and Soda-and-Acid.

6.6.4 Sulfuric acid for photographic use should be purchased under Federal Specification O–S–805. Sulfuric acid, Photographic H_2SO_4.

6.7 Transportation description.—Transportation description applicable to this item is as follows:

Sulfuric Acid

Carload minimum weight 30,000 pounds in glass in barrels or boxes.

36,000 pounds in metal barrels.

Truckload minimum weight 30,000 pounds in barrels or boxes; subject to Rule 34 of National Motor Freight Classification.

36,000 pounds in metal barrels; subject to Rule 34 of National Motor Freight Classification.

Notice. — When Government drawings, specifications, or other data are used for any purpose other than in connection with a definitely related Government procurement operation, the United States Government thereby incurs no responsibility nor any obligation whatsoever; and the fact that the Government may have formulated, furnished, or in any way supplied the said drawings, specifications, or other data, is not to be regarded, by implication or otherwise as in any manner licensing the holder or any other person or corporation, or conveying any rights or permission to manufacture, use, or sell any patented invention that may in any way be related thereto.

MILITARY INTERESTS:
Army—C E M O Q
Navy—Sh
Air Force.

Copies of this specification may be purchased for 10 cents each.

O-S-801a

AUGUST 8, 1956

SUPERSEDING
Fed. Spec. O-S-801
August 4, 1952

FEDERAL SPECIFICATION

SULFURIC ACID, ELECTROLYTE;
FOR STORAGE BATTERIES

This specification was approved by the Commissioner, Federal Supply Service, General Services Administration, for the use of all Federal agencies.

1. SCOPE AND CLASSIFICATION

1.1 Scope.—This specification covers sulfuric acid for use in electrolytic solutions for storage batteries.

1.2 Classification.

1.2.1 *Classes.*—Electrolyte, sulfuric acid shall be of the following classes, as specified:

Class 1. — Concentrated sulfuric acid, specific gravity 1.828 minimum at 26.70°C. (80°F.)

Class 2. — Diluted sulfuric acid, specific gravity 1.395 ± 0.005 at 26.70°C. (80°F.)

Class 3. — Diluted sulfuric acid, specific gravity 1.280 ± 0.005 at 26.70°C. (80°F.)

2. APPLICABLE SPECIFICATIONS, STANDARDS, AND OTHER PUBLICATIONS

2.1 The following specifications and standards, of the issues in effect on date of invitations for bids, form a part of this specification:

Federal Specification:

GG-H-941—Hydrometers; Syringe, Battery.

(Activities outside the Federal Government may obtain copies of Federal Specifications and Standards as outlined under General Information in the Index of Federal Specifications and Standards, and at the prices indicated in the Index. The Index, which includes cumulative monthly supplements as issued, is for sale on a subscription basis by the Superintendent of Documents.

(Single copies of this specification and other product specifications required by activities outside the Federal Government for bidding purposes are available without charge at the General Services Administration Regional Offices in Boston, New York, Atlanta, Chicago, Kansas City, Mo., Dallas, Denver, San Francisco, Los Angeles, Seattle, and Washington, D. C.

(Federal Government activities may obtain copies of Federal Specifications and Standards and the Index of Federal Specifications and Standards from established distribution points in their agencies.)

Military Specifications:

MIL-P-207—Packaging and Packing for Domestic and Overseas Shipment and Storage, Electrolyte; Storage Battery.

MIL-C-17932—Carboy, Slatted Crate, Carboy, Fully Enclosed; and Carboy, Tilter Top Crate.

Military Standards:

MIL-STD-105 — Sampling Procedures and Tables for Inspection by Attributes.

MIL-STD-129—Marking for Shipment and Storage.

(Copies of specifications, standards, and drawings required by contractors in connection with specific procurement functions should be obtained from the procuring activity or as directed by the contracting officer.)

2.2 Other publication.—The following publication forms a part of this specification. Unless otherwise indicated, the issue in effect on date of invitations for bids shall apply.

Interstate Commerce Commission:

49 CFR 71–78 — Interstate Commerce Commission Rules and Regulations for Transportation of Explosives and Other Dangerous Articles.

(The Interstate Commerce Commission regulations are now a part of the Code of Federal Regulations (1949 Edition-Revised 1950) available from the Superintendent of Documents, Government Printing Office, Washington 25, D. C. Orders for this publication should cite "49 CFR 71–78 (Rev. 1950).")

3. REQUIREMENTS

3.1 Material.—Material shall be non-fuming sulfuric acid, suitable for electrolyte in storage batteries. The acid shall be free of sediment, and shall meet the requirements specified herein.

3.1.1 *Color.*—The acid shall preferably be colorless, but in no case shall its color be darker than that of the standard color solution, when tested as specified in 4.3.2.

3.1.2 *Specific gravity.*—When measured as specified in 4.2.2, the specific gravity of the acid, corrected to 26.70°C. (80°F.) shall be as follows:

Class 1 — 1.828 minimum
Class 2 — 1.395 ± 0.005
Class 3 — 1.280 ± 0.005

3.1.3 *Purity.*

3.1.3.1 *Strength of acid.*—The H_2SO_4 content, by weight of the acid, shall be as follows:

Class 1 — Not less than 93.2 percent.
Class 2 — 49.5 to 50.5 percent.
Class 3 — 36.5 to 37.5 percent.

3.1.3.2 *Impurities.*—When determined as specified in section 4, the permissible maximum limits of impurities in the acid shall be as specified in table I.

TABLE I.—*Limits of impurities in acid*

Item	Calculated as	Maximum limits, percent		
		Class 1	Class 2	Class 3
Organic matter	--------	1	1	1
Fixed residue	--------	0.03	0.015	0.011
Iron	Fe	.005	.003	.0019
Sulfurous acid	SO₂	.004	.002	.0015
Arsenic	As	.0001	.00005	.00004
Antimony	Sb	.0001	.00005	.00004
Manganese	Mn	.00002	.00001	.000007
Nitrates	NO	.0005	.0003	.0002
Ammonium	NH	.001	.0005	.0004
Chloride	Cl	.001	.0005	.0004
Copper	Cu	.005	.003	.0019
Zinc	Zn	.004	.002	.0015
Selenium	Se	.002	.001	.0007
Platinum	Pt	1	1	1
Nickel	Ni	0.0001	0.00005	0.00004

¹ To pass test (see section 4).

4. SAMPLING, INSPECTION, AND TEST PROCEDURES

4.1 Sampling for lot acceptance.

4.1.1 *Inspection lot.*—For purposes of sampling, a lot shall consist of all sulfuric acid of the same class manufactured as one batch or in one continuous process run and offered for delivery at one time.

4.1.2 *Sampling for inspection of filled containers at contractor's plant.* — A random sample of filled containers shall be taken by the Government inspector in accordance with Military Standard MIL–STD–105 at inspection level 1 and acceptable quality level of 2.5 percent defective to verify conformance to all stipulations of this specification regarding fill, closure, marking and other requirements not involving tests.

4.1.3 *Sampling for tests.*—From each inspection lot the Government inspector shall take two containers at random. From each of the two containers enough acid to perform test shall be taken and placed in separate clean, dry containers, sealed, marked and forwarded to the testing laboratory designated by the bureau or activity concerned.

4.1.3.1 *Procedure.*—Portions shall be withdrawn from the containers in such a way that the upper layer, which is liable to dilution if the container has not been properly closed, and the bottom layer, which may contain sediment, will be about equally represented in the portion taken from each container.

4.2 Inspection.

4.2.1 *Inspection of containers at contractor's plant.*—Each sample filled container shall be examined for defects of construction of the container and the closure, for evidence of leakage, and for unsatisfactory markings. Each filled container shall also be weighed to determine the amount of contents. Any container in the sample having 1 or more defects, or under required fill, shall be rejected, and if the number of defective containers in any sample exceeds the acceptance number for the appropriate sampling plan of Military Standard MIL–STD–105, the lot represented by the sample shall be rejected. Rejected lots may be resubmitted for acceptance tests provided the contractor has removed all nonconforming containers.

4.3 Lot acceptance tests.—The sample specimens selected in accordance with 4.3 shall be subjected separately to the tests specified in 4.4. If either specimen fails one or more of these tests, the lot shall be rejected. Rejected lots may be resubmitted for acceptance tests provided the contractor has removed or reworked all nonconforming products.

4.4 Test procedures.

4.4.1 *Inspection of acid.*

4.4.1.1 *Visual inspection.*—Visual inspection shall determine whether the acid contains more than small amounts of suspended matter or sediment or has more than a slight brownish color. If so, the material shall be

rejected without further inspection or test (see 4.4.2.2).

4.4.1.2 *Specific gravity.*—The specific gravity shall be determined by means of a hydrometer conforming to class A, style 1, or class B, of Federal Specification GG–H–941.

4.4.1.2.1 *Hydrometer.* — The hydrometer shall be calibrated to read correctly at 26.7°C. (80°F.). The hydrometer shall have at least 1 scale division for each 5 points (0.005). Temperature corrections, when necessary, shall be made for deviations from the standard temperature as shown in table II. When the temperature of the acid is above the standard temperature, the correction shall be added to, and when below, subtracted from, the observed value to reduce this to the correct reading at the standard temperature.

TABLE II.—*Temperature corrections*

Acid	Correction per degree	
	°C.	°F.
Class 1 --------------	0.00099	0.00055
Class 2 --------------	.00079	.00042
Class 3 --------------	.00075	.00040

4.4.1.3 *Inspection for shipment.*—Inspection of acid for shipment shall be made to determine whether containers, packing, labeling conform to the requirements of this specification.

4.4.2 *Tests.*—Tests to determine whether the acid complies with the detail requirements of section 3 shall be made as follows:

4.4.2.1 *Strength.*—The strength of the acid shall be determined by titration. Using a pipette, about 1 ml. of the acid shall be put into a small tared weighing bottle with a well fitting stopper and weighed accurately. After suitable dilution it shall be titrated with standard sodium hydroxide solution (approximately N), using methyl red as the indicator.

3

4.4.2.2 *Color.*—Color shall be determined by comparing 50 ml. of the acid in a Nessler tube with a standard containing 0.12 mg. of copper, 1 ml. of $N/10$ hydrochloric acid, and 5 ml. of freshly prepared hydrogen sulphide water, diluted to an equal volume. The comparison is to be made immediately after the preparation of the standard. The depth of the color shall not exceed that of the standard. The Nessler tubes used shall have a length of about 30 cm., a diameter of 2 cm., and a capacity of 50 ml. In all cases observation shall be made by viewing the solutions vertically.

4.4.2.3 *Chemical tests for purity.*—Chemical tests for purity shall be in accordance with recognized chemical assay methods for such impurities for classes 1, 2, and 3 (see table 1).

5. PREPARATION FOR DELIVERY

5.1 Packaging and packing.

5.1.1 *Level A.*—Sulfuric acid shall be packaged and packed in 13-gallon carboys, 5-gallon carboys, with tilter top conforming to Military Specification MIL–C–17932, or 1-gallon bottles. Contents of carboys and bottles shall be of the approximate weight shown in table III. Packaging and packing in 1-gallon bottles shall conform to Military Specification MIL–P–207. Packaging and packing in carboys shall be in accordance with Specification 1A of the Interstate Commerce Commission Regulations for the Transportation of Explosives and Other Dangerous Articles by Freight. When approved by the procuring activity (see 6.2) and when permitted by the above specifications, polyethylene carboys may be used. Unless otherwise specified, 5-gallon and 13-gallon carboys shall be furnished with a leakproof plastic screw cap made of polystyrene and fitted with a cap liner made of polyethylene, so constructed as to permit venting of pressures in excess of 10 pounds without permitting contamination of the contents of the carboy. Caps shall be secured by a self-shrinking plastic band.

5.1.2 *Level C.*—Surfuric acid shall be packaged and packed in conformance to Interstate Commerce Commission Regulations for Transportation of Explosives and Other Dangerous Articles by Freight, in standard commercial, glass-stoppered carboys, in 50-gallon lead-lined steel drums, or in bulk.

5.1.3 *Level D.*—Sulfuric acid shall be packaged and packed in accordance with the requirements of 5.1.2 and applicable carrier rules and regulations for ocean shipment.

5.2 Marking.—Packages and shipping containers shall be marked in conformance to Military Standard MIL–STD–129.

5.2.1 *Special marking.*—In addition to any special marking specified by the procuring activity (see 6.2), the following marking shall be applied:

(*a*) The top side of the shipping container shall be marked "THIS SIDE UP" in 1-inch high letters.

(*b*) Labels marked "FRAGILE" shall be attached to 3 faces of box (top, 1

TABLE III.—*Approximate weight of contents*

Acid	Containers			
	13-gallon carboys	5-gallon carboys	1-gallon, U.S., bottles	1-gallon, Imperial, bottles
	Pounds	*Pounds*	*Pounds*	*Pounds*
Class 1 _____	200	76	15.5	18.5
Class 2 _____	150	58	11.7	13.9
Class 3 _____	140	53	10.7	12.9

end, and the side containing the contract data).

(c) A white "A" label conforming to Interstate Commerce Commission Regulations for the Shipment of Acid shall be attached to 1 end of the box.

(d) Each shipping container shall have precautionary labels permanently affixed to three of its surfaces with water adhesive. The labels shall be white with black print and shall bear the following legend indicating that the container contents are dangerous.
"*DANGER: CAUSES SEVERE BURNS.*

Do not get *in eyes, or on skin,* or on clothing. In case of contact immediately flush skin or eyes with plenty of water for at least 15 minutes; for eyes, *get medical attention.*

Do not add water to contents while in a container because of violent reaction."

5.2.1.1 *Level C.*—Shipping containers containing sulfuric acid packaged in accordance with level C, if for the military, shall be conspicuously marked "MIN MIL PKG".

5.2.1.2 *Level D.*—Unless otherwise specified, shipping containers shall be marked with the name of the material, the class, specific gravity, and the quantity contained therein, as defined by the contract or order under which the shipment is made, the name of the contractor, and the number of the contract or order.

6. NOTES

6.1 **Intended use.**—Sulfuric acid covered by this specification is intended for use in electrolytic solutions for storage batteries. Class 1, concentrated sulfuric acid should be diluted to density specified for class 2 or class 3 acid before use. Concentrated sulfuric acid conforming to class 1 should not be used undiluted in lead storage batteries.

6.2 **Ordering data.** — Procurement documents should specify the following:

(a) Number, title and date of this specification.

(b) Class required (see 1.2.1).

(c) Level of packaging and packing and quantity per container (see 5.1).

(d) Whether containers are to be returned or retained (see 5.1).

(e) Whether polyethylene carboys may be used (see 5.1.1).

(f) Special markings required (see 5.2.1).

6.3 Sulfuric acid should be purchased by weight, the unit being the avoirdupois pound.

6.4 It is believed that this specification adequately describes the characteristics necessary to secure the desired material and that normally no samples will be necessary prior to award to determine compliance with this specification. If for any particular purpose, samples with bids are necessary, they should be specifically asked for in the invitation for bids, and the particular purpose to be served by the bid sample should be definitely stated, the specification to apply in all other respects.

Patent notice.—When Government drawings, specifications, or other data are used for any purpose other than in connection with a definitely related Government procurement operation, the United States Government thereby incurs no responsibility, nor any obligation whatsoever; and the fact that the Government may have formulated, furnished, or in any way supplied the said drawings, specifications, or other data, is not to be regarded by implication or otherwise, as in any manner licensing the holder or any other person or corporation, or conveying any rights or permission to manufacture, use, or sell any patented invention that may in any way be related thereto.

MILITARY INTEREST:
Army—C E M O Sig T
Navy—A MC Or Sh S Y
Air Force.

★ U. S. GOVERNMENT PRINTING OFFICE: 1956

Copies of this specification may be purchased for 10 cents each.